IT'S NEVER LONG ENOUGH

A Practical Guide to Caring for Your
GERIATRIC DOG

Dr. Mary Gardner

This book may be purchased in bulk for educational, promotional or business use. Please contact the publisher for more details.

ISBN:
Hardcover - 978-1-956343-00-7
Paperback: 978-1-956343-01-4
Ebook: 978-1-956343-02-1

Ed: 1

Library of Congress Cataloging-in-Publication Data

Includes bibliographical references and an index.

Researcher and editor: Dr. Theresa Entriken

Copy editor: Mindy Valcarcel

Doodles by: Portia Stewart

Interior design by: Ljiljana Pavkov @ bookwormsdesign.com

Book cover design by: Victoria Black @ thevictoriablack.com

Front cover photo credit: Mandi Pratt @ greyboypetprints.com

Disclaimer

This book is not intended as a medical textbook. Every pet should receive an examination by their veterinarian prior to starting any treatment.

I've shared my patients' stories in this book with their families' consent, and in a few instances where appropriate, I've changed their names and other identifying details.

I am not paid by any of the companies whose products I recommend. These are simply products that I have found useful for pets and their families. Except for Lap of Love Veterinary Hospice, of which I am co-founder and shareholder, and a company that I co-own with my brother called Monarch Pet Memorial Services, I have no other financial affiliations.

I do love cats! So please don't take offense that this book is focused on dogs. The cat book is coming soon!

Publisher: Rolled Toe Publishing (Books@GreyMuzzleVet.com)

   /drmarygardner **greymuzzlevet**

I dedicate this book to my mom. She was who first taught me about compassion and undying love towards animals.

"Over all the years that I've been honored to serve as the world's personal finance expert, the one major expense that I've noticed that usually becomes the biggest strains on a family's finances is the money that is needed to take care of the declining health of the families aging dog. Not only will this book educate you on how to personally and practically best take care of your dog's health - in my opinion - it will also help you take care of your wealth! I know every single one of you will benefit from reading this book and following the advice that's in it."

—SUZE ORMAN,
New York Times best-selling author,
Host of the Women & Money podcast

"Thank you Dr. Gardner! This book is practically veterinary school between two covers, brought into plain language, plus all the love needed to make sense of the science and provide practical tips to care for your aging dog with confidence. Mary has an outrageous wealth of wisdom to match her devotion to our furry family members, and she shares it all here. You will be informed and prepared, and you will be touched."

—DR. BJ MILLER,
Human hospice and palliative care doctor,
TED Talk alumni and author

"It's Never Long Enough is a book for every dog owner. It is easy to read without being demeaning to the reader's intelligence, yet contains a depth of knowledge available for those readers that want a complete understanding of the topic."

—DR. MIKE PETTY CVMA, CVPP, CCRT

FOREWORD

Dr. Faith Banks

If you have a senior or geriatric pet, you should know the name: Dr. Mary Gardner. She is a veterinarian who has dedicated her life to her grey muzzle patients and helping their families. She has committed her career to educating other veterinarians about respectful and compassionate care that meets the particular needs of aging pets, including through that component of life that is death. Whether pets' lives are long or short, at the end, every pet deserves a good death. Through her veterinary practice, educational conferences, journal articles, and veterinary medical textbook, Dr. Mary has made it her mission to teach veterinarians how to better provide care for pets during their late life stages as she spreads her messages across the globe.

Now, by writing this book, Dr. Mary continues to expand sharing her knowledge and experience with pet parents directly. It is a must-read for all pet owners who have aging dogs. Filled with wisdom, pets' and their families' stories, healthcare information, humor and love, it is an invaluable guide for pet parents who are navigating their beloved dogs' senior and geriatric years. The caregiver tips, backed up by veterinary medical knowledge and experience, make this book a bible for pet parents caring for their aged canine companions. This book will prepare you for the ups and downs of living with an elderly pet, and help lighten the load moving forward.

Drs Faith and Mary at a hospice conference

I first met Dr. Mary at an international conference for pet hospice and palliative care in 2011. She quickly became a close friend as we compared stories, successes, best practices and a deep understanding of this relatively new type of care called animal hospice. I continue to be inspired by her dedication and passion for educating new and seasoned veterinarians and all pet parents throughout the world. From building an incredibly successful, nationwide veterinary in-home hospice and end-of-life practice, Lap of Love, to becoming a highly sought-after international speaker, to opening an aquamation and memorial center for pets, Dr. Mary has the insight and expertise to guide those willing to learn. These pages are a road map for pet parents as they traverse the potentially bumpy caregiving path ahead.

I have been a mobile hospice veterinarian in Canada for over a decade, and I am so excited to be able to recommend this groundbreaking book to my clients. It covers countless pieces of information families will need throughout their dog's golden years. When I consult with pet parents, I try to empower them with the knowledge they need to understand why their pets are acting the way they are and what it means. I support and encourage them to be able to care for their pets at home, thus eliminating middle-of-the-night trips to the emergency room. This book empowers pet parents to better understand and effectively care for their aging pets. You will find answers to the most common questions pet parents ask about their elderly dogs. You will learn about the aging process, how to recognize age-related ailments, and what it means if your dog has them. You will

Good friends - Drs Faith and Mary

obtain tools and support to help you manage those ailments, and to plan for the moment your beloved dog passes. And because your elderly ailing dog may need your intensive caregiver energy, this book also emphasizes how caregivers can care for themselves. In short, Dr. Mary shares how pet parents can extend and enhance their geriatric dogs' lives and experience more joyful moments with their cherished, wagging-tail family members.

How lucky I am to call Dr. Mary my colleague, visionary mentor and dear friend. How lucky you are to care for a beloved pet, and to gain insight into Dr. Mary's life and share in her love, humor, positive spirit and knowledge.

TABLE OF

Contents

PART THREE: AGING WELL AND CARING
FOR THE GREY MUZZLES 299

PART FOUR: ENDURING THE UNENDURABLE — PREPARING FOR AND SAYING GOODBYE 413

ADDITIONAL

resources and supplements:

 Website dedicated to this book containing additional resources, tips and product information broken down by chapter:

 Activity book to help children going through the loss of a dog:

 Workbook for journaling your dog's care plan, multiple assessments tools (cognition, quality of life, etc), goals of care, bucket lists, joys of living list, life quality calendar and more:

A shopping page containing recommended products that are sold on Amazon:

Dr. Mary Gardner's YouTube channel which contains a ton of resources:

Dr. Mary Gardner's website which has blogs, videos and more:

IT'S NEVER
LONG ENOUGH

INTRODUCTION:

How my voyage began

"The best way to approach happiness is expansion of yourself...
with creation... with love... with sharing... with knowledge."

— JACQUES COUSTEAU

Oddly, I never wanted to be a veterinarian when I was growing up—which doesn't mean I didn't always love animals, because I do! Ideally, I wanted to follow in the fin strokes of Simone and Jacques Cousteau. My father owned a dive shop on North Caicos, a remote island within the Turks and Caicos, where we spent a few summers taking tourists on scuba trips. I was too small to scuba but I snorkeled and played tour guide from our dive boat as best as an 8-year-old could. I thought the ocean was my calling!

Besides those few summers on the island, I grew up in rural Orange County, New York. My brother, sister, and I had a cornfield to dash through, an old barn to hide in, snowy hills to sled down, flowers to harvest, and wild critters to stalk. I liked animals, as most kids do, and we had dogs to grow up with—usually Great Pyrenees. My first one's name was Lump. And cats usually came to us via the typical stray route—they strolled in one day and treated us as their family.

Me in North Caicos – now in hindsight – I probably should not have done that to the fish!

Me, our family dog Lump, and my older sister, Sharon.

My parents divorced when I was 9. After that I spent most of the time with my mother. We lived in low-income housing, and some weeks we had to count coins to get our necessities at the food store. I desperately wanted a pet, but we often rented rooms or had other temporary accommodations, which made it impossible. I was too embarrassed to bring friends to where I stayed, but a dog or cat wouldn't care where I slept or what my humble dwelling was as long as they could be with me. A pet would give me the friend I wanted but couldn't have.

When I was in high school, we were able to move into a 768-square-foot home with a small backyard. I could finally have my own dog! I immediately went to the humane society to find my new best friend.

As I scouted the kennel rows, I wanted to take every dog home with me. Then I spotted this fuzzy, dirty beige, sweet-faced thing with dark eyes that melted my heart. Her name was Schmoo and the shelter identified her as a Samoyed (with a touch of Great Pyrenees). I had no idea what a Samoyed was and I didn't care—I adopted her.

I brought her home and immediately bathed her because she was covered in dirt. And seemingly magically (and with a bit of horror), all the dirt turned blood red when her coat got wet! I didn't understand what was happening. I soon realized Schmoo had fleas. And I later learned that most of the "dirt" was flea poop, which contained the digested blood from the meals the fleas were enjoying at Schmoo's expense.

Me and Snow White

16

After giving her the longest bath, I toweled her off and, voilá, she turned pearly white—as a Samoyed should! The prettiest dog I had ever seen. We thought she needed a new name for her new life and new look. Snow White was most fitting.

Snow White and I were instant buddies. She was a friend to all who met her. She slept in my bed and loved riding in the car. Having my own dog was the best!

The hardest moment in my life was leaving Snow White behind when I left home to attend the University of Miami. While I studied marine affairs full-time, I also got a job and worked hard so I could afford off-campus housing to bring Snow White to Miami. In hindsight, South Florida is not the best place for a furry Samoyed! But like most of us, she lived in air-conditioned comfort and went out after sunset. She was my companion throughout college and my first job working for a maritime lawyer.

Although I loved my boss, my first job was not one that I envisioned for my future. So I resigned and accepted a position as a trainer at my family's software company. I knew nothing about software, but I enjoyed learning it and had the gift of gab and no fear of public speaking. Eventually I moved up in the company and became a product manager who worked with the research and development team. I loved designing the software that the programmers coded. But the job required travel, and about 40% of the time I was on the road.

While traveling in October 1999, I received a horrible phone call from my dog sitter. Snow White had gotten into a terrible fight with another dog and was admitted to the veterinary hospital. I raced home the next day to see her.

I'll never forget the day they wheeled her into the room where I waited. They had shaved her coat to uncover and clean the huge gashes in her flesh. She had over 50 bite marks, with tubes protruding from under her skin to help drain the fluid from her wounds. Her jaw was wired because it had been broken. As miserable as Snow White must have felt, she still wagged her tail when she saw me.

About a week later, the veterinarian allowed me to take Snow White home to care for her. That was the most difficult thing I ever had to do. I tried for several days, but she was not eating well, she wouldn't take her pills, and I couldn't clean her extensive wounds sufficiently. I took her back to the veterinary hospital because I knew they could care for her better than I could.

After another week, Snow White's condition had worsened. The veterinarian called to tell me they gave her a blood transfusion and suggested I come visit her. I left work immediately. I was escorted to the treatment room, where my beautiful Snow White was lying on a blanketed pad on the floor, being well cared for. But I could tell she was not well. She looked yellow to me (at the time, I didn't know that her abnormal color indicated liver failure).

Once again, she wagged her tail when she saw me. It seemed like Snow White could never have a bad day—a trait I wish I possessed.

I spent two hours with her, sitting on the floor, petting her head in my lap, and talking to her about my day. Snow White was now 12 years old. Besides this

 Me and Snow White shortly before her accident.

setback, she had been very healthy her whole life. But as I would later learn, an older dog has a hard time fighting infection and recovering from organ damage.

At 6:01 p.m. Snow White looked at me. Then her head arched back and her legs stretched out in front of her. I knew instantly that she was dying.

I screamed for the doctor, and the whole veterinary team ran in and lifted her onto the exam table. The veterinarian started CPR. As hard as they tried, they could not bring Snow White back. I watched in shock, and I stood there, stunned. I had been certain Snow White would recover and return home with me one day soon.

The veterinary clinic team was so kind to me. They gave me time alone with my beloved friend, and eventually I asked if I could take her home to bury her. They helped me carry her to my car, and I made that dreadful drive home. My friends met me there and helped me bury Snow White.

Losing Snow White was horrible. And it hurt me when people would say, "Well, she was old," or "She was just a dog." I was so blessed to have had her in my life. She will always be my first angel to watch over me.

Snow White's inspiration

It took a few months before I was ready to invite another dog to share my life. I had fallen in love with Samoyeds, so my eventual search led me to a joyful puppy who I named Serissa. Soon after I also welcomed a new Doberman puppy named Neo. I was excited to watch Neo and Serissa grow up together.

 Serissa and Neo

Shortly after I lost Snow White, I started to yearn for more knowledge about animal health and diseases. Although I was 29 years old, I realized I wanted to start the long journey to become a veterinarian!

So I began volunteering at the humane society. It was a mix of incredible fun—sharing my time caring for the animals and learning about anesthesia and surgery in the spay/neuter ward—and dreadful heartbreak: saying goodbye to animals who weren't adopted and had to be euthanized.

When I was 30, I quit my software job and began working as a kennel assistant at a veterinary hospital. This was a humbling move. One week I was training CEOs of large corporations on their new software, and the next week I was cleaning kennels and picking up dog poop in the hospital lobby.

I also enrolled in the undergraduate courses that were required before

I had the honor of delivering the student commencement address to my veterinary school class.

admission to veterinary school. The moment I met the minimum requirements, I applied only to the University of Florida College of Veterinary Medicine. The average starting salary for a veterinarian was about $55,000 at that time, and the in-state tuition would allow me to graduate with less student loan debt than if I went to school elsewhere. My grades were not sterling, but somehow I earned an interview at the college! Luckily my gift of gab helped in the interview, and I was fortunate to be accepted after my first application. In August 2004, I started veterinary school at the age of 31.

Serissa and Neo helped me through those wonderful, scary, tiring, amazing, and fact-filled four years of veterinary school! I am proud to have graduated with the University of Florida College of Veterinary Medicine Class of 2008. I wouldn't have changed one step in my path to become a veterinarian.

I've got the veterinary degree—now what?

Finding a great fit in a veterinary practice as a new graduate can be a challenge, and I was lucky to be hired into a wonderful clinic in Deerfield Beach, Florida:

Pet Vet Animal Hospital. I worked with three other fantastic and fun veterinarians who mentored me and a staff who appreciated my antics. I loved general practice! I loved the pets, I loved the clients, and I loved what I was learning. Yet I began to feel I needed to make a bigger impact in my life and help animals in a different way...

So I started exploring options to work elsewhere within the animal health industry. Maybe in the pharmacology field, or maybe for a technology company? I was still searching when my friend and fellow gator Dr. Dani McVety called to catch up and to ask if I was interested in partnering with her in her new endeavor.

For about a year, Dani had been providing in-home veterinary hospice and euthanasia services. I knew of another veterinarian in Deerfield Beach who provided a similar service and I thought that it must be depressing as a full-time job, so I had never considered it. But the way Dani explained her home visits—the comfort she saw in her patients, how the families reacted, and how much satisfaction and gratitude she received—I wanted to hear more about how I could help Dani.

I visited Dani in Tampa, Florida, and we brainstormed for two days straight. I fell in love with this idea, and something inside me lit up! The reason I left my good software job, cleaned kennels, and went through veterinary school was because of the death of my dog Snow White. I realized I wanted to make an impact in my career by focusing on helping families who were losing their pets to advanced age or irreversible medical conditions. It was perfect for me!

Dani and I dreamt of ways we could grow and expand the business to help more families. We would also need a unique kind of veterinary practice software, and I started designing it in my head that night.

Driving back to South Florida after that meeting was exhilarating. I was so excited to start this new type of work in veterinary end-of-life care and grow the company to offer these services nationwide one day.

In the summer of 2010, our company, which is full-heartedly named Lap of Love, employed only Dani and me. We answered phones, scheduled appointments, and visited patients at home whenever and wherever families needed us. We were tired and nearly broke—but excited as the company started to grow.

Fast-forward 12 years, and in 2022 Lap of Love employs more than 200 full-time veterinarians offering end-of-life care in over 100 locations across the country. We help over 100,000 families a year with end-of-life medical care for their pets who are terminally ill or have such advanced aging problems that their quality of life is poor. I have transitioned out of making in-home visits to full-time management of the company and helping our Lap of Love family.

Aren't I depressed?

I hear that question often. One might imagine, as I once did when I first learned about veterinary end-of-life services, that euthanizing animals as a full-time job is depressing. And, make no mistake, it can be because you see the sorrow in the families' eyes. But it is rewarding to make a tremendously difficult experience a wee bit better for the pet and the family. The hugs I've gotten are fantastic! The thank-you messages I receive bring me tears of gratitude. For me, I cannot imagine a better niche of veterinary medicine than hospice and euthanasia. If only I could possess a tail to show how truly happy I am in life!

But the one thing that weighed on me heavily was the visits I would make to homes where the pets had not seen their veterinarian in a very long time. It became clear to me that not only could veterinary care have helped the pet sooner in some way, such as by alleviating pain or anxiety, a veterinarian could have made simple sugges-tions to help the owner manage their ailing pet better and provide the pet and pet parent a better quality of life.

I loved my hospice patients. I could do so much for them and their families before the end. But I wanted so many of them to see their veterinarian even sooner and more regularly because they could have received care for months to years to enhance and likely extend their lives—long before my help was needed.

I realize that it may be diffi-cult to get many pets, especially

I love getting love from grey muzzles.

older pets, into the carrier or car for veterinary visits. I realize that some families may presume (or may even be told) that their pet is old and there is nothing they can do. But in so many cases, there is so much we can and should do!

Sailing on in my journey of sharing

I've spent years researching the ailments that plague our aging pets and the ways we can help manage and protect them in their homes. I travel the world teaching veterinarians these simple tips and have written numerous articles in the veterinary literature and co-edited a veterinary textbook on these topics.

I am inspired to write this book because I also want to reach more families directly.

As you skipper your dog's voyage through his or her* golden years, I hope this book gives you healthcare insights and guidance that sparks new thoughts on how you can help your senior dog continue to live happily and comfortably. I also hope to give you a few good laughs and maybe a wee cry along the way. Throughout these chapters, I share experiences from caring for my own dogs and describe lessons learned from my patients and their families' love and heartbreak.** You'll find the latest information on aging and common ailments of older dogs, checklists to help you monitor your dog for aging changes and illnesses, questions to ask your veterinarian, tips to manage your dog at home, and product suggestions.*** I also cover the importance of checking in on yourself and other family members as you manage the challenges of caring for an ailing older dog, how to assess your pet's quality of life, and what to consider before and after your pet earns angel wings.

Me and Serissa a few months before she became an angel.

Geriatric pets are now my life's passion, and there is nothing better to me than a grey muzzle, a weak and wobbly dog, and a skinny, crusty cat. They are the best! And so are the families who love them.

---

* Instead of the impersonal pronoun "it" that you'll see in a lot of scientific literature when referring to a singular pet, throughout this book I wanted to be more personal and use "he" and "she" and related pronouns in the singular sense. All pets are loved, no matter their sex, so every "he" or "she" I refer to remains a cherished representative for your pet.

** It bears repeating that the content in this book is based on my professional and personal knowledge and experiences and is not intended as a substitute for a veterinarian-client-patient relationship. Always partner with and consult your veterinarian about your pet's healthcare.

Part One:

GETTING TO THE GREY MUZZLE LIFE STAGE

In every relationship there comes a time when many more days lie behind you than ahead. When we're granted the benefit of that keen awareness, our remaining days together become even more precious. You may have already begun to recognize the subtle changes that signal that shift in the sands of time as your dog ages... less pep in her steps, diminished sparkle in his eyes, shrinking muscles, and maybe even dwindling enthusiasm about activities that once brought your dog unreserved joy.

It may seem like only yesterday that you celebrated "Gotcha Day" (adoption day!) with your new furry family member. And our dogs have indeed become family members, especially compared with many of their counterparts of years past. Although time typically marches on too quickly in many aspects of our lives, time seems to really hoof it when it comes to our dog's lifetimes. Why is that? Why can't they live as long as we do? Why do large dogs have even shorter lifespans than other dogs do? Why do some dogs age more successfully than others? What's the difference between a senior dog and a geriatric dog? Can dogs become frail, like some elderly people do? I explore these questions, and more, to help you ponder the mysteries and mechanisms of aging in dogs.

CHAPTER 1:

A part of the family: A dog's place in the home sweet home

> "If aliens are watching us through telescopes, they're going to think the dogs are the leaders of the planet. If you see two life forms, one of them's making a poop, the other one's carrying it for him, who would you assume is in charge?"
>
> —JERRY SEINFELD

Think of the classic, beloved animal stories from the past. Lassie, a devoted collie, romped around the farm with her best human buddy, Jeff. Lassie mostly stayed outdoors, keeping an eye out for trouble and helping Jeff's dad run the family farm. Always ready with an excited bark, Lassie helped straighten things out.

How about your own Lassie? A little different? In all likelihood, she mostly stays inside. She curls up on the couch or snuggles beside you in bed at will.

How times have changed ...

Dogs and cats have lived alongside people for centuries. The human and non-human animals found mutual benefit in hanging out together. Classically, domesticated dogs were guardians, warning of threats or barking off invaders.

Were friendships struck? Attachments made? Of course! But most dogs were considered "just animals" and held a different place in a household. Our relationships with pets have changed over the last few decades.

I remember as a child growing up with our family dog Lump. We gave him a doghouse and he primarily lived outside. He occasionally graced our living room but was never allowed in the bedrooms. Contrast that with my household today. As I write this, my two cats are snoozing on my bed pillow and my dog is on the couch nestled in my throw blanket! Pet hair everywhere is the decor of love.

According to a 2015 poll, more than 95% of pet owners consider their pets members of the family (Shannon-Missal 2015). And we demonstrate this kinship love: 45% of owners bought birthday presents for their pets, and 81% of cat owners and 72% of dog owners let their pets sleep in their bed at night. The fact that you are reading this book shows that the four-footed critters who share their lives with you are cherished family members and need attentive care as they age.

Where the pets are

So how many pets are out there in the U.S. today? How many families share their lives with pets?

At the end of 2016, research showed that nearly 57% of households have at least one type of pet, whether they be dogs, cats, fish, frogs, ferrets, or other furry and feathered and not-furred pets! (San Filippo 2018) The numbers vary by state, with Wyoming, West Virginia, Nebraska, Vermont, and Idaho having 70% or more of households with pets.

Based on the 2019-2020 American Pet Products Association National Pet Owners Survey, that number has climbed, with 67% of U.S. households that now have at least one type of pet (APPA). Another 2019-2020 survey reported that 63.4 million households (about 52%) in the U.S. have dogs and 42.7 million households (about 35%) have cats; 1.6 million (1.3%) have horses. (Bedford 2020)

Even amid the COVID-19 pandemic, a separate market research publisher, Packaged Facts, estimated a 4% growth in the percentage of pet-owning households in 2020. (Packaged Facts)

For the family

What do we do for our family members? Ensure their basic needs are met—a home, food—absolutely. We also let our family members know they are needed and loved. We want them to have certainty and significance. We do whatever we can to help them. They are a part of us.

My friend Steve Dale is a certified animal behavior consultant, famous pet journalist, stellar pet parent educator, and cat and dog disciple extraordinaire. When his dog Ethel passed, one of his readers expressed sympathy by writing, "I feel bad for you, but she was only a dog." Steve replied:

She was only a dog

Only a dog sees you every day with the same joy she did on the previous day. A dog's love is the most dependable guarantee of a relationship there is at a time when few relationships are guaranteed.

Only a dog will always tell you the truth. Dogs don't lie.

Only a dog knows exactly how you're feeling .... dogs innately take our emotional temperatures, arguably better than your significant other or your own children.

Only a dog will love you—always and forever and unconditionally.

You are right dear reader—she was only a dog.

 Ethel with her stick and her dad, Steve.

Veterinary care for the ages

Veterinary education and the profession have shifted along with the shifts in animals' roles in society and humans' overall relationship with pets. For example, horses used to be integral to daily life because they were our mode of transportation. So while some veterinarians still care for horses, most veterinarians today focus on dogs and cats. The American Veterinary Medical Association (AVMA) reports that more than 50,000 veterinarians in private clinical practices provide companion animal care (dogs, cats, pet birds, and exotics) exclusively, while about 4,100 care for horses predominantly or exclusively. (U.S. veterinarians 2020)

Despite the focus on dogs and cats, most veterinary students are still trained to care for many animal species. They complete medical and surgical rotations in equine and large-animal (cows, pigs, sheep) care, even if they plan to become dog and cat docs. And the education we receive in veterinary school continues to advance and expand. Of course we learn basic medical care, but we also learn about specialized orthopedic surgeries, heart surgeries, dialysis for kidney failure, chemotherapy for cancer, acupuncture, and so much more.

Pets' changing status in the family, along with advances in veterinary medicine that mirror those in human medicine, have increased pets' life expectancy. Just as healthcare is crucial to us, veterinary care for our pets is paramount. Routine care such as vaccinations and parasite preventives not only ward off disease in our pets, they help keep other pets and even people in the household healthy. Pets' veterinary care may range from a physical examination and quick nail trim to a kidney transplant or radiation therapy.

Did you know that most any disease that can affect a human can affect a dog, too? Dogs commonly have gum disease, cataracts, heart disease, arthritis, cancer, dementia, and other familiar human ailments. Basic to advanced diagnostic tests and simple to complex treatments are at the ready from your primary care veterinary team or veterinary specialists.

The great news is that basic, routine veterinary care goes a long way in keeping pets healthy family members during their lifetimes of happily shared adventures

FUN FACT: BEST FRIENDS, BEST MEDICINE

Through the years, we've learned about the health benefits of sharing our homes with dogs, cats, and other pets. Most family physicians (97%) agree that pets provide health benefits for people. And 74% said that with medical evidence to support it, they would prescribe pets to improve their patients' overall health. (New Survey HABRI 2014) Studies show that pets help their owners be happier and more physically fit, with health benefits that include:

- More opportunities to socialize, exercise, and spend time outside
- Lower cholesterol and triglyceride levels and blood pressure
- More companionship and less loneliness and depression (Centers for Disease Control 2019)

with you. Seeking veterinary advice and following veterinary recommendations can also help prevent some of the costly health problems that may otherwise emerge as a pet ages.

So how much do pet parents typically spend on pet care? The same 2015 poll that reported 95% of owners think of their pets as family members assessed how much the owners typically spend annually: (Shannon-Missal 2015)

- Food/treats—$476.60
- Medical costs (veterinary appointments, medications, procedures)—$425.70
- Pet sitting or boarding—$128.50
- Toys—$63.70
- Other (habitats, collars, litter)—$97.40
- Total—$1,191.90

Adjusted for inflation as of February 2021, that total equates to $1,341.36. (CPI Inflation Calculator)

We all vary in our abilities to care for our dogs, especially when they are older. But we all care and don't want our dogs to suffer. So this book focuses on the care we can provide, includes care options that you might not otherwise be aware of, helps you navigate what to expect as dogs age, and suggests how senior and older dogs with health problems can be managed in the home, including at the end of their lives.

The intent of this book is not to cover every disease a dog can get, but rather to focus on age-related changes. What causes them? And how can you care for a dog who may be plagued by them? The care suggestions in this book will range from those that are inexpensive and easy to implement to those that are elaborate and time-intensive.

Regardless, my intent with this book is to help you keep your beloved dog a healthy, active, engaged, and comfortable family member throughout the golden years—may they be many!

CHAPTER 2:

Defining senior vs. geriatric: The fragility of life

"You can't help getting older, but you don't have to get old."

— George Burns, American comedian, actor, and musician

Thanksgiving is one of my favorite holidays. I vividly remember going to my Grandma Gardner's house in New Jersey every November and the phenomenal meal she prepared. After decades passed, our lovely tradition moved from the blustery Northeast to my father's house in South Florida, where my Grandma had also bought a small condominium.

With the move, my Grandma awarded her chef's hat to my father, but our gatherings were still as memorable. (Don't tell

 My grandparents Margaret and Edward.

my father, but Grandma may have been a better cook!) She still insisted on bringing a side dish, but in her late 70s, Grandma also relinquished her driver's seat. That challenged us to provide a suitable "taxi"—one with perfect seat height and legroom for easy entry and exit, with space in the back for a walker. The driver would need to patiently wait while she got ready and not let her forget her sweater. The temperatures in November could still be 80 F, but Grandma got cold easily. The driver would also have to be willing to leave the party early when Grandma got tired.

One Thanksgiving holiday with my grandmother Margaret and my father, Allan.

I loved being Grandma's driver! Her condo on the ground floor was always tidy, and it held all of the same pictures and most of the same furniture from her New Jersey home. It also, somehow, held the same smell—my favorite scent of Grandma. While she got ready, I waited on the couch and picked out my favorite candies from the familiar crystal dish precisely placed on her side table. Each quest brought back wonderful memories of my visits with her over the years.

I loved that Grandma held onto my arm as we made our way to my car. Her hands were thin and her skin was dotted with wisdom spots. Her eyes had a grey haze but still sparkled. Her lipstick was always perfect on her thinned lips, and she never had a bad hair day. I would watch her carefully shuffle her feet to maintain steady contact with the ground and think, "So this is where my size 11 feet come from!" I would gingerly help her into my car, place her carefully guarded secret-recipe apple pie on her lap, and stash her walker in the back—and away we would go. I cherished the time and conversation we had together in the car.

Once we arrived at my father's house, someone would come out to help Grandma. Then off she went to be a social butterfly! She'd sit on the couch and everyone took turns talking with her. My father would come bounding out of the kitchen with his trademark smile and ask me how everything went while chauffeuring Grandma.

At the time of Grandma's move, my father was in his late 50s and nearly retired, but his energy level and activities matched those of his 30s. He golfed three times a week, worked on his dive boat, and treasure hunted.

Yup, my father is a real-life shipwreck diver! He is always as tan as can be because

My father, Allan, the treasure hunter.

he basically lives outdoors. Who knows whether he has age spots? They are camouflaged! He is thin and fit and, although he has slightly bad posture, he moves around with ease.

My father and my grandmother were both senior citizens then, but they were very different. My father was and still is completely independent and mentally sound with no physical limitations or medical problems. My grandmother had decreased vision and hearing, she was weak and walked slowly, but she did not have other known medical problems. Her mind was as sharp as a tack. She depended on family to help her with various things, but not to the point of needing to move to a nursing facility. I didn't know the precise reasons why back then, but I realized my grandmother was geriatric. She was fragile, while my father was not.

As my career started to focus on our older pets, I dove down a rabbit hole to learn about the differences between senior and geriatric.

An older dog by any other name would be as sweet

People tend to be sensitive about age. Consider our various reactions to, "How old are you?" or "You don't look older than 40!" And we tend to transfer some of the same feelings we have about being human to our dogs. What do you call your older dog? A senior? A geriatric? An oldie but goodie? A sugar face? Or my favorite, a grey muzzle?

In 2005, the American Animal Hospital Association suggested that dogs be considered senior when they reach the last 25% of their expected lifespan for their breed. (Senior Care Guidelines Task Force 2005)

In pondering this question of senior vs. geriatric while co-writing the 2017 textbook *Treatment and Care of the Veterinary Geriatric Patient*, I turned to insight from the American Veterinary Medical Association (AVMA) and discovered there wasn't a strict definition for a "senior" pet. Their official take:

> *"It varies, but cats and small dogs are generally considered 'senior' at 7 years of age. Larger breed dogs tend to have shorter life spans compared to smaller breeds and are often considered senior when they are 5 to 6 years of age. Contrary to popular belief, dogs do not age at a rate of 7 human years for each year in dog years."* (Senior Pets/AVMA)

That's right, dog's ages in human years can no longer be determined simply by multiplying their age by 7, and I'll dive into the new calculation in the next chapter.

Based on charts that estimate relative ages of dogs and cats based on human years, pets become senior in relation to their size when they are:

- 10 years old and weigh up to 20 pounds,
- 9 years old and weigh between 21 and 50 pounds,
- 8 years old and weigh between 51 and 90 pounds, and
- 7 years old and weigh more than 90 pounds. (Lobprise [1] 2020)

If pets are considered "senior" between the ages of 7 and 10 years, how about "geriatric"? I found that the AVMA tends to use the terms "senior" and "geriatric" interchangeably. So I turned to insight from the terms used to describe people. The American Association of Retired Persons focuses on issues that affect people over age 50 and begins marketing to people then. Human medicine defines the term "senior" as a person who is 65 years or older. However, the term "geriatric" accounts for aging, health, mental status, and how well a person can function in the world.

And I wondered, does this play out in pets too?

The fragility factor: Handle with care

As dogs age, just like we two-footed folk, things get a little less automatic. You may notice your dog is a little less steady on his feet than he used to be, which can—and should!—cause you concern when he's rip-roaring and ready to jump out of the car and go see the world.

Aging in dogs and people is similar with respect to our nervous, immune, and muscle systems and gene alterations. (Banzato 2019) Dogs share our environments and develop many of the same age-related diseases that we do, such as cancer, heart and kidney disease, cognitive problems, and many others. (Hua 2016)

In people, the concept of the *Fragility Syndrome* (also known as *Frailty Syndrome*) is used in geriatric care, which stems from having diminished physical and cognitive *physiological reserve*. Physiological reserve is basically the body's ability to be resilient, and it helps organs function properly under stress. Physiological reserve decreases with age, but not equally in all people. (Heinze-Milne 2019)

Diminished physiological reserve makes elderly people more vulnerable to stressors—even seemingly mild stressors such as taking a new medicine, having a minor urinary tract infection, or undergoing a minor diagnostic or surgical procedure. With diminished physiological reserve, experiencing a stressor means a person has a higher likelihood of an adverse health outcome. (Clegg 2013) These stressors can cause a drastic change in a vulnerable person's health status. A seemingly healthy elderly person who has experienced a stressor but has diminished physiological reserve may go from having stable posture and balance to being unsteady or experiencing falls, from being mobile to immobile, from being independent in daily activities to being dependent on others, or from being alert and aware to delirious. (Clegg 2013) Thus, the person is considered to be fragile or frail.

People with fragility or frailty also have a greater risk of hospitalizations and death. (Mello 2018) Keeping fragile people well-functioning and safe becomes more and more of a concern. Nearly 10% of people 65 years of age or older are fragile, and fragility increases to 25% to 50% of people aged 85 years or older. (Liu 2014)

The encouraging take from those statistics is that up to 75% of people over age 85 years may *not* be fragile. So strategies to prevent fragility and tools to identify it in human medicine are crucial and have been studied. (Clegg 2013)

Signs of fragility or frailty in people

Physicians use various combinations of these indicators to classify fragility or frailty syndrome in people:

- Unexplained weight loss
- Weakness (including grip strength)
- Slowed motor performance (gait/walking speed)
- Fatigue/exhaustion
- Impaired balance
- Decreased physical activity
- Social withdrawal
- Mild cognitive dysfunction
- Increased vulnerability to physiological stresses

People are considered "geriatric" once they experience three of these signs of fragility or frailty:

- Weakness (reduced grip strength)
- Unexplained or unintentional weight loss (chronic undernutrition)
- Slowed mobility (gait speed)
- Self-reported fatigue or exhaustion
- Low physical activity level

Now we know the same is true for older dogs. They may be "old" in terms of age in years like my father (sorry, Dad!), but there may also come a point when they become fragile, like my grandmother.

Signs of fragility or frailty in pets

These signs and classifications can be applied to dogs, too. Observations like:

- Slight quivers in their legs
- More difficulty rising

- Less interest in food
- Slower walking pace and reluctance to run
- Longer naps or restlessness at night
- Less interest in outings or play

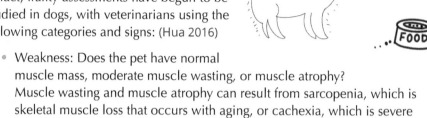

In fact, frailty assessments have begun to be studied in dogs, with veterinarians using the following categories and signs: (Hua 2016)

- Weakness: Does the pet have normal muscle mass, moderate muscle wasting, or muscle atrophy? Muscle wasting and muscle atrophy can result from sarcopenia, which is skeletal muscle loss that occurs with aging, or cachexia, which is severe weight loss plus muscle wasting associated with disease.
- Chronic undernutrition: What is the pet's body condition (overweight or underweight based on assessment of body fat), level of appetite, and coat quality and density?
- Poor mobility: Is the pet's gait normal, or does the pet have stiffness, lameness, or incoordination? Does the pet have joint pain and, if so, is it moderate or marked?
- Exhaustion: Does the pet have normal exercise tolerance, or is exercise associated with tiredness or breathlessness?
- Low physical activity: Is the pet's activity level normal, moderately low, or low?

All of these can be signs that the body is not quite working as it used to, and there can be many causes. But they do signify keeping a closer watch over our faithful friends to ensure that they have all they need to continue to thrive and avoid stumbling blocks.

Keeping an eye out for changes

So how do we stay vigilant? Only recently has a "frailty index" for dogs been proposed to help practicing veterinarians keep a closer watch on our geriatric friends. The frailty index is intended for veterinarians to better assess how close older dogs may be to the end of life and to help determine the best treatment options for them. (Banzato 2019) The frailty index is calculated based on information commonly obtained during veterinary visits: physical examination findings, laboratory test results, and a health status questionnaire.

In addition to helping veterinarians evaluate older dogs, this frailty index will help veterinarians identify patients who have high scores—regardless of the patient's age—and need extra care and more follow-up veterinary visits, compared with patients who have lower frailty index scores. (Banzato 2019)

One of my dreams is for pet parents, together with their veterinarians, to better identify signs of advanced aging, vulnerability, and fragility or frailty in their dogs. Developing, testing, and using standardized health and quality-of-life assessments of geriatric dogs should provide better evidence-based clinical tools. And in using better assessment tools, the care and treatment of geriatric pets can be more closely and individually optimized.

In the meantime, create a Pet Health Journal to help you chart your pet's course during smooth sailing and squalls, which you can review with your veterinarian. See Chapter 23 "Journaling: Tracking your dog's health".

What can be done for frail pets?

Research shows that frailty in people is preventable and its progression can be halted or even reversed! By focusing on nutritional counseling and dietary support (ensuring the correct amount of protein intake and total calories), strength training to prevent muscle loss (individualized to the patient's abilities), mental stimulation, and health education, frailty can be prevented and turned back. (Ng 2015, Travers 2019, O'Connell 2020])

It isn't a stretch to think that frailty may also be preventable or reversible in dogs. In this book, I highlight how you can help your dog best manage the aging process and the associated changes during their senior years, as well as the diseases that most commonly affect older dogs.

CHAPTER 3:

Aging in pets:
Their clocks tick faster

"You must match time's swiftness with your speed in using it, and you must drink quickly as though from a rapid stream that will not always flow."

— SENECA, ROMAN PHILOSOPHER (4 BC – AD 65)

In the blink of an eye, my dog Sam went from being a middle-aged adult who played mischievously, ran hard, slept like a log, and bounced out of bed as agile as a puppy to becoming an elderly lady! Now she lounges in her bed most of the day, takes leisurely strolls, needs assistance getting into the car, and has trouble sleeping through the night. She still enjoys toys but doesn't play with the youthful vigor she once had. These changes happened over a mere four years. The same types of changes in people would take about four decades!

Let's tackle a popular topic of pet life—how old is your dog in people years? The 7 people years to 1 dog year ratio that you've likely heard of is not a magic conversion number. It depends on many factors, and your dog's overall body size is an important one. Large-breed dogs tend to have a shorter lifespan than small-breed dogs, for reasons I'll go into in the next chapter.

A new canine biological clock

Genetic researchers have developed a new calculation that more accurately converts dog years to people years. (Wang 2020) Their research and the calculation is based on assessing molecules called methyl groups that naturally circulate in the body and are added to specific parts of dogs' DNA over the course of their lifetimes. (A look back to your high school biology class: DNA is deoxyribonucleic acid, a molecule that contains the genetic code in all known organisms and in many viruses. The genetic code essentially instructs an organism's development, life processes, and reproduction.) This addition of methyl groups to DNA (called *DNA methylation*) throughout life also occurs in people and in species other than dogs. DNA methylation gives researchers an accurate way to estimate age and is known as an *epigenetic clock*.

The new calculation shows that:

- an 8-week-old puppy is similar in age to a 9-month-old human baby,
- a 1-year-old dog is roughly 31 human years old (remember, most dogs can have puppies starting at around 6 months of age),
- a 4-year-old dog is about 53 in human years,
- a 7-year-old dog is around 62 human years old, and
- a 12-year-old dog is about 70 in human years. (Wang 2020)

As you can see, the canine epigenetic clock "ticks" faster at first than our human epigenetic clock does—a 2-year-old dog is 42 in human years! Then the canine clock slows later in life—a 15-year-old dog is similar in age to a 74-year-old person. (Morrell 2019)

The new calculation was developed based on Labrador retriever data, but one of the study's lead researchers thinks the epigenetic clock can work for all dog breeds and says that the calculation will continue to be evaluated in other breeds. (Gen Eng Biotech News 2020) And as we well know, some dog breeds live longer than others. So once this research is applied to other dog breeds, it may tell us more about why different breeds have different lifespans. (Morrell 2019)

You can calculate your dog's age in human years by using the new formula:

16 × ln(dog age) + 31 = equivalent human years

Dog age calculator

Quick formula translation: On a scientific calculator, enter your dog's age, then hit the "ln" key. Multiply that result by 16, then add 31.

You can also simply plug your dog's age into the new online dog-to-human-years calculator at: **drmarygardner.com/dogage**

Beyond the numbers: no matter our pets' ages in human years, most of us agree that they do not live long enough. But we can make the last life stage smoother—and potentially help them live a longer, better life.

FUN FACT

Based on time perception tests in mice and high-resolution images of their nerves in action, researchers have evidence that animals can judge time. They found a special group of neurons in a part of the brain called the medial entorhinal cortex, a structure that helps with memory and navigation. These nerve cells switch on and count like a clock while an animal waits. (Morris 2018, Heys 2018)

If your dog seems to look at you with reserved panic if breakfast is 15 minutes overdue, or meanders in and out of the kitchen 10 minutes before dinnertime, it's probably no surprise to you that animals seem to know what time it is!

Is old age a disease?

A closing thought as we delve into more details about aging dogs in the next chapters. A popular mantra among veterinarians (and most people) is that "Old age isn't a disease." While that may be technically true, many health issues associated with aging exist and may develop more readily as fragility arises.

In human medicine, it has been suggested that aging *should* be classified as a disease, because such classification might promote more and faster aging research. Officially designating aging as a disease could enhance more development and rigorous study of therapies to address aging processes and age-related diseases. It could also increase funding for aging research and allow health insurance reimbursement for more treatments that have been proven to prevent, slow, or reverse aging processes. (Bulterijs 2015) Classifying age as a disease could affect pets as well, because developments in human medicine often influence diagnostic tests and treatments in veterinary medicine.

For now, age isn't classified as a disease in people or in dogs, yet it's important to notice as changes occur in your dog and know the steps you can take to keep them comfortable and happy. I believe it is imperative that pet parents understand the aging process, how to recognize age-related conditions and what it means for their dog to have them, how to manage their dog's conditions, and where to find appropriate support to help them help their dog.

CHAPTER 4:

Dignity in aging: The mysteries of growing older

"How did it get so late so soon?"

— Source unverified

(the internet attributes this quote to Dr. Seuss)

As the years pass, like us, our dogs get a little greyer, their skin thins, and their get-up-and-go slows. Most living creatures cannot avoid aging, and aging occurs at different rates.

How and why humans age has been a great debate for centuries! And in the last 100 years, oodles of studies have helped us better understand the aging process in people, along with age-associated diseases and other challenges.

FUN FACT:

One species of jellyfish (*Turritopsis dohrnii*) and their small freshwater relatives called hydra do not age!

For people, it's generally accepted that living a long, healthy life is influenced by many factors, including genetics, relationships, environment, culture, education, occupation, income, and behavior. Behavior encompasses many other factors, such as the choices we make about diet, exercise, sleep, smoking, drinking alcohol, getting regular medical checkups, managing stress, engaging socially, and learning new things.

Many studies on aging focus on centenarians—people who live to be 100 and older. For example, large studies of centenarians in China revealed that mental resilience and optimism are keys to longevity, (Zeng 2017) along with following proven preventive healthcare strategies: eating a rich and varied diet full of grains and fruits, keeping up good dental health, quitting smoking, limiting alcohol intake, and sustaining a calm outlook. (Rong 2019)

We can't study exactly the same health strategies in dogs, but I do see many dogs live well and long with good exercise programs, healthy diets (and proper weights), routine veterinary medical and dental care, and a lot of social interaction.

Dogs contribute to aging research in people

How and why dogs age has been less studied than it has been in people. But that is changing because dogs are excellent models of aging in people. (Sandor 2019) Dogs, rather than mice, are now the center stage for research in human aging, in part because dogs in North America, Australia, and Europe are living life most similar to humans.

How are we similar? Let us count the ways! Dogs have medical care similar to that of people: They are monitored and evaluated frequently, receive vaccinations, and get referred to medical specialists when needed. The amount of money spent on medical procedures and exams for dogs is second only to that spent on human medical care. (Greer 2011) We share our homes, neighborhoods, exercise habits (walking, jogging, swimming, and even surfing!), and often our dinner plates with our dogs. (A morsel of consolation for a concern you might have: Sharing healthy table foods with your dog in moderation—about 10% of total calories—is OK!) Dogs develop many of the same age-related diseases humans do, and they live with the same pollutants (e.g. secondhand smoke and other air pollutants, pesticides, herbicides, and other chemicals) and disease-causing bugs that we do.

Cats are pretty close to living the same lives as humans, too, with the exception of exercise. (Even cat yoga is much more strenuous for humans, as is goat yoga!) But, sadly, not a lot of research has been done yet on factors that relate to the aging process in cats.

Because of the heartwarming facts that dogs receive similar healthcare and share our environment, along with the heart-wrenching fact that dogs live shorter lives compared with people, studies on the factors that influence longevity are relatable to people and can be completed much faster in dogs. Two major lifespan

Me and a yoga-loving goat friend.

studies in dogs include the Morris Animal Foundation's Golden Retriever Lifetime Study and The Dog Aging Project.

The Morris Animal Foundation is gathering lifelong health, environmental, and behavioral data in more than 3,000 pet golden retrievers in the United States. These pups started the study between the ages of 6 months and 2 years with no history of cancer or other potentially life-threatening conditions. They'll be monitored and evaluated throughout their lives. The primary goal of the study is to identify environmental, lifestyle, genetic, and nutritional risk factors for cancer and many other canine diseases.

The Dog Aging Project is conducted by researchers at the University of Washington and Texas A&M University College of Veterinary Medicine and Biomedical Sciences. The project will collect information for 10 years on more than 10,000 mixed-breed and purebred pet dogs of all ages, whether they are healthy or have a chronic disease. The goal is to identify what factors are connected with improved health and longer life in dogs, which will shed light on improving the human lifespan, too.

A pill for the ages?

About 500 of the dogs who are enrolled in The Dog Aging Project will be chosen to also participate in a study that investigates whether rapamycin extends their healthspan—the disease-free period of life. Rapamycin is a drug approved for use in people who receive organ transplants, and it was originally discovered in soil bacteria on Easter Island.

A previous study of rapamycin's effects in a small number of dogs showed that some benefits of treatment may include increased activity, improved heart function, and increased affection toward the owner, with no clinical side effects. (Urfer 2017) That study was too small and too short to evaluate rapamycin's effects on the dogs' healthspan and longevity, so the new study aims to address that. The drug has already been shown to boost longevity in mice, flies, and yeast—and much research into the potential anti-aging effects of rapamycin in humans is underway. So I'm keeping my eye on further rapamycin developments!

Chihuahua vs. Bernese Mountain Dog

In general, we know that larger animals live longer than smaller animals do. For example, a mouse lives about two years and an elephant lives about 50 years or more. But the opposite is true for dogs, who have complex body characteristic differences and a wide lifespan range. This has always intrigued me. Why do small-breed dogs like Chihuahuas live longer than large-breed

 My fur friends BD (small one) and Maple (big one).

dogs like Bernese Mountain dogs?

On average, giant-breed dogs (those weighing more than 110 pounds) have an expected lifespan of only 6 to 8 years. Smaller breeds (weighing less than 20 pounds) live 14 to 16 years, on average. When we learned this in veterinary school, I also wondered whether the same is true for people, because at 6'1", I'm like the Great Dane of the human species!

We can't point to one simple explanation for all the changes that occur as we grow older. To talk about why aging occurs, we have to get a little sciency-wiency. A whopping nine main contributors to aging in mammals provide a few explanations! (López-Otín 2013)

FUN FACT:

A large study of people in the Netherlands showed that women taller than 5'9" were 31% more likely to live to be 90 than women less than 5'3" tall. (Brandts 2019, British Medical Journal 2019)

1) GENOMIC INSTABILITY—DNA undergoes a range of irreversible and damaging informational changes. DNA is a molecule that contains our genetic code and is present in nearly every cell in the body—from fat cells to heart cells to brain cells. Most cells are replenished throughout life because they can make copies of themselves, including their DNA. Cells can also repair DNA, but only to a point.

2) TELOMERE ATTRITION—telomeres are repeating sections of DNA that protect the ends of chromosomes (chromosomes are DNA "packages" inside cells). Telomeres get a wee bit shorter each time a cell divides. Telomere attrition is the gradual loss of these protective end caps (they're like the plastic tips on the ends of shoelaces that keep them from unraveling). When the telomeres get too short, the DNA gets damaged, and the cells stop dividing or die. It turns out that large-breed

TELOMERE

dogs start life with shorter telomeres than small-breed dogs do, so this helps explain their shorter lifespans.

3) EPIGENETIC ALTERATIONS—harmful but potentially reversible age-related changes in the ways genes are expressed.

4) DISRUPTION OF PROTEOSTASIS—age-related mishaps in cellular protein processes and production.

5) DEREGULATION OF NUTRIENT SENSING—the cell processes that ensure proper nutrition for optimal metabolism go awry.

6) MITOCHONDRIAL DYSFUNCTION—the energy-producing machinery of cells becomes defective.

7) CELLULAR SENESCENCE—cells no longer divide as they normally would. (Senescence can be a good thing when it happens to cancer cells because we want them to stop proliferating, but it's a bad thing when it happens to cells that should divide to replenish and replace themselves, such as with wound healing.)

8) STEM CELL EXHAUSTION—stem cells can develop into many different types of cells to replace those that are lost through normal wear and tear, disease, or injury, so when stem cell numbers or functions decline, this replacement stops.

9) ALTERED INTERCELLULAR COMMUNICATION—changes in the many ways that cells normally signal one another, such as through hormones. Hormones are the body's chemical messengers that tell many cells what to do. They help regulate development and growth, appetite and thirst, digestion and metabolism, temperature, behavior, reproduction, and more! One of these hormone messengers is insulin-like growth factor-1 (IGF-1), and its main job is to regulate growth hormone, which in turn affects growth and body composition. Research shows that smaller-breed dogs, which have longer lifespans, have reduced IGF-1 levels, and larger breeds, which have shorter lifespans, have higher IGF-1 levels. In addition, obese dogs—no matter their breed—have higher IGF-1 levels and shorter lifespans. (Greer 2011)

Purebred dogs vs. mixed-breed dogs

What about purebred vs. mixed-breed dogs—does one have a longevity advantage over the other? For almost two centuries, selective breeding has given us our modern breeds, which are genetically isolated and, well, fairly inbred. Sadly, this practice has led to a wide range of breed-specific genetic diseases and disease predispositions that are as diverse among breeds as is their appearance. It can be impressive, playing a "disease-by-breed trivia" game with a veterinarian. Name a breed, and we will name its common disorder. Cavalier King Charles spaniel?

Heart disease. Golden retriever? Cancer. Boxer? Heart disease and cancer. German shepherd? Spinal cord disease. There's no coveted grand prize in this trivia game. Any of these problems can reduce any pet's life expectancy.

Some diseases are more likely to occur in breeds with certain body shapes, sizes, or coats. For example, barrel-chested dogs are prone to a life-threatening disease called gastric dilatation-volvulus (GDV) wherein the stomach twists on itself. Large-breed dogs are more likely to develop geriatric-onset laryngeal paralysis and polyneuropathy, a disease I devote an entire chapter to later.

Studies show that purebred dogs have a shorter life expectancy than mixed-breed mutts. One study of more than 2 million dogs seen at 787 primary care veterinary hospitals in the United States showed that the estimated lifespan of a mixed-breed dog was 14.45 years (14.42 to 14.49 years) and a purebred dog was 14.14 years (14.12 to 14.15 years). (Urfer 2019) That's less than half a year difference, but it was a statistically significant difference (a difference not due to chance alone).

The study also showed that regardless of whether a dog was purebred or mixed, the two factors associated with a bigger improvement in lifespan included being spayed or neutered (for example, intact females lived about 13.77 years and spayed females lived about 14.35 years) and body size—being smaller is better (but mixed-breed large and giant dogs still did not live as long as purebred small dogs). (Urfer 2019)

A smaller, separate study of more than 20,000 dogs from three independent primary care veterinary hospitals in the United States did not find a statistically significant survival advantage for mixed breeds vs. purebred dogs. (Urfer 2020)

The ultimate goal: Living longer together

It may have taken a few centuries, but many dogs have a life of luxury now. And we dog lovers can benefit in many ways from what researchers discover to help our furry family members. As scientists continue to look into why and how dogs age, we will learn so much about how to prolong the lifespan and healthspan of our dogs. Regardless of how long we can extend their lifespan… it is never long enough.

Dr. Mary's keys to slowing the sands of time for pets

We can help our dogs live longer and happier by using these strategies throughout their lives:

- Feed a healthy, complete, and balanced diet appropriate for your dog's life stage or health issue.
- Exercise every day—matched to your dog's abilities.

- Help your dog maintain a healthy weight and optimal body and muscle condition.
- Include play and mental stimulation.
- Manage stress and anxiety.
- Provide regular veterinary medical and dental checkups and preventive healthcare.
- Be on alert to detect medical and behavioral issues earlier and seek veterinary treatment sooner. To help, keep a pet health journal with a photo diary.
- Consider spaying or neutering your pet (usually an early-life decision, but can be done later in life if indicated).
- Allow nature time—going outdoors is excellent—and prohibit free roaming when appropriate (to prevent car accidents, predation or neighborhood fights, and exposure to infectious diseases).
- Always give extra love!

Because these strategies can become more challenging to implement as dogs age, and after they have developed a medical condition or two, the chapters that follow provide more specific insight into how you can keep your senior and geriatric dogs as happy, comfortable, and healthy as possible during their twilight years.

 My grey muzzle friend Ruby enjoying the beach in Oregon (AKA Ruby in the Sky with Diamonds, Roberta, Rubix Cube, Rhubarb).

 READING RECOMMENDATIONS

- Morris Animal Foundation Golden Retriever Lifetime Study: **https://www.morrisanimalfoundation.org/golden-retriever-lifetime-study**
- The Dog Aging Project: **https://dogagingproject.org/**

Part two:

THE AGING BODY — COMMON AILMENTS THAT AFFECT GERIATRIC DOGS

From dry noses to leaky rear ends, in these chapters I focus on helping you manage the general ailments that most commonly plague senior dogs, and I highlight a few specific diseases that advanced age can bring. Whether your dog has arthritis, a spinal cord disease, overgrown toenails, bone cancer, weak muscles, or obesity, you'll want to manage his comfort and mobility. If your dog has urine accidents in the house because she has an overactive bladder, bladder cancer, or a weak urinary sphincter, you'll still be dealing with sloppy situations. In addition, sometimes you're unlikely to get a specific diagnosed—perhaps because problems with your senior dog make him less tentative to visit the vet, because a specific diagnosis is elusive, or treatment options can be expensive. If, for example, all of the testing and still don't have a

and are without a specific support group to connect with on social media, you'll still want to focus on managing your dog's ailments. In this section you'll learn what ailments to watch for, what the signs look like, and what the signs may indicate. I provide caregiving tips specific to each ailment or disease, offer pointers based on home hacks that my patients' families and I have used, and suggest resources and products. I also list questions to ask your veterinarian that'll help spark discussion so you can take home more information from your visits.

CHAPTER 5:

Nose: The better to smell you with

"The future is smelled on the breeze that brings air from the place you're headed."

— FROM "INSIDE OF A DOG: WHAT DOGS SEE, SMELL, AND KNOW"
BY ALEXANDRA HOROWITZ

Walter's lanky, 12-year-old legs wobbled under his 90-pound Rhodesian ridge-back frame. He was a gentle, happy fella who loved hanging out near his family. I watched him shakily walk in circles in the living room on his supersize ortho-pedic dog bed—one turn, two turns—gingerly preparing to "land." His joints crackled; I winced. Three turns—and finally, he bent his knees and sank his hips to lie down.

I was visiting Walter's home to discuss hospice care with his family. They sus-pected their remaining time with him was short, but they weren't ready to part with their dear, floppy-eared friend. They wanted my suggestions to help him live more comfortably during his final weeks.

They told me Walter had started "ice skating" on the hardwood floor and would also get stuck under the dining room table, so they had blocked his access to that room. Luckily they had a one-story house, so Walter could still easily access most rooms and the backyard. It was clear to me that we needed to manage Walter's mobility struggles immediately. I asked the family whether they were giving Walter any medications.

They told me their veterinarian had prescribed a nonsteroidal anti-inflammatory drug for Walter's arthritis several months ago and that it seemed to help him get around easier and have less pain. But after two months they stopped giving it because they thought the medication gave Walter a dry nose, which to them meant he was sick.

I hadn't heard that a dry nose was a side effect of that drug in dogs, so I told Walter's family I would later contact the drug manufacturer to ask whether this was a reported problem (which I did, and it wasn't). I also told them that even if the medication did cause Walter's dry, now crusty nose (side note: stopping the medication hadn't brought Walter's wet nose back), the benefits Walter gained from the drug—pain relief and better mobility—far outweighed him having a dry nose.

I tell you this story because it's not an uncommon finding in senior dogs—the dry, crusty nose!

How much does the nose know?

If only it were as easy as checking the nose to determine whether a dog is healthy. Veterinarians may be out of business! People often ask me about the correlation between the moistness or dryness of their dog's nose and whether it means they are "coming down with something." The quick answer is, no, probably not. So let's talk about that important beacon—the nose!

My vet says this clown nose is nothing serious.

As you are well aware, dogs sniff almost anything—and usually at inappropriate times! How often have you gone for a walk with your dog, which should take 15 minutes, but it lasts 45 minutes because your dog wants to fervently smell every blade of grass?

The sense of smell is critical to dogs and people. And it's no longer considered conventional wisdom that humans' sense of smell is worse than that of other animals. (McGann 2017) Did you know that people can not only follow a scent trail, we can improve with practice? (Porter 2007) And some evidence suggests people can tell when others are ill, emotionally stressed, or might make a good mate. (Klein 2017, Mujica-Parodi 2009)

But back to the four-footed... the sense of smell is a vital part of dogs' lives. They smell everything! Compared with their distant relatives, most dogs no longer have to sniff to find their meals or catch a whiff of approaching predators. But their noses still convey critical information about their environments. Smell helps dogs recognize their human family members and learn a little about where

they've been. Dogs also communicate by detecting each others' scents and respond by marking their territories. (Another reason for those prolonged dog walks—all those quick tinkle, "I was here!" moments!)

Specially trained dogs also rely on their noses to help us hunt, uncover illegal substances and illicit products, expose explosives, detect illnesses, find invasive species, point to bed bugs and termites, and unmask a cache of ill-gotten cash. They lead us to poached animals and do crucial work in human search, rescue, and recovery.

The nose's business

Like people, dogs breathe primarily through their noses. The nose warms and humidifies air and is a first line of defense against dirt, allergens, and pollution. It also helps the immune system recognize and protect against inhaled bacterial and viral invaders.

Noses trap air and scent molecules and shuttle them up the nasal passageway to specialized cells called *olfactory sensory neurons*. Each neuron has one odor receptor. Those scent molecules stimulate the odor receptors, which send signals to the olfactory bulb in the brain and to the frontal cortex to process and identify the smell.

The sense of smell and taste work together because food aroma travels to the same neurons. If the scent cannot reach the receptors, for example because of inflammation caused by a virus or a tumor, then the food's flavor isn't enjoyed as much.

So why are dogs' noses often wet? Their moist noses help trap the scent particles that are passed to the neurons. A dry nose doesn't necessarily mean your dog is sick, but it can reduce their ability to trap odor (and therefore smell), so they may lick their noses often.

FUN FACTS:

- Dogs can wiggle their nostrils independently.
- Dogs' sense of smell is reported to be 10,000 to 100,000 times greater than humans'. (Walker 2006, Jenkins 2018)

Who smells best?

Different species are more attuned to the scents that mean something to them in their environments, so it's difficult to compare the same scents across species to test which animal has the best sense of smell. The sizes of the olfactory bulbs and the number of olfactory neurons among different species also don't reliably predict smell abilities. For example, the proportion of a dog's brain devoted to interpreting smells is much greater than a human's brain, but that doesn't mean humans can't detect certain smells as well as dogs can. (McGann 2017)

For years it was thought that dogs have more smell receptors than cats do, but it has since been shown that cats have similar numbers of smell receptors. However, some dog breeds, such as bloodhounds, have double the number of receptors compared with other dog breeds.

Animal	Number of Olfactory Receptors
Human	6 million
Cat	150+ million
Dog	150 to 300 million

- The volume of the human olfactory bulb is 0.06 cm³. (Kavoi 2011)
- The volume of the dog olfactory bulb is 0.18 cm³. (Kavoi 2011)
- By volume, the olfactory bulb is about 0.01% of the human brain, 0.31% of the dog brain, and 2% of the mouse brain. (Kavoi 2011, McGann 2017)

Along with the crazy number of smell receptors, dogs and cats (along with pigs and horses) also possess a second olfactory organ called the vomeronasal organ. (Padodara 2014) It's located at the bottom of the nasal passage and above the roof of the mouth. The vomeronasal organ is designed to pick up the scent of pheromones, which are chemicals unique to each animal (and some insect) species. Pheromones send messages that can alter a behavior or bodily function of the recipient.

My dog Sam and friend Mya sniffing their hellos.

Odoriferous influence

We know that smell evokes our memories, triggers our emotions, and sways our behavior. Does the smell of Play-Doh transport you back to a playdate when you were a toddler? How about puppy breath—does it make you happy? Maybe a whiff of ocean air prompts you to take the afternoon off and race to the beach? I'll follow the smell of warm chocolate chip cookies anywhere!

Oh, how often I've yearned for the chance to go back to my grandmother's living room and capture the sweet smell of Grandma. I wish I could invent a way to forever hold onto her scent, and those of my dogs. I keep my dogs' collars after they pass and sniff all I can from them. Such special smells have the power to bring back vivid memories—ones that we might not otherwise readily recall. We also wonder whether our dogs have similar responses to the smells they've learned.

Research revelation: Your scent sparks your dog's joy

In 2014, researchers wanted to study how dogs' brains would respond to different odors, so they trained 12 awake dogs to stay still in a magnetic resonance imaging machine that would evaluate their brain activity. (Pets usually have to be anesthetized for this diagnostic test.) They tested the dogs' responses to five scents: the dog's own, a dog who lived in their household, a dog they had never met, a person they had never met, and a person who lived in their household (either the spouse or child of the dog's primary caregiver) or who was a close friend. (Berns 2014)

The scents had been collected on the morning of the test on separate sterile gauze pads. The scents were presented to each dog by their handler, who was the dog's primary caregiver but not one of the five types of scent donor. The "scent donors" (other than the dog being tested) were not present at the test.

The brain scan images showed that the positive-reward area of each dog's brain was most activated when the dog smelled the scent of their familiar person! And perhaps not surprisingly, the second most active positive brain responses occurred when the dogs smelled the scents of the dogs they knew. Their research suggests that dogs not only remember the scent of their familiar humans and canine buddies, they remember them fondly.

FUN FACTS:

- Many mammals have scent glands that produce pheromones and other chemicals that help them signal territory, mood, and sexual status to other members of their species.
- Dogs have scent glands on the undersides of their paws and rear end.

What can go wrong with the nose?

Some of the common problems associated with dogs' noses as they age range from color change to cancer.

Color change

When my dog Serissa was 11 years old, her jet black nose started to turn tan in spots. Some of the skin cells on her nose cells simply stopped producing normal amounts of pigment (similarly to the way our hair and dogs' muzzle hair go grey). It was not a sign of a disease or an abnormality. It became a sad daily reminder that her age was increasing and my time with her was decreasing!

My dog Serissa, at age 13 years, and me, at age... I'll never tell!

Eugene, a friend's dog, shows off his crusty nose.

Thickened, crusty area around the nostrils

Have you ever seen what looks like a small tree with thick bark growing up from a dog's nose? This is called *hyperkeratosis*—a condition in which skin produces an excess amount of keratin (a protein). It occurs especially in breeds such as pugs, French bulldogs, and cocker spaniels. The nose becomes dry and calluses form.

Mild cases usually don't affect a dog's sense of smell, but in general, a dry nose can reduce a dog's ability to trap scent molecules. With severe hyperkeratosis, blocked nasal passages obstruct the pathway for scent molecules to journey to the brain. The excess tissue can also lead to bacterial infections. If this nasal issue is attended to early enough, your veterinarian may be able to remove the excess skin using laser surgery, and it is a low-risk procedure.

Cancer

Nasal adenocarcinoma is the most common type of nasal cancer in dogs. The signs of nasal cancer? Dogs may excessively rub their noses or sneeze and snort, or they may have nasal discharge, nose bleeds (also called *epistaxis*), snout swelling, or facial deformity. Some of these cancers grow quickly, and I encourage you to seek advice from your veterinarian as soon as possible if your senior dog has signs of nasal disease since nasal cancer is much easier to treat when the tumor is small.

Foreign objects, polyps, and allergies

Dogs who spend a lot of time outdoors nosing around in tall grasses are more likely to inhale plant seeds that lodge in their nasal passages. Snorted materials can cause sudden irritation, intense pawing at the nose, excessive sneezing, and long-term inflammation. If these signs are caught early, veterinarians, with careful examination, can sometimes find and remove the plant material or other object that doesn't belong.

Dogs may develop non-cancerous growths in their nose called *polyps*, which can be surgically removed. And dogs with allergies may have nasal cavity inflammation, so treatment focuses on managing the allergy and its irritating effects.

FUN FACT:

The technical term for sneezing is sternutation. Sun exposure can make some people sneeze, and this condition is called ACHOO syndrome (for Autosomal Dominant Compelling Helio-Ophthalmic Outburst), or photic sneeze reflex. People who have inherited this trait sneeze multiple times in response to bright light.

Infections and autoimmune skin disease

Older dogs sometimes develop bacterial or fungal infections or autoimmune skin problems (the body's immune cells malfunction and start attacking normal skin or mucous membrane cells) that affect the nose. It's always a good idea to have your dog checked out by a veterinarian if you notice dryness and cracking on your dog's nose or see oozing or bleeding erosions or other lesions that affect your dog's nostrils, lips, or gums.

Decreased ability to smell

We don't yet know precisely what happens with a dog's sense of smell as they age. But we know that our sense of smell declines as we age. People 65 to 80 years of age lose up to 50% of their sense of smell, and people over 80 years of age lose up to 80%. (Attems 2015) As we age, oxidative stress (an imbalance between the harmful molecular reactions that can occur during normal cell processes and the mechanisms that prevent them) damages many of our cells, including our olfactory nerve and brain cells. A loss of nerve endings in a dog's nose can reduce the nose's ability to produce mucus, which decreases sense of smell.

In people, a diminished sense of smell is one of the earliest indicators of Alzheimer's disease [Kotecha 2018]. In senior dogs, cognitive dysfunction has been likened to Alzheimer's disease. Smell disturbance is one of the physical signs of canine cognitive dysfunction syndrome, so a diminished sense of smell may be an early indicator of the disease in dogs, too. [Ozawa 2019]

Other factors that can diminish a dog's sense of smell include viruses such as canine parainfluenza and distemper; diseases such as hyperadrenocorticism, hypothyroidism, and diabetes mellitus; severe dental disease; and drugs such as metronidazole (an antibiotic) and doxorubicin (a drug used to treat cancer).

Dental disease

It may sound odd, but if a dog has nasal problems, I always look at their teeth! I have seen some nasty grills in my years as a veterinarian. Unfortunately dental disease can become unnecessarily severe in dogs because many pet parents are nervous about the anesthesia required to have their dogs' teeth cleaned. However, the risks of not treating dental disease may be far greater. Diseased gums and teeth can lead to infection and even abscesses that disturb the scent pathway and cause many other problems throughout the body. So have your dog's teeth evaluated and cleaned regularly!

A nose for words

- Anosmia is the complete loss of sense of smell.

- Hyposmia indicates partial loss of sense of smell.

- Parosmia is a change in the normal perception of odors, such as when the smell of something familiar is distorted or when something that normally smells pleasant now smells foul.

- Phantosmia is the sensation of an odor that isn't there.

- Presbyosmia is the reduction in or loss of sense of smell that occurs with aging.

Sniffing out trouble: When to see your veterinarian

I can't stress enough how important it is to see your veterinarian if your dog repeatedly paws at his nose or face, snorts or snores excessively, or has nasal discharge, a bloody nose, or changes in his facial appearance. I vividly remember one of my canine patients who had a severely bulging eyeball caused by a nasal tumor pressing behind his eye (a tumor that clearly hadn't popped up overnight).

To identify the cause of a nose issue, your veterinarian may recommend blood tests, clotting tests to check whether blood clots form normally, radiographs, a computed tomography (CT) scan, using a special scope to look up the nose, and taking a biopsy.

It can be hard to tell whether your dog has an impaired sense of smell. Perhaps your dog may not be curious to sniff the grocery bags anymore, nor your clothes and shoes when you get home from work. And dogs with diminished smell often have a reduced appetite, or they may begin to show a preference for certain foods—presumably those with odors they can more readily detect.

A weak sense of smell can curtail a dog's appetite because smell and taste are linked. Taste buds play a big role, of course, but the molecules released from chewed food enter the nasal cavity and are processed by the olfactory cells to help detect complex flavors. (That's why if you pinch your nose while sampling Harry Potter™ Bertie Bott's Every Flavour Beans, you'll be unable to tell the difference between the candyfloss and the vomit flavored jelly beans. Talk about mischief managed!)

A decreased appetite can be caused by scores of other medical problems, so If your dog is otherwise in good health and has been checked for other potential causes of inappetence, it may be related to a diminished ability to smell. A reduced appetite can, in and of itself, be of concern, so check out Chapter 9 "Body condition and nutrition: Helping senior dogs eat better and feel better " for tips on appetite stimulation!

Because a diminished sense of smell might also be a sign of cognitive dysfunction, talk with your veterinarian about this possibility. Also see Chapter 19

"Cognition: Cross my mind... or not" for activities and therapies that may help slow the progression of this condition.

If it truly is simply an age-related loss of your dog's wonderful ability to smell, there isn't much veterinarians can do to treat this just yet. Peg it up to one of the many joys of aging.

> **Eek, my dog's nose is bleeding! There can be many causes, from an injury to cancer, but here are some steps to take if you see a bloody nose.**
>
> - Keep your dog calm, and encourage her to lie down and relax. (Elevated blood pressure from excitement can cause more bleeding.) Try to keep your dog's head level or slightly elevated.
>
> - Try holding a cold pack or ice pack wrapped in a towel on the bridge or side of the nose. Note whether the bleeding comes from one or both nostrils so you can relay the information to your veterinarian.
>
> - Avoid trying to place absorbent materials inside your dog's nose, as this will likely lead to sneezing, head shaking, and further bleeding.
>
> - Continue to keep your dog calm and limit their activity for several hours after the bleeding stops. Running, head shaking, and sneezing can disrupt the clot and the nosebleed will start again. Consider providing calming pheromones such as Adaptil.
>
> - Call your veterinarian and schedule an appointment for an examination.
>
> - Depending on the cause of your dog's nosebleed and whether bleeding is likely to recur, ask your veterinarian whether calming supplements or mild sedatives would help manage your dog at home.
>
> - If the nosebleed is severe or lasts more than five minutes, seek immediate emergency veterinary care.
>
> - For dogs accustomed to wearing a basket muzzle: If the nosebleed is severe and you need to drive to the veterinarian without a helper, line the inside of a basket muzzle with thin, extra-absorbent feminine pads. Gently fasten the muzzle behind your dog's head, and take care not to completely obstruct air flow. This helps catch the droplets. For this to succeed, your dog should already be trained to wear a basket muzzle. Otherwise, introducing one during a nosebleed may make dogs more anxious, increase their blood pressure, and make them shake or rub their head to try to remove the muzzle.

CAREGIVER TIPS AND HOME HACKS TO HELP YOUR DOG'S SENSE OF SMELL

- Humidify the air in your home to help keep nasal cells moisturized.
- Apply a balm made for pets (e.g. Nose Butter or Snout Soother) on the external portions of your dog's nose to help keep it moist.
- Warm foods to enhance their smell.
- Stay up-to-date on routine wellness veterinary visits and vaccinations to prevent upper respiratory infections.
- Give dogs intriguing new things to smell to stimulate their noses and provide mental activity. (Avoid essential oils, as many are toxic to dogs if they have skin contact or are ingested.)
- Consider teaching your dog to use nontoxic scent markers. These markers are typically used to help dogs with vision impairment navigate their homes. People who have lost their sense of smell—which has become a more common problem related to COVID-19 infections—may benefit from scent training, although it hasn't been widely studied. Scent training is likened to physical therapy for noses. Human patients take a whiff of strong essential oils such as eucalyptus, clove, and lemon and attempt to identify the odors. (Harrison 2020) This has not been studied in dogs with impaired ability to smell, but teaching a dog to use scent markers could help stimulate their olfactory abilities.
- If your dog is ill and must be hospitalized, send a favorite toy with her, or send a shirt that you've worn recently that you haven't laundered.
- When your dog gets home from the hospital, rub him with a towel that you've first rubbed your other dogs (or your cats) with. This transfers their familiar smells to your dog who smells like the veterinary clinic. Then consider rubbing the dogs (or cats) in the household again with the towel you've just rubbed on your homecoming dog (if your dog doesn't have an infectious condition). This way they'll all smell similarly strange and similarly recognizable to each other.
- Check with your veterinarian for treatment updates. Ultra tiny molecules (called *nanoparticles*) of zinc delivered in a special spray have been shown to enhance odor detection abilities in dogs and in people (Ramaihgari 2018), so such therapy may someday be medically available.

What happened with Walter?

A month after Walter again started receiving his nonsteroidal anti-inflammatory medication, plus the other arthritis medications and Snout Soother that

I prescribed, Walter walked more steadily, laid down on and got up from his bed with more confidence, and sniffed the backyard earnestly with his moisturized snout.

Three months after my first visit with his family, Walter was doing so well that I told the family he no longer needed to be in hospice. Walter lived another two years!

When the time came for Walter to earn his angel wings, I not only gave Walter's family his paw impression in clay, but also his nose impression. His family told me they would miss his wet nose prints on their sliding glass doors.

Walter's nose print.

Sam's nose became dry and flaky with age. I used Snout Soother, and in about a month it improved.

PRODUCT RECOMMENDATIONS

- Nose Butter® (The Blissful Dog):
  https://theblissfuldog.com/collections/nose-butter
- Snout Soother (Natural Dog Company):
  naturaldogcompany.com
- Snout Magic (The Happy Pet Company)
  http://www.snoutmagic.com/
- SightScent™ Sight and Scent Mapping Program
  http://sightscent.com/index.html

CHAPTER 6:

Eyes: "You looking at me?" Vision changes with age

"It is only with the heart that one can see rightly;
what is essential is invisible to the eye."

—Antoine de Saint-Exupéry, from "The Little Prince"

On the second night in the south Florida house I moved to with Serissa after I graduated from veterinary school, I lugged my teeming trash cans to the road for the next day's pickup. Then I moseyed to my new backyard. It was a windless evening, but waves rippled in the pool.

The disturbed water baffled me for about three seconds. Then I spotted Serissa in the deep end of the pool. She was two feet underwater, nearly motionless! Instantly, I dove in, grabbed her tired body, and lifted her over the pool's edge. I laid her on her side. She was stunned, but breathing and clearly exhausted.

I carried Serissa inside and briskly toweled her coat while giving her a ton of hugs. She looked at me with a mixture of terror and adoration—at least I'm sure that's how I was looking at her!

She must've been exploring the bushes near the pool and popped through the hedge, straight into the water. She was

See if you can spot Serissa in this picture!

65

5 years old then and didn't have vision problems. She'd simply made a wrong move in unfamiliar territory. I'm thankful to this day for those full trash bins. Serissa and I got a lucky break that night.

Serrisa steered clear of the pool from that point on. And I eagle-eyed her outdoor whereabouts for several years.

A fainter twinkle

 Serissa safely poolside.

After Serissa's 8th birthday, I noticed she had started drinking more water than usual and asking to go out to urinate more often. She was also eating more, but losing weight. I took samples of her blood and urine for testing, and the results showed that she had diabetes. Her pancreas was no longer producing sufficient amounts of insulin, a hormone that helps regulate blood glucose (sugar) concentrations. And just as some diabetic people do, Serissa needed daily insulin injections and carefully timed meals, plus frequent additional tests to check her blood sugar. Still, she was a breeze to care for.

When Serissa was 10, a white, cloudy haze began to develop in the center of her eyes. Not long after, she began tripping over shoes, toys, branches, and other things she normally would have skirted or jumped over. Then one night while I was stargazing in the backyard, I heard a splash. Serissa had fallen into the pool again, after earnestly avoiding it for the past five years! My sweet baby girl was panic-stricken, but I scooped her out much faster this time. I thanked those lucky stars that I was there for her again.

I knew it was time to thoroughly assess her failing vision. Just like in diabetic people, cataracts are a common consequence of diabetes in dogs. The lens in the eye is unable to absorb and use the excess glucose in the fluid that nourishes the eye, and the lens becomes cloudy and difficult to see through. The next day I made an appointment for Serissa to see a veterinary ophthalmologist.

I learned that Serissa's cataracts were severe and that she had lost about 50% of her vision. She needed cataract surgery, which requires expertise beyond my realm of practice. My gratitude goes to Dr. Susan Carastro and her team at Animal Eye Specialty Clinic in south Florida for removing Serissa's cloudy lenses and placing clear, artificial lens implants. During the postoperative healing period and for many weeks after, Serissa needed daily eye medications. Cataract removal was well worth the expense and recovery care required. It restored Serissa's vision—allowing her to avoid those terrifying surprise swims—and gave me more peace of mind.

A glance at eye structure

Vision plays a fundamental, vital role in our dog's lives—it helps them avoid hazards, find food, communicate, and play. Yet I have met many blind dogs who live wonderful lives.

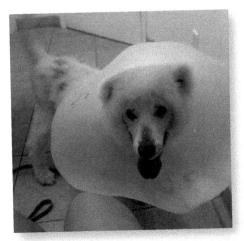

 Shaved-face Serissa at her recheck eye appointment after cataract surgery. A little funny-looking, but happy!

As dogs age, vision impairment is common. It can be caused by an underlying disease, such as the diabetes that triggered Serissa's cataracts, or by typical age-related changes. Eyeballs are quite complex! It's helpful for pet parents to understand the basic structure of the eye to appreciate the things that can go awry.

The eye consists of three chambers—the anterior (front), posterior (rear), and vitreous (gel-like goo that fills the eyeball and helps it keep its shape). Eyes also have three layers:

- The outer *fibrous tunic layer* consists of the cornea (clear portion of the front of the eye) and sclera (white portion of the eye that also contains tiny blood vessels). When you get an eyelash or dust in your eye, the cornea and sclera become irritated and painful.
- The middle section is the *uveal layer*, which contains the iris (the colored ring that surrounds the pupil), ciliary body (sits behind the iris and supports the lens and produces the substances that fill the eye), and choroid (blood vessels that supply the eye's inner layer). Many diseases can cause inflammation in this layer and lead to glaucoma, which is increased painful pressure in the eye from fluid buildup. And excess fluid buildup can cause blindness.
- The inner *nervous layer* contains the retina (tissue that contains light receptors) and optic nerve, which carries the retina's signals to the brain for image processing. If the retina separates from the back of the eye (retinal detachment)—which can occur with some diseases

or trauma—emergency treatment is required to reattach the retina to attempt to prevent permanent vision loss.

FUN FACT:

The best way to visually estimate a mature dog's age is to evaluate changes in their ocular lens! It's similar to counting the rings of a cut tree to estimate its age, but this method is noninvasive—only a dark room and a penlight to illuminate the eye are needed. Not all veterinarians know how to estimate a pet's age this way, but in dogs older than 4 years of age, lens assessment is more than twice as accurate as dental assessment. (From age 1 to 4 years, assessing the number and wear of their teeth is more accurate. So the dental and lens age estimates complement each other.) When I adopted my dog Norrin, I was told he was 3 years old. But two years later when we visited the veterinary ophthalmologist, she told me Norrin was 7 years old!

Norrin would like a birthday recount!

The lens is separate from these three layers. It sits behind the iris to help focus the light that streams through the pupil and onto the retina.

Watch for age-related changes and signs of diminished eyesight

As dogs age, different components of the eye can lose function. Luckily, age-related changes in the eye usually don't lead to total blindness, but they can hamper your dog's daily living activities and safety. Serissa's cataracts were not typical age-related changes; they resulted from her diabetes. Many other conditions, such as infections, tumors, trauma, and high blood pressure, can cause reduced eyesight or blindness. If your dog shows signs of decreased vision, it's important for your veterinarian to examine your dog to determine the cause so that correct treatment and care can be provided.

When to see your veterinarian

The signs of eye disease and changes in vision range from subtle to obvious and include:

- Excessive blinking or squinting
- Rubbing or pawing at the eyes
- Sensitivity to light
- Redness
- Watery eyes or gooey discharge
- Bulging eyes
- Cloudiness
- Persistently dilated pupils
- One pupil that is larger than the other
- Bumping into furniture, doors, or walls
- Difficulty finding food or water bowls, toys, or treats
- Hesitancy to jump on or off furniture or into the car
- Reluctance to use stairs, explore new places, or navigate in dim light
- New or increased anxiety or clingy behavior
- Increased vocalization
- Reduced eye contact
- Startling easily or exhibiting increased irritability
- Taking longer to recognize familiar people from a distance
- A persistently raised third eyelid

FUN FACT:

In addition to their top and bottom eyelids, dogs have an eyelid that moves diagonally from the bottom inner corner of each eye to further protect it. We call this the *third eyelid*, or *nictitating membrane.*

Common eye conditions in older dogs

Whether your dog has eye problems related to an underlying disease or exhibits common age-related changes, protecting your dog and alleviating discomfort is paramount. I'll cover ways to keep them safe and comfortable later, but first let's take a closer look at the most common age-related changes that may affect your dog's eyes.

Corneal edema

The cornea is made up of layers that act like a pump to keep it perfectly hydrated and see-through. With age, the corneal cells degenerate and decline in number, and the pump falters. Fluid begins to build up in the cornea, which is called *corneal edema*. This hampers vision, so an affected dog may show signs of

blindness. If too much fluid accumulates, a small rupture occurs and leads to a corneal ulcer, a painful and serious problem that requires urgent attention and immediate treatment.

My dog Duncan had corneal edema. One day we were sitting outside in the sun, and I noticed mild, grey cloudiness in his eyes. It was yet another sign of Duncan getting older. I was nearly as alarmed as when I found my first grey hair! Because this condition can progress, I monitored him for worsening edema with a tonometer (an instrument that measures eye pressure) and for signs of pain and diminished vision. To help reduce Duncan's edema, I gave him medicated eye ointment every day to help draw the extra fluid out of his corneas.

 Duncan had a bluish grey haze in both eyes because of corneal edema.

 Duncan was the best patient, even when I gave him his eye medication.

I always recommend a post-treatment kiss!

Nuclear (lenticular) sclerosis

Made up of water and proteins, the lens is fairly elastic and can change shape to help focus light onto the retina. With age, the water and proteins decrease and the proteins become compacted in the lens center (nucleus), which reduces lens flexibility. (Reduced lens flexibility is the reason many older people need reading glasses.) As the proteins become more compacted, a white or blue-grey haziness appears in the center of the lens. This is called *nuclear* or *lenticular sclerosis*.

Pet parents often refer to this lens cloudiness as cataracts. But there is a big difference! Unlike cataracts, nuclear sclerosis doesn't usually affect vision. Nuclear sclerosis is usually seen in dogs starting at around 6 or 7 years of age. It is not painful and no treatment is needed. However, your veterinarian should perform an evaluation to rule out other diseases that may look the same.

Senile cataracts

Age-related cataracts can develop in some dogs who have nuclear sclerosis, so continue to monitor visual abilities in dogs with nuclear sclerosis. Senile cataracts can develop when the aging, compacted lens proteins start to degenerate, and it's important to catch this early, when surgery to remove cataracts is most successful.

Cataract surgery carries risks, postoperative complications can occur, and many eye and other medications are typically required afterward. Discuss your expectations and patient care capabilities with your veterinarian to determine whether cataract surgery is right for your dog. Your veterinarian must also determine whether your dog has senile cataracts or has cataracts caused by another underlying problem such as diabetes that also requires treatment.

Eddie had cataracts due to diabetes - her right eye was worse. She was on daily eye meds to make her comfortable.

Iris atrophy

Serissa's irises were deep brown—nearly black—and mine are hazel. Norrin has one brown iris and one blue iris (called *heterochromia*). This colored ring of tissue contains a sphincter muscle that alters pupil size in response to light, certain hormones, or drugs. In low light or scary situations, the pupils dilate to allow as much light in as possible. In bright light, pupils constrict to reduce the amount of light that reaches the retina.

Like many muscles in the body, the iris muscle shrinks with age, and this is called *iris atrophy*. This limits the pupil's ability to change size, so affected dogs may not see as well at night or may squint more than usual in bright sunlight. With iris atrophy, the colored tissue may have a "moth-eaten" appearance or a wavy edge, or the pupils may appear to be misshapen or unequal sizes.

Iris atrophy is an aging change for which there is no treatment, but it shouldn't seriously affect your dog's vision or quality of life. However, it's important to have a veterinary exam to identify the cause of a dog's irregular pupil sizes because it can indicate another more serious problem.

Try not to look sideways at eyeball removal

Severe infection, a traumatic accident, glaucoma, or cancer may necessitate the removal of one or both of a dog's eyes—a surgical procedure called *enucleation*. It's performed as a last resort because the eye is often painful and can't otherwise

be repaired. After an eye is removed, the skin is permanently sutured (stitched) to close the gap. If a family requests it, a prosthetic globe can be placed for cosmetic reasons. Dogs with one or both eyes removed can go on to live joyful, active lives with a little help from their loving families.

After Miley developed bilateral cataracts, she underwent surgical removal of both eyes and still loves being the center of attention.

Jezebel didn't skip a beat after losing her right eye.

CAREGIVER TIPS AND HOME HACKS

If your dog has vision impairment, simple environmental adjustments can keep him happy and secure. Dogs who are blind or visually impaired miss danger signs such as an aggressive dog, a swimming pool (poor Serissa!), stairs, an oncoming car, or an exuberant toddler who is waddling their way. Maintaining familiar routines, creating a safe zone, using positive training techniques to teach new ways to navigate, engaging them in new ways to play, and providing opportunities for mental stimulation and physical activity allows dogs with visual impairment to lead happy lives. They can still enjoy their favorite activities such as chasing toys, going for a walk, hanging out with the family, playing with the neighbor's dog, riding in the car, basking in sunlight, and dreaming of squirrels.

This baby gate prevented Serissa from tripping down a step when I wasn't available to watch her. But I could easily open the door when I was home to help! Here she's carrying a stick she brought in from outside, but can't get through the gate with it!

Preserve familiarity. To prevent your dog's injury or confusion, try not to move furniture or alter her routines. One exception that may require schedule changes: for dogs who are sensitive to light, take walks at dawn and dusk, and plan prolonged outdoor activities for cloudy days or in shady areas.

Hinder hazards. Senior-pet-proof your home, similar to what you would do for a toddler. Ensure your dog is unable to wander into the street or off a balcony or deck. Place baby gates or "stack" tension rods (a lower cost option) to block off potential hazards. Attach soft pads to hard edges that your dog may bump into.

SLOW DOWN

BLIND PET

Heighten visibility. Many senior dogs struggle to see in low light, so help them navigate hallways and stairwells with motion-sensor lights and night lights that turn on when it gets dark. Also place lights near food and water bowls and the doggie door. Prevent run-ins with glass doors by adhering stickers to the glass at dog-eye level.

 Pause for paws! Stickers on a glass partition or patio door help dogs avoid bumping into it.

Be a lifeguard. Monitor your dog (visually impaired or not) at all times near a body of water! As a veterinarian in south Florida, I've encountered innumerable tragic accounts of dogs who die from drowning in swimming pools, waterways, and even hot tubs. Pet sitters must mindfully watch the dog and not be tempted by phone or video game distractions. Pool alarms are also a helpful tool, and it's a good idea to keep the toilet lid closed, too. That closed toilet lid serves double duty for those dedicated toilet-water-drinking enthusiasts. Sorry, Charlie!

Consider a harness. A 2006 study conducted by veterinary ophthalmologists revealed that when a healthy dog pulls against their collar, the pressure within their eyes increases substantially. (Pauli 2006) These findings suggest that dogs who have corneal problems, glaucoma, or other eye problems in which an increase in eye pressures could be detrimental should wear a harness instead of a collar, especially during activities and exercise.

Furnish nutritional support. Whether your senior dog has an eye disease or not, consider a supplement that supports eye health. I recommend Ocu-GLO (**http://www.ocuglo.com/**), which has been formulated by board-certified veterinary ophthalmologists.

Foster enrichment. Toys with sound and smell will thrill most dogs—even older curmudgeons—and keep them engaged. Dogs enjoy treat-dispensing puzzle toys and snuffle mats (small "carpets" that promote foraging for food or treats). Offer your dog's toys a few at a time on a rotating schedule to prevent boredom and keep toys feeling new rather than providing unlimited access to all their toys.

More tips for caregivers of dogs who are blind

Most dogs know their home well by memory and learn to rely more on hearing, smell, and touch as their eyesight diminishes. Sometimes they adapt so well that owners are surprised to learn their dog is blind. Understandably, dogs who lose vision gradually or lose vision in one eye tend to adapt easier than dogs who suddenly become blind, which can be distressing, confusing, and sometimes depressing to them. With your patience, reassurance, support tools, and affection, dogs can adjust to blindness and regain confidence in their environment and instincts remarkably well!

The comfort of a safe zone

Pick a room or specific location where all of your dog's basic necessities are readily accessible, such as his bed, food bowl, water, and toys. Geriatric dogs who are blind are comforted by routine, such as being fed at the same time every day in the same spot. It helps when their necessities are in the same reliable places and that their established safe zone is always there for them, especially if they are distressed by visitors. Consider marking the safe zone with a unique comforting scent like lavender oil as an added cue to help them easily locate their safe zone.

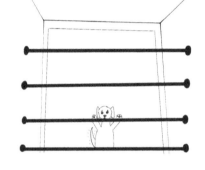

And in case of inadvertent escape from your home or yard, attach a medical alert tag to your dog's collar to indicate he is blind and include your contact information.

A heaven-sent tool

If your dog isn't adapting as well to vision loss as you'd hoped, or if you have to move to a new home, I've seen many pet parents successfully use halos—hard wire or plastic rings that serve as bumpers for blind dogs. Several products are available, but families I know especially like Muffin's Halo for Blind Dogs, or the Walkin' Blind Dog Halo at Handicappedpets.com.

The nose knows

You can use your dog's good sense of smell to your advantage and develop a scent mapping

 Bo rocking his halo.

system with scented oils or special scent tabs. With repetition and positive reinforcement training techniques, you can teach your dog to associate specific scents with desirable objects such as bowls, beds, and crates, as well as locations such as specific rooms, the door that leads outside, and pathways. You can also use this method to teach them about hazardous objects or places like the top of the stairs.

Auditory reassurance

Frequently talking to your dog brings much comfort, as it is helpful to be reminded of the family's presence. Dogs don't understand full sentences, so using key, one-word commands or familiar short phrases are best, such as: "sit," "come," "stay", "lie down," "potty on the grass," "I'm here," and "such a good boy!" Use a calm, upbeat voice to convey happiness, comfort, and safety. Dogs are incredibly in tune with their people, so cultivating your own positive attitude and acting as a grounding anchor for dogs is invaluable, especially for those adjusting to blindness.

Family members may consider wearing a bell or similar item that helps the dog easily identify the location of specific people. Teach visitors how to approach your dog without surprising her. Use a soft voice or other sounds to alert her to your presence and offer your hand near her nose to smell before touching her.

Dogs who are blind will be unable to respond appropriately to the eye contact and body language cues that other dogs use to communicate, so monitor their interactions. Leash a sighted dog who is meeting a blind dog. Attach bells or jingling tags to the collars of other dogs in the home to alert vision-impaired dogs to their whereabouts. Consider placing a bell on the dog who is blind, because it allows you to easily find him if he gets lost in the house or yard!

And lap up this last quick tip: A drinking fountain placed in your dog's safe zone provides a continuous auditory cue and helps them locate their water.

Tactile reassurance

Maintain clear walking paths and consider placing carpet runners so your dog can feel where it's safe to walk.

If you're worried your dog will walk off the edge of your bed, try helping him learn where the edges are by using buoyant polyethylene foam, better known as pool noodles! Place pool noodles under the bottom sheet and a couple of inches away from your bed's edges. (White Dog Blog website) Let your dog explore your bed with the pool noodles in place and praise, pet, and treat your dog for staying inside the noodle boundaries. Do training sessions a few times throughout the day and evening before bedtime. For more pool noodle training details, visit "The White Dog Blog" website at: **http://your-inner-dog.blogspot.com/2020/05/pool-noodles-in-bed.html**

Tips for administering eye medications

Ask your veterinarian to show you how to administer your dog's eye medications. Dogs typically receive eye medications two or more times a day for several days or weeks, so to speed healing, make it a positive experience. Here are my tips:

- Use a warm, damp washcloth to gently clean the area around your dog's eyes. Wash your hands and take extra care not to touch the tip of the medication container to your dog's eye or face, or to your hand. And don't apply the medication to your finger to rub in your dog's eye.
- If you have a small dog, you may want to wrap him gently in a towel with his head exposed and hold him in your lap or on a table. If your dog is especially wiggly or resistant, you may need a helper to hold him. Your dog's eyes may be sensitive and uncomfortable for the first few treatments until the medications start to work.
- Hold the medication container with your thumb and forefinger with the tip pointed down and gently steady your hand on top of your dog's head if needed. With your other hand, slightly tilt your dog's head up (use extra care in dogs with neck pain) and use your thumb to pull the lower eyelid down to help catch the medication.
- Approach with the medication from the top or side of your dog's eye rather than straight on, and dispense the prescribed drug amount at the top outer corner or in the center of the eye. Don't allow the tip of the container to touch any part of the eye. The medication will feel odd or slightly cold, so your dog will blink and may jerk a bit and shake his head.
- Give your dog lots of praise and a favorite small snack after every treatment! And wash your hands again afterward.

Insightful help is out there

If your dog's vision declines or she becomes completely blind, remember that she can lead a wonderful, fulfilling life. I recommend that you meet with your primary care veterinarian to discuss causes, treatment, and environmental adjustments. You may also want to seek guidance from a veterinary ophthalmologist. To find one close to you, ask your primary care veterinarian, or visit the American College of Veterinary Ophthalmologists website at **https://www.acvo.org/**.

Questions to ask your veterinarian about your dog's eyesight

- What's the underlying cause of my dog's vision changes?
- Will additional tests be needed to confirm the cause?
- Should my dog be referred to a veterinary ophthalmologist?
- What is the expected progression of this condition?
- What treatment options are available, and what are the costs?
- What are the risks of treatment?
- What is the expected outcome of treatment?
- Will you show me how to give eye medications to my dog?
- What are my options if I'm unable to medicate my dog?
- Is my dog's condition painful, and, if so, how will pain be managed?
- What tests and how often will they be needed to monitor my dog's condition or response to treatment?
- What environmental changes can I make to enhance my dog's quality of life and ensure safety?
- What products can I use to make life easier for my dog?

 READING RECOMMENDATIONS

- *Living With Blind Dogs: A Resource Book and Training Guide for the Owners of Blind and Low-Vision Dogs* – by Cariline Levin
- *Blind Devotion: Enhancing the Lives of Blind and Visually Impaired Dogs* – by Cathy Symons
- *My Dog Is Blind ... but Lives Life to the Full!* – by Nicole Horsky
- Training website: Karen Pryor Clicker Training: **https://www.clickertraining.com/**

 PRODUCT RECOMMENDATIONS

- Drinkwell Original Pet Fountain (PetSafe) **https://store.petsafe.net/drinkwell-original-fountain**
- SightScent Sight and Scent Mapping Program **http://sightscent.com/index.html**
- Babble Ball (Pet Qwerks) - found through many online retailers
- Wooly Snuffle Mat Paw5: **https://paw5.com/pages/wooly-snuffle-mat**

- Or make your own snuffle mat:
  **https://www.pawsocute.com/dogs/5-diy-snuffle-mats-dogs-fido
  -will-love-4/**
- Ocu-Glo - **http://www.ocuglo.com/**
- Wobble Wag Giggle Ball (As Seen On TV)
  **https://www.asseenontvwebstore.com/Wobble-Wag-Giggle-p/
  wobble-wag.htm**
- Muffin's Halo Guide for Blind Dogs **https://muffinshalo.com**
- Blind Dog Halo from Handicapped Pets
  https://www.handicappedpets.com/walkin-blind-dog-halo/
- Dog Activity Flip Board (TRIXIE Pet Products) **https://www.trixie.de/
  heimtierbedarf/us/shop/Dog/DogActivityStrategyGames/?card=62541**

 SUPPORT RECOMMENDATIONS

- Blind Dogs—Owners and Supporters Facebook group:
  https://www.facebook.com/groups/126150894067756/

CHAPTER 7:

Hearing: Say what? Is it stubbornness, or hearing loss?

Your senior dog snoozes dreamily despite the buzz of your daily household activities, but when you inadvertently touch his food bag, WHOOSH!—he instantly appears at your side! Yet, three minutes before that, you'd tried calling him to another room, and he didn't even open one eye. To many dogs, any sound associated with their food container is like saying "Hey Siri" to an iPhone! With that being said, dogs do lose their hearing ability as they age, and the signs can be subtle.

Ear basics: Wired for sound and striking a balance

At the root of sound is vibration. Objects that vibrate create energy as sound waves that pass through air, water, or solids such as a wall. The eardrum (*tympanic membrane*) and three tiny bones (*ossicles*) in the middle portion of the ear catch and transmit sound wave vibrations, where they travel to a structure in the inner ear called the *cochlea*. The cochlea looks like a mini spiral seashell or snail shell. It contains teeny hair receptors that convert sound waves into electrical activity that the brain interprets.

You've no doubt noticed your dog perks up to interruptions in the sound of silence more easily than you do. Dogs have better hearing than humans do for many reasons. Because dogs' cochleas contain more spirals, they can hear a wider range of high-pitched and softer sounds than we can. And their awesome outer ears use several muscles that swivel, acting as funnels to capture sound waves. This helps them detect noises that are farther away, so they hear the delivery driver—or a rabbit—approaching much sooner than you do.

Another component of the inner ear is the *vestibular apparatus*—structures that help the body orient to stay balanced, maintain posture, and stabilize movements. See Chapter 18 "Balance: Is the room spinning?" for more on that topic.

Why hearing loss happens

Age-related hearing loss is called *presbycusis* and it's a common cause of deafness in dogs. Presbycusis typically progresses gradually during the last third of a dog's lifespan, and they lose the ability to hear certain sounds before others. That may be why many people, myself included, say their dog has selective hearing. Pet parents often tell me their dogs are "just getting ornery" in their old age or ignore commands because they're "stubborn" and "set in their ways." But, in reality, hearing loss has likely begun, and pet parents may not recognize it until their dogs are deaf.

Deafness is classified in numerous ways, and presbycusis falls into the sensory classification, which means the cochlear structure is disrupted. With age, the teeny hair cells in the cochlea degenerate and lose the ability to transmit sound waves.

Causes of deafness other than presbycusis include genetic abnormalities, birth defects, ear infections, tumors, polyps, a foreign body (so *that's* where the Lego went!), a skull fracture, a ruptured eardrum, adverse reactions to drugs or inappropriate use of certain medications, and exposure to extremely loud noises. (Flashback to my teenage heavy metal music phase in the 80s!)

A bit of good news for those of you with younger pups. You may be able to help protect your dog from some types of hearing loss. Avoid exposing your dog to loud noises in close proximity, such as overly loud televisions and music, blow dryers (yours and the groomer's), lawn mowers, leaf blowers, boarding kennels, shooting ranges, concerts, and fireworks. (Jarmon 2019) Ear muffs made especially to protect dogs' hearing are available through many retail outlets.

Staying attuned to hearing changes: When to see your veterinarian

Because age-related hearing loss progresses slowly and can take years, you may first notice a subtle change in your dog's behavior—perhaps she no longer barks at doorbells ringing on TV. Dogs heavily rely on their sense of smell to navigate their world, so it's easy to miss signs of diminished hearing for quite some time.

Pooches with hearing loss or other ear problems may:

- Sleep more
- Not wake to sounds that would normally rouse them—like the garage door opening or a key or keypad unlocking a door
- Easily startle when touched
- Fail to respond to normal verbal cues
- Fail to respond appropriately to sound communication cues from other dogs, resulting in aggression
- Fail to respond to sounds that normally elicit a tizzy—like your home's doorbell!
- Stop howling at nearby sirens
- Seem confused or disoriented
- Excessively bark or make other odd vocal sounds
- Exhibit increased anxiety (which may be related to a fear of being startled)
- No longer fear thunderstorms or fireworks, although they previously had a noise phobia
- Shake their heads often, scratch or rub at their ears, or flinch or vocalize when their ears are touched
- Have unusually smelly, moist, dirty, swollen, or inflamed (reddened) ears
- Stumble, walk in circles, lean while standing, be unable to sit upright, or otherwise seem off balance

On a related note, dogs who have underlying muscle or bone pain may:

- Develop sensitivity (fear or anxiety) associated with noises that didn't used to bother them (more on this topic next)

If you notice any of these changes, visit your veterinarian to check your dog for causes of hearing loss that may be treatable, as well as for other conditions.

Research revelation: Noise sensitivity can be such a pain

What about dogs who seem to be super sensitive to sounds, particularly when they get older? Has your dog suddenly started flinching when a cabinet door shuts or hiding when you pull back a dining room chair? If so, your dog hasn't gained new superhero noise detection abilities, but something may be going on that should be checked out.

A 2018 study showed that dogs who had muscle or bone pain were more sensitive to loudness, different pitches, or sudden noises than dogs who were sensitive to noise but didn't have pain. (Lopes Fagundes 2018, Science Daily 2018)

This suggests that in some dogs, fear or anxiety related to noise could be associated with underlying pain. The theory is that when a dog who is already sore from inflamed joints or muscles is startled and tenses up in response to a loud, unexpected noise, the tension puts extra stress on these areas and causes more pain. The dog then associates pain with the noise and becomes more sensitive to the noise—and may even avoid situations where that sound is made because they anticipate pain.

In that study, dogs who had a painful condition had begun to show signs of fear (e.g. shaking, hiding, trembling) associated with noises (e.g. thunderstorms, fireworks, motorcycles, gunshots, airplanes, cars) much later in life. On average, they were four years older than dogs who were fearful of noises but had no pain. All the dogs in the study who were treated for pain showed improved behavior.

Thus, the study authors recommend that dogs with noise-related behavior problems have a veterinary examination to determine whether a painful condition is related to their fear or anxiety. If a painful condition is identified, it can be treated appropriately. The authors caution that even after pain is successfully treated, a dog may still exhibit noise sensitivity because she has learned to associate noise with pain. So the dog may require further treatment with behavior modification techniques to control or eliminate her response to the noise. (Lopes Fagundes 2018)

Additional sounds that might trigger fear in dogs with painful conditions include slammed doors, kids squealing in a park, construction racket, and others. In some instances, the sound itself may be so loud that it causes ear pain and possible hearing damage.

Now when a pet parent tells me that their older dog has behavior changes associated with noise, I thoroughly evaluate whether underlying pain is a factor. Noise sensitivity may be a red flag that signals a painful issue that I can treat, possibly eliminating their dog's anticipatory fear!

Say what? Hearing assistance for dogs

Now let's get back to hearing loss. If you learn that your dog has age-related hearing loss, unfortunately there is no cure. Devices to improve hearing in people are technological wonders! But in dogs, not so much. Hearing aids for dogs may be an option, but such devices have been said to "treat" owners more than the dogs because dogs adjust well to hearing loss. (Scheifele 2012)

Hearing amplification options for dogs may be difficult to find, can be costly, are challenging to fit and adjust (the sounds won't necessarily sound normal and dogs can't tell us what they're hearing), and require intensive training (for dogs and pet parents). (Scheifele 2012) No research has been done to evaluate the social or emotional effects of hearing loss in dogs. However, dogs are so attuned to using other senses, they can manage their environment well even when they are deaf.

A cautionary tale in managing geriatric dogs with hearing loss

My biggest concern when helping a family with a dog who is hearing impaired is that someone will startle the dog when he is resting, sleeping, or otherwise not expecting to be touched—and, in response, the dog snaps at or bites them.

I'll never forget Bella, a lovely 13-year-old Labrador retriever. Bella's family had called me to euthanize her. Labradors are sweet dogs and rarely have a bad day. Bella seemed to be no exception. She greeted me at the door with kind, greying eyes and slowly led me back to the family room. Her hips swayed from side to side like Marilyn Monroe's! She had severe arthritis, but no other debilitating disease for the family to manage. Bella's primary care veterinarian had determined that the lumps and bumps dotting Bella's sides and back were benign fatty tumors (called *lipomas*) that are common in middle-aged and older dogs. Bella's appetite was good, she had no incontinence or accidents in the house, and she was still smart and interactive.

Bella's real trouble was that she often easily startled because she was almost fully deaf. A few days before I arrived, the family's 7-year-old daughter had invited a friend to visit. Bella had been sleeping soundly in the living room and the young visitor plopped down next to Bella and leaned against her to pet her. Of course, the friend didn't know that Bella had arthritis and that leaning on her would hurt her, or that Bella couldn't hear her coming. Bella woke, startled, and snapped at and bit the girl's hand. The girl didn't need sutures and was otherwise OK, but the bite had to be reported.

Fortunately, Bella's rabies vaccination was up to date. But the family was still faced with the decision to euthanize Bella because they also had a 1-year-old starting to toddle around the house. They were afraid Bella would bite again in a similar situation. While I supported the family's decision, Bella's euthanasia was an especially sad time, and we all cried hard that afternoon.

Bella lives on as I share her story when I talk with other families about the importance of recognizing and adjusting to the special needs of dogs with hearing and vision impairments and painful conditions.

 ## Questions to ask your veterinarian

- What is the underlying cause of my dog's hearing impairment?
- Is my dog's noise sensitivity related to an underlying painful condition?

- My dog won't let me touch his ears, so how can I best clean or medicate him when needed?
- What environmental changes can I make and what products are available to enhance my dog's quality of life and ensure safety?
- Will behavior modification techniques (such as counterconditioning—changing a dog's emotional response to a certain stimulus, and desensitization—safely and gradually exposing a dog to low levels of the stimulus before it provokes a response) help my dog respond more appropriately when she is anxious or afraid? (Horwitz [1] 2020)
- Will my dog benefit from anti-anxiety medications or supplements?

CAREGIVER TIPS AND HOME HACKS FOR HEARING-IMPAIRED DOGS

- Avoid startling your dog and teach others, especially children, how to approach her appropriately. If your dog is sleeping and is startled, she may snap automatically in defense just like Bella did. Children may not understand that their dog is going deaf or has painful areas. Teaching children the safe way to approach and "love on" their dog will mitigate many issues.
- Before touching a dog who is hearing impaired, make them aware of your presence by first allowing her to smell your hand or a familiar object. If they do not respond (let's face it, sometimes they're simply in a deep sleep and dreaming about chasing squirrels!), rouse them otherwise. Tap the surface they're sleeping on or gently and slowly touch a part of their body that is less likely to be painful, such as between their shoulders or on their chest. Many older dogs have painful joints, so avoid their hips and limbs. Also avoid poking or touching them sharply and quickly, and avoid their face.
- Closely monitor your dog's interactions with visitors, and move him to a different location if needed. Teaching your dog to wear a head halter, body harness, or basket muzzle can give you extra control over their interactions during social encounters and help you keep young children and other dogs safe. (Horwitz [1] 2020)
- Use behavior modification techniques (as directed by your veterinarian) to help your dog manage fear- or anxiety-inducing situations safely.
- Always supervise your dog outdoors, and leash walk or use a secure outdoor enclosure. Dogs can easily wander off and may not notice oncoming cars, approaching dogs or cats, or other potential threats.

- Attach a bell to your dog's collar so you can find her if she escapes from your sight.
- Place a medical alert on your dog's tag or collar to indicate that he is deaf.
- Rethink a common old wives' tale: Old dogs *can* learn new tricks! Dogs eagerly learn new things, but usually only when you are interested as well. Learn and teach hand signals as soon as you notice that your dog doesn't hear as well, or if your dog is deaf. Or do this anytime earlier in your dog's life—hand signals are a fun, additional way to communicate and keep that bond you have with your dog!
  - o Use different hand signals for different commands (e.g. come, sit, down, no, stay, go to your spot, quiet, get your toy) and situations (e.g. time to eat, all done, let's go, I'm leaving, we have visitors). Give small treats or pet your dog as a reward, use lots of eye contact, and employ other communication cues (like a blinking flashlight or porch light to signal it's time to come inside) as needed.
- If your dog seems to be more anxious, talk with your veterinarian about medications or supplements (also called *nutraceuticals*) that can help alleviate anxiety.
- Remember that your dog who is hearing impaired can enjoy a happy life and do everything that a dog who has normal hearing can, except hear!

CAREGIVER TIPS AND HOME HACKS FOR DOGS WITH NOISE SENSITIVITY

- Lubricate all hinges and door latches, cabinet doors included.
- Explore the availability of quiet/silent door latch options.
- Apply rubber stoppers on cabinet doors and drawers to prevent slamming noises.
- Install a self-closing, touchless, slow-closing, or quiet-close toilet seat.
- Attach felt pads to the bottoms of chair legs.
- Place non-slip carpet runners with rubber backing or yoga mats where needed to dampen sounds of clicking or heavy heels (senior dogs also greatly benefit from traversing these non-slippery runways).
- Muffle your coffee grinder with a folded towel.
- Lower the volume on your audio system (home theater, video games, music) to reduce the sound of explosions, gunfire, heavy metal, bass, and more.
- Use your paper shredder in a room with a closed door or far enough away from your dog to dampen the sound.

READING RECOMMENDATIONS

- "Living With a Deaf Dog: A Book of Training Advice, Facts and Resources About Canine Deafness Caused by Genetics, Aging, Illness" - By Susan Becker
- D for Dog: Website with tips for living with deaf dogs: **https://www.dfordog.co.uk/blog/deaf-dogs.html**

 SUPPORT RECOMMENDATION

- Facebook group for owners of dogs with hearing impairment: Deaf Dogs Really Do Rock! **https://www.facebook.com/groups/IHaveADeafDog**

 MEDICATION RECOMMENDATION

- Sileo – made by Zoetis is the first FDA-approved medication indicated for the treatment of canine noise aversion. Ask your veterinarian about it.

CHAPTER 8:

Oral care: Keep them grinning

In veterinary school I learned many things about many creatures. From infectious diseases and diabetes to skin problems and complex surgical procedures, I studied and helped treat dogs, cats, ferrets, rabbits, guinea pigs, hamsters, rats, mice, birds, chickens, cows, horses, llamas, Florida black bears, turtles (so many pet and wild turtles in Florida!), snakes, lizards, and even fish. And the one thing I wish I could've spent more time studying was the oral cavity. Yup—the mouth and teeth!

Veterinary schools have limited time to teach students about pets' dental conditions, yet nearly every dog I see has some form of dental disease. And as dogs age without proper dental care, their dental issues worsen. Senior dogs *always* bring a smile to my face! But when I was in primary care practice and examined the mouths of just about every small-breed dog over 7 years old, I braced myself for a hot mess! And the smaller the dog's mouth, the worse their teeth!

Baxter's breath of new life

Baxter was a 6-year-old terrier mix, and his owner told me Baxter had lost weight and his breath smelled "pretty gross." Baxter didn't want me to touch his mouth (which I attributed to pain), and based on what little I could see, it was bad. And his breath smelled like hot garbage!

Baxter's owner agreed with me that Baxter needed a professional dental cleaning including dental radiographs, along with tests that would help me assess Baxter's health status before anesthetizing him. Baxter's urine test results were normal, but his blood tests showed mild abnormalities that indicated potential liver and kidney disease. I suspected these results were related to his dental problems and not serious enough to postpone his dental treatment.

Once Baxter was anesthetized and I could fully examine his mouth, I learned that Baxter had such severe dental disease that he needed all but two teeth surgically extracted—40 total! Eight of his teeth were so loose that they nearly fell out on their own.

A couple weeks after Baxter's dental extraction sites had healed, Baxter's owner excitedly told me Baxter was now begging for treats, playing with toys, nudging his hand to be petted, and chasing squirrels. He realized these were all activities that Baxter had gradually stopped doing since he was 3 years old!

Two months later I rechecked Baxter's blood tests, and his results were normal—no indications of potential liver or kidney problems. Of course Baxter's future professional dental cleanings were much shorter because he only had two teeth, but Baxter lived a happy, active life for 10 more years!

 Me and veterinary technician Jasmine cleaning teeth!

A dog's first dental visit

Far too often, pet parents don't schedule their dogs for their first dental visit and cleaning until their dog is middle-aged or older. Yet most dogs who go without dental care exhibit dental disease by 3 years of age!

The American Animal Hospital Association recommends that small- and medium-breed dogs have a professional veterinary dental cleaning starting at 1 year of age, and that large-breed dogs have their first cleaning at 2 years of age. Small-breed and brachycephalic (short-headed) breeds such as boxers or pugs are more prone to dental problems than are large-breed dogs. They have a smaller bone-to-tooth-root ratio (less bone to support the tooth roots) and shorter skulls, so their teeth are crowded and sometimes rotated. In these breeds, veterinarians may have to remove a tooth (that usually is not helping the dog chew anyway) simply to make room to treat the dog's other teeth or to provide overall better oral health.

When I was a primary care practitioner, I typically didn't hear concerns from pet parents about their dog's teeth until their dog's breath smelled bad, they saw blood on their dog's chew toys, or they realized that their dog wasn't eating well. But by the time pet parents notice something amiss, the damaged oral tissues and infection have already wreaked havoc. Many pet parents of older dogs are shocked to learn from their veterinarians that not only is their dog long overdue for teeth cleaning, their dog's dental disease has progressed so far that the dog needs several tooth extractions—sometimes 10, 20, or more teeth (like Baxter's astonishing 40)! Most of my middle-aged dog patients had to have multiple teeth pulled during their first professional dental cleaning. And sadly, many of their owners didn't bring them back for routine veterinary dental cleanings for the remainder of their dogs' lives because their first experience turned out to be an extremely costly surgical procedure. Routine dental care and professional cleanings are important at all ages.

When dental care is irregular

Unlike people, dogs infrequently get cavities. But like people, they do get gum disease (also called *periodontal disease*), and it can begin when they're young. Periodontal disease is the most common problem in the adult dog population because most dogs do not receive consistent dental care. Playing with a chew toy once a week or eating dry food daily isn't sufficient dental care. If I was still in general practice, I could probably see *only* dogs with dental disease all day, and the majority would be senior or geriatric dogs!

Dogs can't brush and floss their teeth every day or schedule their own teeth cleanings, so accumulated food particles and saliva provide a great environment for their oral bacteria to multiply and leave deposits (*plaque*) on the teeth and below the gums. When plaque weasels its way beneath the gum line, the bacteria and their byproducts incite inflammation. Plaque that isn't removed by brushing continues to build up and hardens into dental tartar (also called *calculus*). Ultimately, tartar irritates the gums and other structures that support the teeth and causes infection.

Teeth, gums, and the bones that support the teeth are badly damaged after years of tartar buildup and infection, which leads to loose teeth and tooth fractures, necessitating tooth extractions. It breaks my heart to think how much pain these dogs must have endured for so long. At a veterinary conference, a veterinary dental specialist once shared something she learned from a dentist for people. Some of her homeless human patients who had previously been unable to seek dental care described that having to eat with a fractured tooth feels like always having to walk on a sprained ankle, or they perceived it to feel like they were chewing on broken glass!

In some dogs, infection and inflammation from severe dental disease leads to bone loss around the teeth, which weakens the jaw bones. Weakened bones may allow small fractures to develop. This is called *osteomyelitis* of the jaw and it occurs more commonly in smaller breed dogs. So when diseased teeth are

FUN FACT:

Adult cats have 30 teeth and adult dogs have 42. Adult people have 32 teeth, unless their wisdom teeth have been removed!

extracted during a dental procedure, the jaw may easily break, which requires a longer surgery to repair, as well as longer, more intense patient care afterward.

Untreated gum disease may also lead to trouble elsewhere besides the mouth. Bacteria from infected teeth and gums may travel through the bloodstream and cause abnormal microscopic changes in the heart, kidneys, and liver. (Pereira Dos Santos 2019, Trevejo 2018) Dogs with diabetes have a higher risk of gum disease, and, in turn, gum disease may hamper glucose metabolism, which can make diabetes worse. (Lewis 2018) In people, chronic inflammation associated with periodontal disease is recognized to adversely affect a person's overall general health. (Bellows 2019) Likewise, and especially in senior dogs, if a dog's dental health can be improved, the dog's health overall will likely also improve. (Lobprise [3] 2020) I saw this with many patients, including Baxter. Not only did he show more zeal for life after his dental surgery, but his blood test results returned to normal.

It may be helpful to think of an infected, diseased mouth as a giant wound that's been left to fester. On top of that, if your dog has fractured teeth (keep in mind that broken teeth aren't always seen unless radiographs are taken), your dog likely endures tremendous pain every time she eats. You can easily imagine how much misery and poor health that causes.

Chewing on all the alarming details I've presented above, it's easy to see why regular veterinary dental examinations (at least once a year) and routine professional dental cleanings are necessary.

Is anesthesia really necessary to clean dogs' teeth?

Wouldn't it be great if dogs would cooperatively sit back once or twice a year, open wide, stay still, and let the veterinary technician examine, x-ray (bite down to hold the radiograph film, and hold still for the picture!), probe, scrape, rinse, suction, and polish their teeth for an hour?

Because dogs won't allow this, they must be anesthetized for teeth cleaning. I know many pet parents are afraid to have their dog undergo anesthesia—particularly an older dog. This fear, along with the cost of veterinary dentistry (most pet insurance plans don't yet cover routine dental cleanings) and the well-meaning but mistaken pet parent belief that dogs don't need regular dental healthcare like people do, all serve to justify some pet owners' decisions to forgo their dogs' routine professional dental cleanings. That is, until a dog's oral disease has progressed so far that the problem can't be ignored. And at that point, a much longer time under anesthesia and a costlier procedure (typically with tooth extractions, as I mentioned earlier) are required.

This is why anesthesia-free dentistry, also called nonanesthetic dentistry, has gained popularity and appeals to many pet owners and to some veterinarians. [Burns 2016] With this service, the dog is awake while the tartar—above the gum-line only—is removed and the teeth are polished. While this makes the dog's teeth look shiny and white on the surface, tartar and other problems below the gums continue to lurk and can progress. This is especially concerning in areas like the tooth roots and jawbones that can only be properly evaluated with radiography (x-rays).

Anesthetizing dogs for dentistry is needed to prevent patient pain or injury during a thorough examination and cleaning. It's also needed to prevent harm to the person cleaning the teeth. Using a dental probe to measure tooth socket depths and a dental scaler to remove tartar under the gumline are often prickly and uncomfortable, plus these instruments are sharp and perilous to use in awake, wiggly dogs who may also bite! In addition, dogs who are not anesthetized can inhale the debris created by removing the tartar from, or scaling, the teeth, which can lead to a serious lung infection. (Dogs who are anesthetized have a breathing tube in place that protects their airways from this debris.) The anesthesia also ensures dogs stay still for correct x-ray positioning, and obtaining radiographs are another vital part of evaluating and maintaining oral health in every dog.

Some veterinarians and technicians believe nonanesthetic dentistry can be used successfully, when done under veterinary supervision and for those dogs whose owners otherwise won't allow a full anesthetic procedure because of the cost or potential risks. But, of course, if a dog needs additional evaluation (which they do, because dental radiographs are considered the standard of care in veterinary practice) or treatment (e.g. tooth extraction), an anesthesia-free procedure is impossible.

The tradeoffs for dogs who undergo nonanesthetic dentistry are that they may experience stress and pain during the service, and undetected or untreated dental disease may stay hidden longer, which leads to disease progression, further

Petunia had to have all her teeth pulled at age 12 years (she is 16+ years old now) and has been happy and healthy ever since. Apart from her tongue always sticking out (which sometimes happens after multiple tooth extractions, especially in small breeds), you would never notice.

pain, and increased cost to treat later. For these reasons, I strongly discourage nonanesthetic dental procedures.

Keep in mind that the risks related to anesthesia can be greatly reduced with a proper preoperative patient history and examination, diagnostic tests (checking the blood and urine to assess a dog's health status, and performing other tests as needed), and high-quality anesthetic and supportive care techniques. If your dog has a medical condition that makes him a higher risk for anesthetic complications, such as diabetes, chronic kidney disease, or heart disease, your veterinarian may recommend referral to a veterinary dental specialist or that the procedure be done at a hospital with a veterinarian who specializes in anesthesia. As with Baxter, I have seen many miraculous patient outcomes after professional dental cleaning.

So don't be nervous if your veterinarian tells you your dog needs professional dental cleaning (all dogs do!) and that he or she may (or does) need one tooth or several teeth pulled. It's crucial to remove the source of oral problems and pain and prevent future or more serious disease—both in the mouth and in other organs. Dogs who have had some or even all of their teeth extracted can still eat well (and even better than with diseased teeth!). They'll also feel better and have a better quality of life, compared to living with rotten, painful, or fractured (like chewing broken glass!) teeth.

Other common oral problems in seniors

As I cover in the chapter on body condition and nutrition, age-related muscle loss is called sarcopenia and it's common and expected in senior dogs. This type of muscle atrophy is especially noticeable in the hindlimbs and can cause trembling and unsteadiness while a dog is standing or walking. Sarcopenia is also apparent in the muscles of the head and can affect the jaw muscles and those involved in swallowing. Affected dogs may have difficulty picking up, holding, chewing, and ingesting food. Dogs can also develop inflammatory or immune-mediated diseases that affect these muscles.

Veterinary examinations that include a good look in your dog's mouth are important not only to assess the teeth and gums but also to look for swelling, wounds or sores called ulcers, masses, or abnormal pigmentation. Oral ulcers can stem from a variety of problems such as irritation, infections, kidney disease, cancer, or even an autoimmune response to excessive plaque buildup.

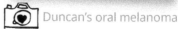
Duncan's oral melanoma

Senior and geriatric dogs have a higher risk of cancer, and cancer can start in the mouth. Malignant melanoma, squamous cell carcinoma, and fibrosarcoma are the most common oral cancers in dogs.

If detected early (which can be difficult without regular, careful veterinary exams), some oral cancers, especially those nearest the front of the mouth and whose tumor cells haven't spread to other parts of the body, can be treated to stop or delay progression. Surgery, chemotherapy, radiation therapy, and even a vaccine (to prevent malignant melanoma from spreading to other organs) may be of benefit. My own dog Duncan had oral melanoma, which I discovered while examining his teeth! His melanoma was surgically removed, and he received a series of vaccinations designed to fight remaining melanoma cells.

News to savor

The good news is that the vast majority of periodontal disease in dogs is preventable!

In addition to regular examinations and an annual professional dental cleaning, here are important ways to promote your dog's oral health at home:

- Brush your dog's teeth daily (use toothpaste formulated specifically for dogs—do not use yours!). You can even teach many senior dogs to accept this, with small steps and patience.
- Feed a therapeutic veterinary dental diet specifically designed to slow plaque buildup (discuss the options with your veterinarian).
- Provide safe toys and chew products.
  - A chew treat that is so rigid you can't bend it or dent the surface with your fingernail is way too hard, and your dog can break its teeth by chewing on it. Don't give your dog cow hooves, animal bones, sticks, hard nylon bones, or antlers.
  - While tooth wear from frequent chewing is uncommon, if your dog obsessively chews tennis balls or other abrasive soft toys, permanent tooth damage may occur.
  - Heed product labels and provide only treats and toys appropriate for your dog's size. Avoid items your dog can choke on or that, if swallowed, can cause gastrointestinal upset, injury, or blockage such as bones, pig ears, and chews or toys too small for your dog's size.
- Water additives and oral gels, sprays, wipes, and powders may help slow plaque buildup. See the Veterinary Oral Health Council website for a li: approved products for dogs.

I HAVE... DOG BREATH?

When to see your veterinarian

Keep in mind that signs of oral problems can be difficult to detect in dogs. Your dog's broken tooth may not be obvious to you, but a tooth with even a minor fracture can be sharply or dully painful and ultimately lead to serious infection and an abscess. In addition to your dog's regular exams, schedule a veterinary visit if your dog:

- Has foul-smelling breath
- Has yellow, brown, grey, or greenish discoloration or buildup on her teeth—this is tartar that needs to be removed from above and below the gum line
- Eats less—dogs may seem hungry but eat very little or walk away from their food because it's painful or difficult to chew
- Drops food frequently, which may indicate that it's painful to hold onto or chew food
- Paws at his mouth or rubs his face often
- Drools excessively (may be hard to detect in Saint Bernards, mastiffs, or Newfoundlands!)
- Has red or swollen gums, or bleeding gums
- Has oral ulcers
- Has swelling in or around the mouth, nose, eyes, or jaw
- Seems painful or gets defensive if you touch her mouth
- Has obviously chipped or broken teeth, or loose or missing teeth

 CAREGIVER TIPS AND HOME HACKS

Regardless of the cause of a senior or geriatric dog's oral cavity problems, they should be able to consume enough calories to meet their nutritional needs and maintain basic daily activities, and they should be enthusiastic about and enjoy eating. Embracing a love of eating factors into a dog's quality-of-life assessment.

- Feed moistened dry or canned food and soft treats to dogs with muscle atrophy, those who have lost most or all of their teeth, or those who have had oral surgery to remove a tumor.
  - Use low-sodium beef or chicken broth to soak kibble
  - Feed freshly made dog food (delivery options are available), such as FreshPet **https://freshpet.com**, JustFoodForDogs **https://www.justfoodfordogs.com** and The Farmer's Dog **https://www.thefarmersdog.com**

- Consider elevating food and water bowls, which may make swallowing easier and may also help dogs with neck discomfort. (Avoid this for large- and giant-breed dogs, who may have an increased risk of bloat and twisted stomach associated with raised food bowls. (Glickman 2000)
- Serve refrigerated food at or warmed to room temperature.
- Teach your dog to accept having his mouth touched so you can look inside and eventually teach him to accept toothbrushing or dental wipes. Pair these lessons with a favorite treat or play activity afterward, so your dog starts to look forward to it!
- If your dog has oral ulcers, your veterinarian can prescribe a special mouthwash used often in human medicine which they call "magic mouthwash." It has to be made at a compounding pharmacy and contains lidocaine, diphenhydramine, and sucralfate and is used as a soothing and protective mouth rinse. This is not to be confused with other over-the-counter trademarked dental rinse products with similar names.

 ## Questions to ask your veterinarian about your dog's professional dental cleaning

- If my dog's age or other medical condition increases the risk of complications from anesthesia, what measures are taken to help reduce this risk?
    - o Do you have a veterinary anesthesia-certified nurse available to assist?
- What is the cost of a professional dental cleaning?
    - o What is the cost if my dog needs tooth extraction?
    - o If my dog needs multiple extractions that exceed my budget, what will be the treatment plan?
- What pain management measures will you use before and after the procedure, especially if my dog needs tooth extraction?
- Can my dog eat and drink normally in the evening after the dental procedure? Will my dog's food need to be softened for a few days? Will my dog need additional supportive feeding methods?
- What dental care can I do at home if I can't brush my dog's teeth?
- For diabetic dogs: How should I fast my diabetic dog before a dental procedure? Will my dog need any diet alteration to ensure they'll eat on schedule afterward?

PRODUCT RECOMMENDATIONS

- Refrigerated, fresh pet foods: freshpet® **https://freshpet.com**, Just-FoodForDogs® **https://www.justfoodfordogs.com**, The Farmer's Dog **https://www.thefarmersdog.com**

READING RECOMMENDATIONS

- American Veterinary Dental College
  https://avdc.org/animal-owner-resources
- Veterinary Oral Health Council accepted products
  http://www.vohc.org/all_accepted_products.html

CHAPTER 9:

Body condition and nutrition: Helping senior dogs eat better and feel better

"Food is symbolic of love when words are inadequate."

— ALAN D. WOLFELT, AUTHOR, EDUCATOR, GRIEF COUNSELOR

As our thoughts turn to what goes into your dog's belly, you may be wondering: Why do many dogs become overweight as they get older? Why do some older dogs lose weight or show less interest in food? Is unintentional weight loss and reduced appetite normal in senior dogs? What food is best for my senior dog? How do veterinary therapeutic diets differ from over-the-counter pet foods? How can I encourage my dog to eat when she doesn't feel well?

I'll address these questions and more, and begin with important considerations for keeping an eye on your dog's physique. Unless we monitor our dogs' weight along with assessing whether they have a healthy amount of fat and muscle, gradual changes in their body composition can creep along and surprise us one day.

Portly pooches

Sadly, many adult dogs of all ages in the U.S. are overweight, but their owners may not realize it. In 2018, the Association for Pet Obesity Prevention estimated that 56% of dogs (and 60% of cats!) were overweight or obese. (Association for Pet Obesity Prevention website)

We've surpassed our pets in this respect. According to the CDC, 73.6% of adult people in the U.S. are overweight or obese. (Obesity and Overweight/CDC website) In people, obesity is considered a disease and is a risk factor for developing diabetes, cardiovascular disease, osteoarthritis, cancer, and more. People with obesity also have a higher mortality risk.

NOT HAVING MUCH FUN FACT

One 2017 study revealed that adult people spend more time on the toilet (3 hours and 9 minutes) each week than they spend engaged in moderate activity (1 hour and 30 minutes) such as bike riding or walking fast. (UK Active 2017)

Likewise, our dog's health, quality of life, and longevity are negatively affected by obesity. (German 2016)

When I worked in general veterinary practice, weight loss in pets topped my discussion topics with pet owners, with dental disease being a close second. (The irony, right? Pets with bad teeth can still overeat!) The veterinary technicians at our practice were always prepared for me to talk with clients about their chunky pets—typically a delicate topic.

And I haven't changed! I recently visited my neighbors to return something. Their large-breed dogs Sailor and Ursa greeted me with smothering kisses when I knelt down to say hello. I noticed their chubbiness right away. I HAD to say something.

"Jeff, these guys are overweight. Can we talk about how much food they are getting?" Jeff gave me the customary, surprised response. "Really?! Are you sure??"

On my phone's web browser I pulled up a canine body condition score chart—a subjective way to assess how much fat a dog has—to show Jeff where Sailor and Ursa landed. The scale runs from 1 (severely underweight) to 9 (severely over-weight), and a score of 4 or 5 indicates optimal body condition—not too fat, not too thin. I gave each of my neighbor dogs a score of 8, which indicates obesity.

I talked with Jeff about a diet and physical activity plan (including food puzzle toys) for his dogs and recommended he drop by his veterinary clinic with them every couple weeks for a weigh-in to track their progress.

When I borrow something else from Jeff in a few months, I look forward to seeing Sailor's and Ursa's results! Trimming his dogs' weight now and keeping it off will help them as they get older. Both dogs are German shepherd mixes, so they may already have underlying hip dysplasia—a common hip joint deformity in large-breed dogs. Dogs with hip dysplasia have a higher risk of developing hip arthritis. So carrying additional weight into their senior years would be especially difficult for his dogs and contribute to severe mobility issues.

Other problems that Jeff's dogs may be able to avoid by trimming fat are decreased lifespan, cancer, diabetes, and respiratory disease. (German 2010) Excess fat stimulates inflammation throughout the body, which can put pets at higher risk of developing other diseases.

It's best for dogs to maintain a healthy weight throughout their lives. Dogs who remain lean throughout their lives have a longer healthspan (the generally healthy and disease-free period of life) and a longer lifespan (Kealy 2002, Huck 2009). But never fear—if your senior dog has fat to lose, it isn't too late to start! A recent study evaluated body composition and survival in 39 Labrador retrievers starting at around 6.5 years of age and followed them throughout the rest of their lives (up to 17.9 years!). The study results suggest that diet and activity to control body weight and the lean-to-fat-mass relationship in middle-age and older dogs allows them to enjoy an increased healthspan and a survival benefit. (Penell 2019)

How to assess fat mass

As dogs age, their metabolism slows, so their nutritional requirements may change, especially as their youthful physical activity levels decrease. They tend to gain fat and lose muscle.

A dog who is at a healthy weight is not necessarily in the eye of the beholder. I believe that most pet parents in the U.S. tend to incorrectly perceive overweight pets as normal and healthy-weight dogs as underweight. I have often been told by well-meaning pet owners that my dogs are "too skinny," when in fact they have a perfect body condition score of 5 out of 9. And based on my interactions with clients before we discuss what an optimal body condition looks like, most pet owners see their dogs who have a body condition score of 7 or 8 as normal and healthy. They also think that a score of 9 might indicate that their pet is "a little overweight" rather than severely obese.

Body condition scoring helps estimate a pet's fat mass by checking how easy it is to feel their ribs, assessing whether they have a "waist" as viewed from above, and evaluating whether their belly has a tuck or hangs down as viewed from the side. Illustrations and charts are readily available that describe body condition scoring. To score your pets, check out the World Small Animal Veterinary Association Body Condition Score scales for dogs: **https://wsava.org/wp-content/uploads/2020/01/Body-Condition-Score-Dog.pdf**

Dog Body Condition Score

A handy way to check for fat cats and bony dogs

Hold your hand out flat with your fingers extended, palm facing down. With your other hand, gently run your fingers over the knuckles on the back of your hand. This is how a pet's ribs feel when their weight is ideal.

Then turn your hand over with your palm facing up and your fingers straight and feel your knuckles on the palm side of your hand. If your pet's ribs feel like this, your pet is too plump.

Turn your hand back over, palm down, and make a fist. Feel the knuckles on the back of your hand. If your pet's ribs feel this prominent, your pet is too thin.

Trimming the fat

Helping an overweight or obese dog lose weight can seem overwhelming, and dogs must rely on their caretakers' willpower. Dogs can't (usually!) help themselves to the food, so their route to a healthy weight starts with their pet parents simply dishing out less food and fewer treats. Overweight dogs who are being fed free-choice need scheduled mealtimes on the menu instead. Overfilling dogs' bowls, giving table scraps, and offering treats are some of the ways that we show dogs love every day. But if our dogs have become rotund, we're also shortening their healthspans and diminishing their quality of life. Talk with your veterinarian about a meal and weight loss program tailored to your dog's needs.

Keeping dogs at an optimal weight while they're young, middle-aged, and senior, including while you're managing their conditions or illnesses throughout their lives, makes a world of difference in your dog's mobility, activity level, attitude, and ability to recover—and will quite likely help your dog live longer. Feeding less of their regular food when appropriate or feeding a veterinary-recommended weight loss diet to help your dog stay trim also saves you money—both in food costs and potential future veterinary bills!

Skinny seniors

Other than putting an overweight dog on a diet, many conditions in senior dogs can cause weight loss. Severe dental problems can make eating too painful, stomach or intestinal diseases reduce nutrient absorption, and a variety of other illnesses and some medications can cause nausea and unwillingness to eat.

As dogs enter their senior years, they may also lose weight because of muscle loss, even without an underlying disease. This type of muscle loss is called *sarcopenia*, and it occurs as people age, too. Another type of muscle loss in people and dogs is associated with underlying disease and is called *cachexia*. Sarcopenia and cachexia also contribute to other health problems.

Unintended, unexplained weight loss always warrants a veterinary evaluation. If dogs have a condition that curbs their appetite or hampers nutrient absorption, they can lose weight because they don't eat enough calories or process nutrients effectively. Their body condition changes can be dramatic and difficult to reverse. Unfortunately, because senior dogs often also have an underlying disease, they may confront both sarcopenia and cachexia. Your senior dog health journal comes in handy for tracking your dog's zeal for food and treats, along with changes in their appearance over time.

Neo, Duncan, Serissa, and Sam—each of my dogs stayed trim and fit for most of their lives, but they each lost weight as they became geriatric. As they lost muscle and fat, their faces and the tops of their heads appeared bonier, and their spines, hips, and shoulders became too easy to feel. They each gradually showed less interest in their meals and dropped at least 10% of their body weight. I had to tighten each one's collar or harness. In contrast to the joy I felt after dieting and being able to cinch my belt by one more hole, their weight loss—some of which was associated with aging, and some with illness—was not joyful to me.

Sarcopenia

I think of my Grandma Gardner, who was a fit woman her entire life. But as she aged, her hands looked bony, her face lost its fullness, and she was a twig. Most people lose muscle mass as they age, even if they are otherwise healthy. Sarcopenia starts at around 30 years of age, and, shockingly, we can lose 30% of our muscle mass by 80 years of age, as compared with the muscle mass we had at age 20. (Freeman 2012)

The danger of sarcopenia? In people, it reduces muscle strength and contributes to fragility, leading to falls and injuries as well as decreased immunity. (Freeman 2012) Sarcopenia is also linked to a risk of adverse outcomes such as physical disability, poor quality of life, and death. (Santilli 2014) Factors that likely contribute to sarcopenia in people as they age include being physically inactive, changes in muscle fibers, chronic inflammation, decreased protein production, insulin resistance, and decreased testosterone and growth hormone. (Freeman 2012)

Sarcopenia has been less studied in dogs than in people, but evidence suggests that dogs also lose muscle with aging. (Freeman 2012, Freeman 2018) Sarcopenia in dogs probably results from similar mechanisms associated with aging in people and contributes to similar adverse outcomes.

Parents of dogs with mobility issues often ask me to prescribe medications to alleviate pain in their dogs. But in some cases, after I perform a physical examination and assess their dog's weight, body condition, and muscle condition, some dogs don't appear to be in pain or have arthritis—but they do have sarcopenia.

You might think that signs of sarcopenia will be obvious in your dog since she should look skinnier than normal. But as muscle is lost with age, more fat mass tends to accumulate, so muscle loss may not be as noticeable, and a dog's weight may stay steady or even increase rather than decrease. This can mask sarcopenia.

Cachexia

Cachexia is closely related to sarcopenia, but cachexia occurs when a disease leads to loss of muscle mass. (Freeman 2018) It most often happens in pets with chronic diseases, such as heart failure, cancer, or kidney disease. But cachexia can also occur in dogs who have sudden severe illnesses and critical injuries. (Freeman 2018)

Animals with cachexia often also have weight loss, which is sometimes extreme, especially as their disease progresses. But you may not notice weight loss in the early stages of cachexia. The weight loss that occurs in dogs with cachexia differs from weight loss that occurs in healthy dogs. In healthy dogs who lose weight because of reduced caloric intake, they lose fat first and preserve muscle. But in dogs with chronic disease, muscle is catabolized (muscle protein is broken down to amino acids to use for energy) before fat stores are used. (Freeman 2018)

> In people, cachexia is also called wasting syndrome. As it is in pets, cachexia in people is a complex disorder that messes with the body's use of nutrients and is associated with long-term disease or sudden, severe illness. People who have cachexia lose muscle with or without losing fat, have unintentionally lost 5% or more of their body weight in 12 months or less, and experience other problems such as less interest in food, being tired all the time, and muscle weakness. (Evans 2008)

Cachexia can occur even in dogs who are eating well. With cachexia, protein, carbohydrate, and fat metabolism go awry and the body doesn't properly process the energy it needs, even if the dog is eating normally. This faulty metabolism results in muscle breakdown and inhibits muscle growth, which contributes to weakness. Cachexia is also associated with triggering inflammation and immune system malfunction, which means the body has less ability to heal and more susceptibility to infections. And dogs with cachexia often have a reduced appetite, which only makes the problem worse.

It's no surprise that cachexia diminishes quality of life in a number of ways. Affected dogs become weaker (and wobbly), which can lead to accidents and

 Cachexia is evident in Dakota, age 15 years. She has a chronic disease, is underweight, has little to no visible body fat (body condition score of 1), and has severe muscle loss. Her hindlimb, hip, back, rib and facial bones are prominent.

injuries that require more caregiving. Cachexia can also hamper a dog's ability to respond to treatment, escalate symptoms of the underlying illness, and reduce life expectancy.

My Anatolian shepherd, Sam, weighed 80 pounds during her healthy adult years. Now, with her cancer and a decreased appetite, she weighs only 67 pounds. Despite my best efforts to ensure she gets the calories she needs as well as daily exercise, her body condition score is a 3 or 4 (out of 9) and her muscle condition score indicates moderate muscle loss. She even goes to physical therapy three times a week. Her fur tends to visually mask her thinness, but petting and palpating her reveals the prominent outlines of her bones.

How to assess muscle mass

Your veterinarian should assess not only your dog's weight and body condition but also your dog's muscle condition to check for muscle loss associated with age or disease. The body condition score primarily assesses a dog's fat mass, so it can be misleading with respect to a dog's muscle mass. For example, despite being overweight or obese, dogs may still have severe muscle loss, and this is called *sarcobesity* (Parr 2013). So dogs whose scale readout drops primarily because of muscle loss aren't necessarily making weight loss progress. Similarly, a dog who is underweight may have normal muscle mass but an insufficient amount of body fat.

Assessing a dog's muscle condition takes more practice than assessing a dog's body condition. It requires looking at and feeling the muscles next to the spine, on the head, and over the shoulders and hips. The score is graded as normal muscle mass or as mild, moderate, or severe muscle loss. You can find information on how veterinarians assess muscle condition by reviewing the World Small Animal Veterinary Association Muscle Condition Score scales for dogs: **https://wsava.org/wp-content/uploads/2020/01/ Muscle-Condition-Score-Chart-for-Dogs.pdf**

Muscle Condition Score

What can be done for dogs with muscle loss?

The goals of therapy for sarcopenia or cachexia are to rebuild strength and slow or reverse the muscle loss associated with aging or disease. Cachexia can't be cured, so the most effective way to help affected dogs is to treat their underlying chronic illness and provide supportive therapies. Treatments that hold promise for helping dogs with sarcopenia or cachexia include exercise, appetite stimulation, fish oil and myostatin inhibitor dietary supplements, and the proper diet in the right amounts. (Freeman 2018) Your veterinarian can help determine whether your dog may benefit from these or additional therapies.

EXERCISE. Increasing dogs' activity through exercise that includes resistance training to slow or reverse muscle loss is key. (Freeman 2018) Endurance exercises build aerobic power generated by the heart and lungs, and resistance exercises maintain and build muscle. A three-day-a-week balanced resistance and endurance exercise program is physically and mentally beneficial for dogs. (Perkins Johnson 2017) Talk with your veterinarian about an appropriate activity plan for your dog. Also consider visiting with a veterinary physical rehabilitation specialist.

> "In my 30s I exercised to look good,
>
> In my 40s, I exercised to stay fit
>
> Then in my 70s I exercised to stay ambulatory
>
> In my 80s I exercised to stay out of assisted living
>
> In my 90s, I'm exercising out of pure defiance!"
>
> — DICK VAN DYKE (CURTIS 2015)

APPETITE STIMULANT. Capromorelin is an oral medication that promotes appetite by making the body's hunger hormone (ghrelin) more readily available. Ghrelin also increases other hormones that boost metabolism and affect muscle mass: growth hormone and insulin-like growth factor-1. (Freeman 2018)

FISH OIL. Omega-3 fatty acids (called eicosapentaenoic acid [EPA] and docosahexaenoic acid [DHA]) help reduce inflammation, decrease muscle loss, and improve appetite. Welactin (Nutramax Laboratories Veterinary Sciences) and Omega-3 Pet (Nordic Naturals) are omega-3 fatty acid supplements available in separate forms for dogs and cats. Some dog foods already contain omega-3 fatty acids, so talk with your veterinarian about whether your pet needs a supplement.

Avoid flaxseed oil (it contains an incorrect ratio of EPA and DHA) and cod liver oil (the amount of vitamin A and vitamin D are too high for the amount of this oil that would be needed to deliver the right dose of EPA and DHA). (Freeman 2010) Always ask your veterinarian whether fish oil or any other type of supplement is appropriate for your dog and, if so, what brands are best formulated for your dog's needs and what doses are safe.

MYOSTATIN INHIBITOR. Muscle cells make a protein called myostatin to limit muscle growth. Without it, dogs (and we!) would have double the amount of normal muscle mass. Researchers think that blocking myostatin may help slow muscle loss associated with cachexia or sarcopenia. Two types of myostatin-reducing agents have shown promising results in two studies that evaluated a small number of dogs. (Freeman 2015, White 2020) One myostatin inhibitor is available as a fertilized egg yolk product in a supplement called MYOS Canine Muscle Formula. More studies are needed in dogs, and myostatin inhibition is also being studied for its potential benefits in people.

DIET. Providing optimal nutrition formulated for your dog's life stage and, when indicated, feeding a therapeutic diet specifically designed to support pets with certain chronic diseases is crucial. Ensuring that dogs with cachexia consume enough calories—especially protein and other nutrients—that also help manage their underlying disease is particularly critical. Pet foods labeled as senior diets won't necessarily provide optimal nutrients for seniors who have underlying diseases. For example, dogs who have heart failure need a lower salt diet. Dogs with kidney disease have special dietary protein and mineral needs. So, especially for dogs with cachexia, consider asking a veterinary specialist in nutrition for help. A veterinarian who is board-certified in veterinary nutrition can tailor a pet's diet and feeding recommendations, and some provide remote consultation. Ask your veterinarian for help in connecting with one, or visit the American College of Veterinary Nutrition website **https://acvn.org/nutrition-consults/**.

Increasing food intake often involves making the food more palatable, which I discuss later in this chapter. Getting the most out of mealtimes may also mean you need to prevent competition for food from other pets in the household.

Which diet is best for senior dogs?

Now that we've covered the portly and the skinny issues that might pop up, let's look at nutrition in general and the topics pet parents often ask me about.

A plethora of diets have been formulated to support a variety of factors that make up the uniqueness that is your dog:

- Life stage (e.g. pediatric or growth, adult, reproduction, mature, senior)
- Breed (e.g. Chihuahua, Labrador, Great Dane)
- Body system support (e.g. dental health, sensitive stomach, haircoat, weight management)
- Disease (e.g. diabetes, kidney disease, joint issues, heart disease, cognitive problems, intestinal disorders, seizures, allergies, urinary tract disease).

It can be overwhelming! Many diets are available over the counter (OTC) at grocery stores and pet stores, and others—veterinary therapeutic diets—are available only through veterinarians. You can face decision paralysis with all the options!

What's the difference between veterinary therapeutic diets and OTC options?

Veterinary therapeutic diets must undergo extensive testing and research to show that they are precisely formulated to address the nutrient needs of pets who have a specific disease or condition. These diets often contain special high-quality ingredients or nutritional supplements that are not included in OTC pet foods. In addition, therapeutic diets have rigorous manufacturing controls, and the companies test every batch of food produced. (ACVN website 2021)

Therapeutic diets typically cost more than OTC diets. The rigorous diet formulation, ingredient selection, and manufacturing technique all add up and make them seem expensive compared with OTC diets. This may be true if you compare them solely on a bowl-to-bowl basis. So if your veterinarian recommends a therapeutic diet for your dog, account for the amount you would spend on an OTC diet anyway, then factor in the benefits of feeding a therapeutic diet as a component of your pet's overall medical treatment to prevent, slow, or reverse the ailment, thus potentially reducing future veterinary medical costs. You'll likely find that therapeutic diets are invaluable support for your pet and you.

Why are therapeutic diets available only through veterinarians?

The FDA Center for Veterinary Medicine requires dog and cat foods that claim to treat or prevent disease be available to the public only through or under the direction of licensed veterinarians. (Center for Veterinary Medicine website 2016) Pets with chronic diseases need veterinary evaluation and monitoring to help ensure that their therapeutic diet (which is often used along with medical treatment) is the right choice for that condition and continues to help the pet. Veterinary oversight is also needed to determine at what point it may be acceptable to discontinue the therapeutic diet and switch to a different therapeutic diet or back to an OTC diet.

It's vital to have a diagnosis before feeding your pet a therapeutic diet, especially if your pet has more than one health problem. You can inadvertently cause a nutrition-related medical problem if you feed a therapeutic diet that your pet doesn't need. The nutrients in therapeutic diets are specially formulated for pets with specific diseases, so the levels of these nutrients are not always suitable for long-term feeding in healthy pets, or the nutrients could be inappropriate for a pet who has multiple conditions. (Again, for pets with multiple conditions, consultation with a veterinary nutritionist about an optimal food is especially helpful!) The bottom line is that therapeutic diets are not available for sale at grocery and pet stores because veterinarians must approve of their use in each pet. (ACVN website 2021) So along that line, don't presume that other pets in the household can eat the same therapeutic diet— ask your veterinarian.

On the other hand, OTC diets are most often based on a recipe that meets a healthy pet's nutritional needs and may have less rigorous manufacturing controls and product tests. Some OTC pet food labels suggest that the diet helps prevent specific health issues, but such diets may contain only one or two of the same supplemental ingredients that veterinary therapeutic diets contain and in amounts that may not be helpful in managing the pet's condition. This is why, for example, an OTC "haircoat support" diet you find at a pet retail store probably costs less than the therapeutic diet that your veterinarian recommends for your dog's allergies. And despite what a pet store employee may tell you, the OTC diet is not "the same thing" as the veterinary therapeutic diet.

Senior diets

Many diets marketed as senior pet diets contain fewer calories because as pets age they tend to have decreased energy requirements or may be overweight. Some senior diets contain additional fiber to support gastrointestinal health or to help with weight loss. Other senior diets may contain slightly higher potassium and lower sodium and protein to help support a pet's aging kidneys. But if your senior dog's kidneys function normally, she doesn't need these nutrient adjustments. Plus, protein restriction isn't needed in healthy senior pets, and, as we've learned, less dietary protein could make matters worse for pets who have sarcopenia or cachexia.

Diets marketed for senior pets must meet the same legal ground rules as diets marketed for younger adult pets. No best senior diet exists for all senior pets, and not all senior pets will benefit from a senior diet. Senior pets who are already receiving a good quality commercial adult pet food may even be able to continue eating that diet. (Clinical Nutrition Team March 2016)

With that said, there are no AAFCO guidelines for 'senior diets'. Which means food companies can say "Senior" on the front of the bag but put whatever they want on the inside. So take a moment and look for the AAFCO statement in small print. If the food has the statement "For all life stages" that means it needs to meet the needs of those dogs with the highest caloric requirement which are puppies and lactating dogs – and may not be the best for your senior pet.

Precision home-cooked nutrition

Many pet owners consider venturing into preparing home-cooked diets for their dogs and cats. I tip my hat to those who do this well! I personally have a hard time feeding myself properly with home-cooked meals, let alone my pets! And most of my dogs are large breeds, so storing all the ingredients and supplements needed, along with the preparation itself, can become space- and time-consuming. But I know many pet parents who manage it and enjoy making meals for their furry kids.

If you want to be your pet's personal chef, please consult with a veterinary nutritionist before embarking on this home-cooking journey. It's crucial that you provide the correct basic nutrients in the right amounts for your pet, because not all sources of proteins, carbohydrates, fats, vitamins, and minerals are equal. On top of that, it's especially critical to seek veterinary guidance to properly nutritionally manage your pet's ailments. And be sure to follow recipes provided by a veterinary nutritionist precisely. Do not substitute, reduce, or boost ingredients.

For those dogs that eat a homemade diet, there is a supplement designed by nutritionists called Annamaet Enhance Dog Supplement which you may want to add to your dog's meal. **www.heartypet.com/products/ annamaet-enhance-dog-supplement**

Quibbles about kibble

If you're looking for simple, healthy feeding alternatives or to add spice to your dog's weekly menu, alternatives to kibble or home-cooked diets include frozen, fresh, or freeze-dried options produced by companies whose pet foods are formulated by a veterinarian board-certified in nutrition or a PhD in animal nutrition. For fully prepared pet foods delivered to your door, I suggest The Farmer's Dog or Just Food For Dogs (and cats).

Heart problems in pets eating grain-free diets?

A concerning increase in reports of dogs (of all ages, not only seniors) developing a specific type of heart disease called dilated cardiomyopathy (DCM) has occurred since 2018. (US FDA 2019) With DCM, the heart muscle stretches, thins, and weakens, which leads to enlarged heart chambers that pump blood less efficiently.

Some dog breeds are known to be predisposed to develop DCM because of heredity, such as Doberman pinschers, Great Danes, boxers, and Irish wolfhounds. In other cases, a deficiency of taurine or carnitine (amino acids that are components of protein) can lead to DCM.

However, with these new reports of DCM, a variety of breeds not known to be genetically susceptible have been affected. To date, the condition is thought to be associated with the diets that these dogs had been eating. And the diets vary—it's not only a grain-free diet association. The nontraditional diets that have been associated with this heart problem included dry, canned, raw, and home-cooked dog foods that were formulated without grains (e.g. the diets used peas, lentils, chickpeas, potatoes, or sweet potatoes as grain substitutes), contained exotic ingredients (e.g. kangaroo, alligator, brushtail possum, rabbit, duck, ostrich, venison, bison, flaxseed, fruits), or were produced by boutique brands (small companies that may not perform long-term diet tests). (Fried 2020, Freeman and Stern 2018)

Specific dietary deficiencies or toxicities haven't yet been identified as causing DCM. Early reports suggested that a deficient amount of taurine (an amino acid important for heart function) may play a role, but not all affected pets have low taurine levels. (Fried 2020) More studies are needed to evaluate each potentially contributing factor. (McCauley 2020)

If your dog receives a DCM diagnosis, give heart medications as prescribed by your veterinarian, and ask your veterinarian to measure your dog's taurine levels. (Freeman and Stern 2018) If your dog has DCM and is eating a nontraditional diet, save the pet food label and samples of the food, and talk with your veterinarian about switching your dog's diet to a low-sodium, standard-ingredient diet (e.g. beef, chicken, corn, wheat, rice) made by a long-established pet food company. Studies show that dogs with diet-associated DCM who were receiving a nontraditional diet and whose owners then switched to feeding a traditional diet had improvements in heart function and longer survival times than affected dogs whose owners did not switch to a traditional diet. (Fried 2020) Taurine supplementation is also recommended in all dogs with diet-associated DCM, even if the taurine levels are normal, so talk with your veterinarian about that, too. (Freeman and Stern 2018).

If other dogs in the family are also eating a nontraditional diet, it is recommended that those pets also be screened for heart disease. Each case of suspected diet-associated DCM should be reported to the FDA by your veterinarian or you. (Freeman and Stern 2018)

Changing diets

If you need to switch your dog to a new diet for any reason, try to introduce it when he is feeling relatively normal. If he feels lousy when you try out a new food—such as a veterinary therapeutic diet—your dog may reject it and never take another nibble.

Veterinarians most often recommend that you switch to a new diet gradually. This gives your pet's gut microbiome time to adapt and helps prevent vomiting and diarrhea that sometimes occurs with sudden diet changes.

To switch gradually, reduce the total daily amount of your dog's regular diet and make up the difference with the new diet over a two-week period:

- on Days 1 – 4, feed 75% of the regular diet mixed with 25% of the new diet
- on Days 5 – 8, feed a 50:50 mix of each diet
- on Days 9 – 12, feed 25% of the regular diet and 75% of the new diet
- on Day 13 and thereafter feed 100% of the new diet.

If your dog shows signs of stomach upset at any time, decrease the proportion of new food and add back the regular food and lengthen the transition time. Also tell your veterinarian about the signs of your pet's upset stomach.

One exception to a gradual diet transition is for dogs who experience a sudden bout of vomiting or diarrhea, such as with gastritis or pancreatitis. In that case, your veterinarian will likely recommend an abrupt, immediate switch to a specific type of bland diet for a few days, among other therapies if needed. But never fear, bland diets are intended to calm and help reset normal gastrointestinal function and microbiome balance.

What's a microbiome? And did you say *"poop* transplant?"

The gut microbiome consists of gazillions of tiny critters such as bacteria, protozoa, viruses, and fungi that live in our pets' (and our!) digestive systems, primarily in the colon. Some of these organisms are beneficial and others can be harmful, particularly when their balance is disrupted. The microbiome is crucial for proper digestion and helps produce vitamins and amino acids (the building blocks of protein). It also communicates with the brain through various complex mechanisms and influences metabolism, immune function, and mood.

Every individual's microbiome is unique. It is delicate and can be disrupted by sudden diet changes (including overabundant treats or inappropriate snacks), various illnesses, stress, and some medications. Influencing or altering the microbiome has potential for treating or helping manage various diseases.

Therapy to modify the gut microbiome can include changing the pet's diet to better support the individual's microbiome needs, giving certain antibiotics to eliminate bad bacteria, adding good bacteria by feeding probiotics, and supplementing the diet with prebiotics—special plant fibers that supply nutrients that good bacteria like. In some cases, transferring organisms from a healthy microbiome to an unhealthy microbiome restores a healthy balance of good bacteria to keep the bad bacteria in check. This is called *fecal microbiota transplantation*, or poop transplant! It has been used successfully in people with overgrowth of bad gut bacteria and is gaining ground for use in veterinary patients. (Chaitman 2021, Chaitman 2016)

Overabundant appetite

Flagging an overzealous appetite (also referred to as *hyperrexia*) as a problem can be tricky because many pet parents presume that dogs who eat well must be healthy. It's true that sick or injured dogs usually have a decreased appetite, but some behaviors, diseases, and medications produce an increased appetite.

For example, dogs may learn that begging results in consistent food rewards, which can lead to obesity and an increased appetite. Cushing's disease (also called *hyperadrenocorticism*, which is overactive adrenal gland function) commonly causes polyphagia (another word for abnormally increased appetite and eating). Diabetes, some gastrointestinal disorders, or a diet with insufficient nutrients can also cause increased appetite. Medications such as corticosteroids and appetite stimulants make pets hungrier. So if your dog eats like a horse and isn't receiving a medication that's known to spark his appetite, a veterinary evaluation is warranted!

Apathetic appetites

As I described earlier, dogs' nutritional requirements may decrease as they age, so they may not eat as much as they used to. And their sense of smell may diminish with age for a variety of reasons, which can lead to a reduced appetite. So if your dog is otherwise healthy and maintains good body and muscle condition scores—and your veterinarian has reviewed your dog's diet history and caloric intake—you don't have to worry too much.

However, decreased interest in food (also called *inappetence*) caused by an underlying disease is worrisome, and it is also common in older dogs. Decreased appetite is one of the main reasons pet parents elect to euthanize their dog. Many diseases can cause a decreased appetite. Cancer, kidney or heart failure, and even cognitive decline can bring on:

- hyporexia (decreased appetite);
- dysrexia (altered appetite that manifests as rejection of the pet's typical balanced diet and acceptance of only certain other foods such as extremely tasty treats); or
- anorexia (complete absence of appetite).

Many mechanisms are at work in causing disease-related decreases in appetite, and nausea is one of those culprits.

Talk with your veterinarian about your dog's waning appetite. They can adjust treatments for underlying diseases, provide anti-nausea and appetite-stimulant medications, and determine whether a feeding tube is indicated.

If despite all efforts, your dog is still not consuming enough calories, consider a feeding tube. Dogs tend to tolerate feeding tubes well, and feeding adequate calories keeps the gastrointestinal cells functioning and promotes overall strength, immune function, and comfort. A bonus: if your dog is a picky pill-taker, a tube better ensures your dog gets the oral medications he needs.

Your veterinarian will evaluate which type of tube is best for your dog: a feeding tube inserted through the nose (nasogastric) or one surgically placed through the esophagus (esophagostomy) or stomach (gastrostomy). Your veterinarian will teach you how to use and clean the tube at home, and what, how much, and when to feed your dog. Dogs with feeding tubes can still eat and drink on their own, and the amount they consume helps gauge when your veterinarian can remove the tube. Some critically ill patients may need a tube placed in the intestine (jejunostomy) or intravenous feeding (parenteral nutrition), and these patients stay in the hospital while the tube is in place.

Pet parents sometimes draw the line on feeding tubes for their pets for many reasons. But feeding tubes can be incredibly beneficial to support dogs through an illness that they might otherwise succumb to. Feeding tubes can also provide support at the end of life to give owners more time with their pets and still allow a good quality of life.

Veterinarians can also suggest other ways to nourish your dog's interest in food that are specific to your pet and their environment. I've garnered oodles of tips from my experiences with my patients, which I share here.

Encouraging dogs to eat

For senior dogs who aren't feeling well or who have a chronic condition that requires a special diet, we often need to change diets or add special goodies to their regime to encourage them to eat. And as the end of life draws ever closer, the nutritional goal focuses more on getting calories and protein into their bodies vs. worrying about maintaining a delicate balance of nutrients related to their specific disease. So if your dog is receiving a veterinary therapeutic diet that he refuses to eat despite your attempts to make it tastier, then you need to talk with your veterinarian about changing the diet to one he will accept.

A senior dog's finicky tendencies can really stress a caregiver. Creativity comes into play during these desperate times.

CAREGIVER TIPS FOR GETTING RELUCTANT DOGS TO EAT

- Avoid putting medications directly into your dog's food because she may reject the food altogether.
- Keep in mind that dogs who refuse to eat their dry kibble may gobble up canned food, and vice versa.
- Offer a mix of dry kibble and canned food.
- Reduce competition for food from other pets in the household.
- Try warmed (to body temperature) food.
- Try refrigerated food.

- Change your dog's mealtime.
- Try feeding in a different bowl or on a plate.
- Change the location in which you feed your dog.
- Feed smaller portions more frequently.
- Add low-sodium beef or chicken broth to your dog's food.
- Ask your veterinarian about adding an omega-3 fatty acid supplement made from fish oil to your dog's food. It may help stimulate appetite and has the added benefit of supporting muscle mass.
- Add high-value treats to your dog's food. For example, I often mix small bits of steak or chicken into my dog Sam's regular food to encourage her to eat.
- Always provide clean, fresh water to help your dog stay hydrated and support nutrient absorption. Consider providing filtered water if your dog doesn't seem to like the taste of your tap water. Simply adding water to dry kibble or canned food, or making a dilute, flavored broth from gravy that remains in the can helps. Drinking fountains may entice some dogs to drink. Flavored broths for dogs are also available.

Then, once you think you have finally found the new food or the treat-enhanced diet that your dog will eat and you have their meal routine back under control, they decide to turn away from their food bowl again!

When you've reached that point, and perhaps before then, appetite stimulants prescribed by your veterinarian can be extremely helpful. One that is available for dogs is capromorelin (Entyce), which I mentioned in the section on sarcopenia. I love Entyce for dogs and have used it in many of my canine hospice patients and in my dogs Duncan and Sam. It is a liquid oral medication given once a day, so you don't have to try to get your pet to swallow a pill. (Sam's reaction to it tells me it is not the best thing she has tasted, so your dog may appreciate receiving a high-value treat afterward.) About an hour after receiving a dose, the pet usually shows interest in food. It's not a guarantee for all pets, but it has been really successful for me.

Eventually dogs will dramatically reduce their food intake near the end of their lives, and this is natural. There are few more emotionally loaded issues than the loss of appetite at the end of life. I have heard an insightful saying from human hospice caregivers that I share with all the families that I help. "Food and water are for the living. A body won't eat or drink for a future is knows it doesn't have." In the late stages of terminal illness, bodies will not desire and will even reject food and water. This is a symptom of death approaching, it is not the cause of death.

Although I'm a veterinarian and understand that my dog Sam's decreased appetite is related to her underlying illnesses and that cancer has caused her cachexia, I, like many pet parents, anxiously stare at my dog while she eats. I breathe a huge sigh of relief each time she munches that last bit in her bowl.

Andy's attitude

Andy was a wee 12-year-old mixed-breed dog with chronic inflammatory bowel disease. He had inappetence, then anorexia, and had become a shell of his former self. His owner had taken him to see nearly every veterinary specialist in Southern California. Then she contacted me for guidance on hospice.

I was a bit intimidated to help Andy's mom because she had already visited the best veterinary clinicians. What was I going to suggest that they hadn't? She tried everything they recommended: changing his diet, giving appetite stimulants, heating his food, giving anti-nausea medications, making home-cooked diets with input from a veterinary nutritionist, changing his mealtimes, switching up his feeding locations, and more. But she held the line on allowing them to place a feeding tube.

Andy did not like strangers, so he greeted me with "intensity." Actually, I never was able to touch Andy during my visit! But I liked this about Andy. I told his mom that if Andy stopped hating strangers, then he was too weak to care. We had a long discussion about Andy's quality of life, and we knew time was short for Andy. His mom decided to create a bucket list for Andy and get a professional photo shoot with him pronto.

As I packed my bag to leave, I said, "Try baby food. Get a couple different flavors and see if he's interested."

The next day, I received the best picture ever! Andy was happily licking the baby food off his nose! He seemed to have a grateful sparkle in his eyes.

Andy continued to enjoy a variety of baby foods, so I suggested that his mom add a few pieces of his kibble to it. And to her surprise, Andy also ate the kibble! Over the next couple weeks, I told her to gradually add more kibble and reduce the baby food. It worked! Andy went back to eating regular amounts of his kibble with a little "baby food gravy."

For whatever reason, only the baby food had kick-started Andy's appetite. I suspect that getting him to eat helped gradually rebalance Andy's gut microbiome. Andy lived happily for another year before his family decided to say goodbye.

Baby food did the trick to kick-start Andy's appetite.

When the day came for me to deliver his angel wings, Andy let me into his house and personal space without any bother or even a bark. I had no doubt Andy was tired, and he was ready.

 ## Questions to ask your veterinarian

- Has my dog's weight changed? Has my pet's weight shown an increasing or decreasing trend?
- What is my dog's body condition score? (Or, is my pet underweight, just right, overweight, or obese?)
- Will my dog benefit from a food puzzle toy or other type of food or treat dispenser?
- What is my dog's muscle condition score? (Or, is my pet's muscle mass normal, or does my pet have mild, moderate, or severe muscle loss?)
- How can I help prevent muscle loss in my dog?
- Does my dog need any dietary adjustments or nutritional supplements?
- Is a therapeutic diet available that is specifically designed to help manage my dog's illness or condition?
- Will my dog benefit from an appetite stimulant or anti-nausea medication?
- What other measures can I take to help my dog eat?
- Will a feeding tube help my dog?

 ### READING RECOMMENDATIONS

- Cummings Veterinary Medical Center at Tufts University Clinical Nutrition Service. Petfoodology blog articles. **https://vetnutrition.tufts.edu/**
- NC State Veterinary Hospital. How to evaluate food for your pet. **https://cvm.ncsu.edu/wp-content/uploads/2019/01/Evaluating-Pet-Foods-v2-1.pdf**
- World Small Animal Veterinary Association Global Nutrition Guidelines. Tools for Pet Owners. **https://wsava.org/global-guidelines/global-nutrition-guidelines/**
- US Food and Drug Administration. FDA Investigation into Potential Link between Certain Diets and Canine Dilated Cardiomyopathy. FDA Website. June 27, 2019. Accessed 1/13/21. **https://www.fda.gov/animal-veterinary/outbreaks-and-advisories/fda-investigation-potential-link-between-certain-diets-and-canine-dilated-cardiomyopathy**

CHAPTER 10

Thermoregulation: Cool canines and hot dogs

"No animal is a better judge of comfort than a cat."

— JAMES HERRIOT, BRITISH VETERINARY SURGEON AND AUTHOR

I'm writing this chapter from my patio, in the 90 F Florida heat. I'm sitting in the shade, but the humidity is stifling so it feels like 110 F. My dog Norrin is on a lounge chair nearby, basking in the direct sun as if he's on spring break in Daytona Beach! He's been there for 30 minutes, and I'm unsure how he hasn't already melted. My dog Sam would never lie in the sun like that. But unlike Norrin who is a young adult with short hair, Sam is a senior with a thick, furry coat. I can see her through the sliding doors, stretched out napping on the cool tile floor. Norrin also loves to snuggle on the couch and bury himself under blankets and pillows. Sam will have nothing to do with that. I know their personal temperature preferences can result from a variety of factors: genetics (body type, coat), age, and underlying medical issues. So because Sam is a senior, I worry— does the cold floor feel better on her joints, or does she have a condition that prevents her from cooling down efficiently? Or am I too worried?

Regulating normal body temperature

In the exam room, pet parents often got wide-eyed during a routine wellness visit when the veterinary technician reported their dog's temperature: "It's 101.5, Dr. Mary."

The dog's owner would immediately ask, "Why does he have a fever?"

I would explain that dogs' normal temperature range is 101 to 102.5 F (38.3 to 39.2 C)— higher than our normal temperature range of 97 to 99 F (36.1 to 37.2 C).

COOL FUN FACT

Chickens' normal body temperature range is a whopping 105 to 107 F!

Typically we think of maintaining a comfy body temperature by adjusting the ambient temperature or altering our exposure to the environment. We change the room thermostat setting, cozy up near a fireplace or best furry friend, open a window to allow breezes to drift through, jump into a swimming pool, and dress appropriately—shorts in summer and sweaters in winter!

The temperature at which animals (including people) don't have to expend energy to stay warm or cool off is called the *thermoneutral zone*. Our thermoneutral zone is not precisely known and depends on our body composition, clothing, age, sex, and other factors. Based on studies done in the 1930s, our thermoneutral zone is presumed to be 82 F to 90 F (28 C to 32 C), and it isn't necessarily the same as our thermal comfort zone. (Pallubinsky 2019) Dogs' thermoneutral zone is 68 F to 86 F (20 C to 30 C). (National Research Council 2006)

We and our dogs also have an internal "thermostat." The anterior hypothalamus is the part of the brain that helps maintain core body temperature within a narrow range, called the *hypothalamic set point*. This narrow temperature range is essential for cells to function normally and to prevent tissue damage and organ failure.

Temperature sensors (called *thermoreceptors*) throughout the body send messages to the hypothalamus about cold and hot within the body and in the environment. This helps the hypothalamus control the ways in which the body conserves or loses heat to maintain this set point temperature. This process is called *thermoregulation*. A healthy thermoregulation process maintains core body temperature despite big differences in ambient temperature.

Generating heat

Dogs and people produce heat internally through metabolism, which involves all the chemical reactions in the body that keep cells functioning, including muscle activity, food digestion, and nutrient processing. (Bates 2017) To retain body heat when it's cold, blood vessels near the skin surface can narrow (called *vasoconstriction*) so that less heat is delivered for transfer through the skin. Fat cells under the skin also help hold heat in.

In addition, a pet's hair can stand up (called *piloerection*, also known as goosebumps in people) in response to cold. Raised hair traps air next to the skin, which insulates against heat loss. (Piloerection can also occur when pets are upset—like the raised hackles on those notorious black cats of Hallow-een!) Many dog breeds also have undercoats to help them stay warm. Those of you who have dogs with thick undercoats may be familiar with how much help a FURminator grooming tool can be with their seemingly perpetual hair shedding!

Another way dogs (and people!) conserve heat is by curling up, because exposing less body surface area to the environment retains heat.

Cooling off

Dogs and people cool off by reducing activity so we produce less heat. We also lose body heat by stretching out to expose more body surface to the environment, through evaporation (people sweat and dogs pant), and by widening our blood vessels (called *vasodilation*) to deliver more blood to the skin surface to release heat.

 LIFE-SAVING TIP: This heat-releasing vasodilation is why you never want to place an overheated dog in cold or ice-cold water or pour it over them. Cold water contact with the skin makes those blood vessels constrict, which reduces blood flow to the skin and hampers a dog's ability to cool off. Instead, use cool water or fans.

Staying hydrated

Proper hydration has numerous health and well-being benefits, including body temperature regulation. We get to enjoy slushies in the summer and hot choco-late in the winter. For dogs, access to fresh water at all times and especially on hot days or during exercise is crucial to keep them comfortable.

Hydration is essential because it supports thermoregulation in other important ways: replaces fluids lost during sweating and panting, eases the heart's work-load, and boosts the blood flow needed to transport heat that's released through vasodilation. (Baker 1984, Doris 1981)

How aging and disease affects thermoregulation

Changes in body functions can throw a monkey wrench into the thermoregula-tion process. As dogs age, thermoreceptors and other thermoregulation mech-anisms may change, which can lead to easily feeling chilled (hypothermia) or overheated (hyperthermia). Geriatric dogs have diminished ability to regulate body temperature so they don't adapt as readily to ambient and internal tempera-ture changes as younger dogs do. This leaves geriatric dogs more susceptible to their cells not functioning as they should, which can lead to illness and slower recovery from illness.

The same goes for senior people. I remember how we always had to be sure my Grandma Gardner took her cardigan wherever we went—even during Florida's summer heat! With advanced age, her body had difficulty maintaining the hypothalamic set point. Older dogs can't put on a sweater at will, so those who have a hard time conserving body heat seek a sunny spot or your lap! On the flip side, some functional changes and diseases that affect older dogs can predispose them to hyperthermia and even heat stroke.

Why older dogs feel colder

Muscles generate heat during physical activity and shivering, and geriatric dogs have less muscle mass overall. Just like us, dogs shiver when their core body temperature drops. The muscle activity from shivering helps restore normal body temperature, but shivering consumes lots of oxygen. This can lead to *oxygen debt*, a particularly dangerous situation in dogs with conditions like heart or lung disease, because oxygen delivery to tissues is already stretched.

Geriatric dogs also tend to lose some of the fat layer right under their skin, which allows heat to escape. In addition, blood vessels lose elasticity with age, so they don't constrict as well in response to cold, allowing heat loss. And senior dogs who have a reduced appetite and eat less have fewer nutrients available, which slows their metabolism and metabolic heat production.

You're as cold as ice! The chilling effects of hypothermia

Hypothermia is an abnormally low body temperature that occurs when cold input or heat loss exceeds heat production. Prolonged exposure to cold ambient temperatures and low blood pressure from blood loss or other causes of a sudden drop in blood flow (shock) can cause hypothermia. Dogs become hypothermic during anesthesia, too, so veterinarians use warm fluids and warming devices (pads, blankets, forced air) to support patients' body temperatures during dental and surgical procedures.

Signs of hypothermia in dogs include intense shivering, tiredness, weakness, reduced awareness, and pale gums. If your dog's temperature is less than 98.5 F (36.9 C), wrap your dog in a blanket and seek veterinary care.

Otherwise, you can help your dog warm up at home using blankets or towels warmed in the dryer or other types of heat sources (see "Tips for warming up"). Check your dog's temperature every 10 minutes. You can remove the heat source (such as a towel-wrapped hot water bottle) once their temperature is above 100 F (37.8 C), but keep them cozy with a blanket in a warm room until their body temperature climbs back up to normal.

Sidebar: Take your dog's temp

Keep a separate thermometer at home for your dogs! The easiest way to check their temperature is rectally. Yup—the old-school method. Put a dab of petroleum jelly on the end and insert it just past the silver tip.

Remember, normal body temperature for dogs is 101 to 102.5 F (38.3 to 39.2 C). Call your veterinarian if your dog's temperature is less than 99 F (37.2 C) or higher than 103 F (39.4 C).

Why elder dogs swelter

Sweating is one way humans cool down, but dogs do not possess the same ability. Dogs only have sweat glands in their paws!

But those glands are so small that dogs need a better way to cool off. Panting is the primary and most efficient way dogs release excess body heat. Panting allows evaporation from the mouth and upper respiratory system.

It's also easier to regulate body temperature if you have more body surface area. So smaller dogs have a harder time regulating their body temperature because they have a higher body surface area to body mass ratio. (Bates 2017)

As I mentioned earlier, staying hydrated helps thermoregulation. Conditions common in older dogs such as diabetes, Cushing's disease (overactive adrenal glands), and kidney disease can cause dehydration and, therefore, also make it harder for them to maintain a normal body temperature. Medications that geriatric dogs may be receiving such as diuretics (prescribed to help dogs with heart disease retain less water), can cause extreme dehydration if the dog's water intake is insufficient. Prolonged or severe vomiting and diarrhea associated with a variety of illnesses can quickly cause dehydration.

My dog Sam had a severe bout of diarrhea. After she pooped nothing but liquid for six hours, along with the fact that she refused to drink water, I worried about dehydration and hyperthermia. And I was right—her temperature shot up to 105.5 F, and I knew she needed

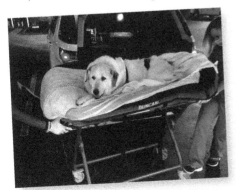

Sam arriving at the veterinary ER for treatment of dehydration, severe diarrhea, and fever.

immediate intensive medical care. We took an emergency trip to the veterinary hospital, and after four days of receiving intravenous fluids and antibiotics, she got to come home!

It's like a heat wave! The stifling effects of hyperthermia

Hyperthermia is an abnormally high body temperature that occurs when heat production or heat input exceeds heat loss.

Fever is a natural, *controlled* form of hyperthermia. Substances in the body called *pyrogens*, which are produced by activated immune cells (or by bacteria), trigger the body's thermostat to rise so the body conserves more heat to try to reach this new set point. This is the body's protective reaction to a disease or other insult because fever activates immune cells, slows bacterial and virus growth, reduces appetite (which leaves more energy for fighting infections), and promotes sleepiness. (El-Radhi 2019)

Heat stroke is a form of *uncontrolled* hyperthermia where the body's thermoregulation processes fail. It can cause dangerous malfunctions in many organs and damage the central nervous system. Heat stroke can result from external factors like a high ambient temperature and a lack of shade or water. And internal, disease-related factors such as obesity, larynx (voicebox) disorders, or trachea (windpipe) collapse increase a dog's risk of heat stroke. (Hall 2016) When any of these external or internal factors affect an already fragile senior dog who has diminished thermoregulation ability, the dog could be primed for an emergency situation!

Signs of hyperthermia in dogs include excessive panting, abnormal drooling, dark reddish mucous membranes, confusion, weakness, labored breathing, vomiting, diarrhea, and collapse. If your dog's temperature is 104 F (40 C) or higher, seek immediate veterinary care.

Otherwise, you can cool your dog at home by spraying cool (not cold or ice-cold) water on them and directing a fan to blow air on them, applying isopropyl alcohol to paw pads and ear flaps (see "Tips for staying cool"), and placing cool, wet towels under them until their temperature is 103 F (39.4 C). Call your veterinarian, and continue to monitor your dog's temperature.

Mind trickery

In addition to its cooling effects, did you know a fan can "trick" the brain into thinking it has adequate oxygen? (Morélot-Panzini 2017) Receptors in the nose sense rapidly flowing air, and they send signals via the trigeminal nerve to the hypothalamus. You can play this "mind game" by placing a fan in front of a dog who is panting excessively or experiencing respiratory distress. It

helps them calm down while you determine whether something else needs to be done to assist them. I recommend this to help manage dogs who have a chronic disease that impairs breathing, such as a dog who has laryngeal paralysis and is overexcited or anxious.

Which is better—a cold spot or a warm spot?

The simple answer is to let your dog decide! Providing a comfy environmental temperature with additional opportunities for your dog to warm up or cool down is important for all dogs. Imagine what it would be like to live where you have no control over the temperature and to be perpetually uncomfortable.

Giving geriatric dogs options that allow them more control over their comfort helps keep them healthy, reduces stress, and allows quicker recovery from illness or injury. Dogs will pick warm or cool places depending on the ambient temperature and what feels best to help them relieve their pain or other discomfort. So offer a buffet of options. They'll decide whether they want to feel as cool as a cucumber or hot as a potato that day.

 ### Tips for warming up

- Use your fireplace (if applicable), open curtains to allow sunbeams in, and keep areas near heating vents clutter-free.
- Create a cozy resting spot in a small draft-free room that has its own warming device, such as a space heater (with automatic shutoff for overheating or tipping over and a cool-enough-to-touch external surface) or a heated pet bed.
- Put an extra blanket on your dog's bed and place blankets or towels in various spots around the house. Consider putting a sweater on dogs who tolerate them.
- Dress them up for the outdoors—shorthaired dogs who live in particularly cold and windy climates benefit from wearing jackets and booties when they venture outside.
- Brush your dog to remove dead hairs from the coat and undercoat, which helps prevent matting, permits hair to fluff up, and allows more air to act as an insulating layer near the skin.
- Help your dog maintain an optimal body weight with good nutrition. Dogs who are too thin have less fat and muscle to keep them warm.
- Provide a heated blanket under their favorite bedding, heated pet beds, radiant heat lamps, heated rice bags, or heated water containers. When using these types of heat sources:
  o At least 60% of the dog's body surface area must be in contact with or close to the external heat source for effective warming.

o The dog must be able to move away from the heat source if she becomes too hot. I have seen many burns and overheating in dogs from heat sources that are used inappropriately, such as in a kennel where the dog cannot move away or near or under a dog who cannot move without assistance.

o Place a barrier like a towel or blanket between the heat source and the dog.

o When using electric heating pads, keep liquids such as water bowls away from the area because of electrocution risk.

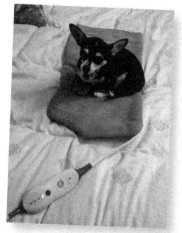

 BD enjoys her dad's heating pad.

 Tips for staying cool

- Place a fan near the dog.
- Keep the ambient temperature at a comfortable level. This is especially important for dogs who are "at risk" of overheating such as brachycephalic (short head, "smoosh face") breeds; dogs who have respiratory disease, collapsing trachea, or laryngeal paralysis; or dogs who are obese.
- And remember, your dog may love car rides, but being left in the car while you run errands can be dangerous for them. Dogs may experience heat stress within only 10 minutes (which can progress to heat stroke) inside a parked car, even when the windows are cracked and the temperature outside is a pleasant 70 F (21 C).

 LIFE-SAVING TIP: Leaving a dog unattended in the car is dangerous in any season—they may rapidly become too hot or too cold!

- Treat your dog to a summer trim—by a professional groomer if needed.
- Brush your dog to remove dead hairs from the coat and undercoat, which prevents matting and keeps air moving near the skin.
- Help your dog maintain an optimal body weight with good nutrition. Dogs who are obese are more susceptible to heat exhaustion and heat stroke.
- Keep isopropyl alcohol spray bottles close at hand for quick administration to the paw pads and ear flaps (take care to avoid their eyes) if

you suspect overheating or heat stroke, and call your veterinarian. Heat stroke can occur suddenly.

- Remember, do NOT cool an overheated dog by pouring ice water or cold water on them or placing them in it. Applying cold water causes the blood vessels under the skin to constrict and impairs heat loss from the body. You can use cool to lukewarm water and put cool wet towels under your dog.
- Help dogs stay cool with special products:
  - o Kool Collar (Leerburg), which comes with a tube insert that is cooled in the freezer and then placed inside the collar to provide a cooling sensation around the dog's neck
  - o Cooling mats and cooling cots or beds, which are available in many sizes at many retailers
  - o Dog beds that allow air flow

 My dog Sam and her cooling mat.

 Sam on her raised bed that has a mesh resting surface to allow air flow. g mat.

Comfy is key

Remember, be especially mindful about providing the appropriate temperature support for geriatric dogs who have any chronic disease, whether it's kidney disease, respiratory system dysfunction, heart disease, arthritis, adrenal disease, diabetes, cancer, or thyroid dysfunction. Help your dogs warm up (and towel them off if they're rain-soaked or covered in snow) or cool down (perhaps with a fan) after outdoor excursions, and help them stay warm if they are receiving subcutaneous (under the skin) fluid therapy at home.

CHAPTER 11:

Skin: Senior beauty is deeper

"Why are people afraid of getting older? You feel wiser. You feel more mature. You feel like you know yourself better. You would trade that for softer skin? Not me!"

— Anna Kournikova, professional tennis player

Did a shoe-loving gorilla take up residence in my living room? Some mornings I'd emerge from my bedroom and wonder who had tossed their giant, smelly sneaker into some corner of my house. But then Sam, my faithful Anatolian shepherd, would trot over to greet me and I'd remember… she's the pungent culprit! My lovely dog has a beautiful coat, but was battling a skin infection beneath her thick fur. I had a stash of Yankee Candles at the ready to mask the overly smelly days.

The skin, along with its diverse population of bacteria, viruses, mites, and fungi—collectively called the *skin microbiome*—is the largest organ in the body. It protects us from infections, regulates our body temperature, and gives us the sensation of touch. And like other organs, it can start to fail as the effects of age creep in. The barrier to the outside world that skin provides weakens and can lead to problems that are often overlooked under all that fur. (If you have a Chinese crested dog or other hairless breed, problems are easier to spot—lucky you!)

Hair and skin are made of a protein called keratin. Genes influence our hair length and determine whether dogs and cats will be long-haired or short-haired (or no-haired!). Our hair tends to grow long and bountiful on our head (and is genetically programmed to stop growing at a certain length, and this length differs among individuals) but short and sparse on our arms and legs. Pets' fur tends to be short and cover most of their bodies.

Senior dogs can have mild skin changes such as greying around the muzzle, or they can develop drastic skin changes that make them resemble a greasy elephant with funky foot pads! But no matter what, in my eyes, the sweetest, most beautiful furry faces belong to senior and geriatric pets. Their years of love and companionship—or for some, their years of endurance—are sculpted within their bony heads; hazy, wise eyes; and grey-speckled muzzles. I treasure every one of them!

Age-related skin and fur changes

Me and one of my smiley grey-muzzle patients, Briland.

Mature dogs' fur turns grey or white in spots as the skin loses pigment-producing cells. Greying occurs particularly around the muzzle and eyes and stands out best against dark fur. Their coat may also thin with age because their hair follicles are less active.

Samson showing the beauty of a sugar face.

Geriatric dogs often have either excessively oily or dry skin. Sebum is a natural oil produced by small sebaceous glands all over the skin surface. The oil keeps skin from drying out and cracking. Their fur may appear dull if their sebaceous glands produce less sebum.

Like our skin, dogs' skin loses elasticity with age. Their skin, footpads, and nostrils can also thicken. They may have misshapen, brittle toenails. Believe it or not, dogs also get age spots, and they develop them at a much faster rate than people do. But fur helps hide their age spots, those lucky ducks!

Senior dogs often develop "senile warts" (*sebaceous adenomas*) and fatty tumors (*lipomas*) that are benign growths, but your veterinarian will need to check every one of them to determine whether they're cancerous.

Because our dogs don't share the vanity trait that we humans have, does their senior appearance really matter? Is a smelly dog suffering? I approach their benign skin issues from two perspectives: Does the dog have any discomfort? Is the human-pet bond strained?

A grey muzzle brings no discomfort to the dog. And a grey muzzle may strengthen the human-pet bond, because we recognize it as a marker for our beloved dog entering old age.

But not all skin disorders are benign. Many can be uncomfortable or painful for dogs. Skin problems can also strain the human-animal bond when the dog smells too gross or scratches too much!

Conditions that cause skin and fur abnormalities

Much research is done to investigate various diseases that affect people's skin, but it's also done in relation to the multi-billion-dollar (and growing) anti-aging skincare and cosmetics industry. For dogs, it's not about keeping their youthful appearance. Skin research in dogs focuses on combating disease—especially allergies, cancer, infections, and autoimmune disorders.

No skin disease is exclusive to senior dogs. If your dog had itchy skin from environmental allergies (called *atopy*, or *atopic dermatitis*) or food allergies as a young dog, their allergies will likely continue to flare and they'll need life-long treatment. Parasite prevention remains important during the geriatric years because fleas, ticks, mites, and mosquitos won't refuse the chance to latch on for a meal—no matter your dog's age. Structural changes in the skin during the golden years can increase the risk of infection and reduce healing ability. Microscopic bugs can overgrow on the skin, so dogs with allergies or parasites can more easily develop bacterial or yeast skin infections—another reason to stay on top of allergy management and to keep up with parasite preventives. If your senior dog undergoes surgery, the incision site may heal more slowly and have a higher risk of bacterial infection than it would have in his boyish days. Senior dog postoperative care is often more intensive than that for a young dog. And skin growths or masses that pop up at any age need to be checked out by a veterinarian to determine whether cancer is present.

Senior dogs are likely to develop one or more chronic diseases, and some of those lead to nutrient deficiencies. Dogs with gastrointestinal, kidney, or liver disease; diabetes; or thyroid or adrenal hormone imbalances often have coat and skin abnormalities. An affected senior dog's coat may be thin, dull, crusty, or brittle, or have patchy hair loss. Skin problems can produce a variety of dog body odors. Pet parents have told me their dogs smell like "popcorn and corn chips," "sweaty fish socks," and "hot rotten cheese"—from bizarre yum to repellent yuck!

You can reduce or resolve many skin problems by treating your dog's underlying diseases and infections, correcting nutritional imbalances and supplementing the diet when needed, and helping your dog stay clean and brushed.

Crazy growths on footpads and noses

I have seen some senior dogs whose noses and footpads look like they have trees growing from them! These growths can be a curious characteristic or an alarming marvel.

The reason for this overgrowth of keratin, called *idiopathic hyperkeratosis*, isn't well understood. It can be mild or it can cause serious issues. Footpads can be so badly affected that they lose gripping ability and cause mobility problems. A large growth on the nose can cause discomfort and excessive nose-rubbing, or block dogs' nostrils and make breathing difficult. A veterinarian may be able to use a surgical laser to remove the excess keratin and provide some comfort for your dog.

 Severe footpad hyperkeratosis of a dog who was sliding across tile floors.

Something to lean on

Older dogs commonly develop calluses on their elbows. They're normal to a certain extent because they provide a "bumper" where the elbows contact the ground during rest. If they become too dry, they crack and bleed. Calluses can be painful for your dog. Special ointments are designed for dogs to help soothe those troubled elbows!

A strained bond

What about my "smelly gorilla," Sam? I prescribed a special medicated shampoo for Sam's groomer to bathe her with. I placed waterproof crib mattress covers on her dog bed that helped absorb her odor and were easy to launder every few days.

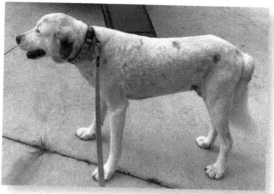

 Sam's fur became thin, with patchy bald spots, and she smelled bad. A thorough trim done by her groomer uncovered several small areas of skin infection.

But Sam's skin problems worsened, and she started losing clumps of fur. I took her back to the groomer for a thorough trim, and found that Sam had developed several moist, infected areas of skin.

I knew something else was brewing to explain Sam's smell, so I ran blood tests and took radiographs. Her results made me suspect she had an endocrine problem called *hyperadrenocorticism*, or *Cushing's syndrome*. Further tests to check her adrenal gland function confirmed my suspicion.

Dogs with hyperadrenocorticism produce too much of an adrenal hormone called *cortisol*, and the signs of the disease include recurring skin infections and patchy hair loss. After three months of treatment to reduce her cortisol levels, Sam's skin infections cleared up and her beautiful coat grew back. And she no longer smelled horrible!

Sam's odor had been the source of a few arguments in my household, and it strained our bond with her, as can happen in many families. Pets with some medical conditions can be so unappealing that family members don't want to be near them. This overstretched caregiver-animal bond is a serious concern. If pet parents isolate the dog in a room away from the family, the dog and the family experience further distress. The dog's problem may spur family arguments, adding even more stress for the caregiver and family.

Helping ensure that ailing dogs are comfortable and not smelly, greasy, bloody, goopy, excessively scratching, or otherwise repulsive in any way is an important part of my work as a veterinarian. Sam's issues helped me understand the strain a smelly dog can cause in a household, and gave me more empathy for pet parents who manage it.

See your veterinarian if your dog has

- Itchy skin, which is characterized by your dog frequently licking, scratching, chewing, or rubbing her skin or fur; shaking her head often; or scooting on her bottom
- Red, swollen, scaly, flaky, crusty, or smelly skin
- Scabs, skin sores, or skin that is excessively moist or has draining pus or pimple-like bumps
- Matted fur that is difficult to groom
- A thin coat or bald patches, or has been pulling out tufts of hair
- Skin lumps or bumps, especially any growth that is pea-sized or larger

Tests your dog may need

- Blood and urine tests to check for underlying medical conditions
- A fecal examination to look for intestinal parasites (Fleas cause skin problems and carry their own parasites, known as *tapeworms*, that can inhabit your dog's intestines if your dog swallows fleas while grooming themselves.)
- Skin tests to obtain cells for examination (Your veterinarian may use a cotton swab, Scotch tape, or a glass microscope slide pressed to the skin or use a surgical blade to scrape the skin surface.)
- Microscopic examination of lumps or bumps by drawing cells out with a needle
- Biopsies or surgical removal of lumps or bumps (These samples are sent to a diagnostic laboratory for evaluation.)
- A food trial (also called a *diet elimination trial*) to check for food allergies

 Questions to ask your veterinarian

- What is the underlying cause of my dog's skin condition?
- What tests will my dog need?
- What medications does my dog need?
- My dog excessively licks and chews his fur; does he need treatment for a behavior problem?
- Does my dog need a different diet or nutritional supplement?
- What shampoos or topical treatments are available for my dog's skin condition?

- How do the medications you prescribe work—will they cure my dog's allergies?
- Is this lump or bump on my dog something serious?

 ## CAREGIVER TIPS AND HOME HACKS

- Regularly brush and bathe your dog to keep his fur mat-free and clean. Use high-quality shampoos designed specifically for dogs.
- Dogs with dry, flaky skin benefit from brushing because it stimulates their sebaceous glands, which produce sebum to lubricate the skin.
- Your veterinarian may prescribe a therapeutic shampoo specific for your dog's skin condition. Follow the instructions for how often you'll need to bathe your dog and the length of time the shampoo needs to remain on her coat.
- Selsun Blue shampoo is sometimes used in dogs with skin infections caused by yeast called *Malassezia*, but check with your veterinarian first.
- Use dry shampoo made for dogs to help them freshen up when needed.
- Keep your dogs' nails trimmed. This helps them get around easier and reduces their risk of snagging and tearing a nail.
- Trim long hair between the toes to keep the areas dry and clean and help prevent infection. Beard trimmers work wonders here.
- Apply nose balm to dry or cracked noses.
- Apply elbow balm to the calluses on your dog's elbows to prevent cracking.
- Use booties for dogs with paw or foot pad problems. Dogs usually tolerate these well within the first few minutes of wearing them.
- Prevent sores and infections from urine scalding by placing absorbent pads under your bedridden dog or use diapers if needed for incontinent dogs, and change them right away when they become soiled.
- Provide comfy, clean, thick-padded bedding.
- If your dog is recovering from surgery or otherwise bedridden, help your dog turn over—from one side, to sternal (chest and abdomen facing the ground), to the other side—so they can rest in a different position every two or three hours. Be vigilant about preventing pressure sores—these can develop on your dog's elbows, shoulders, hocks, knees, hips, and even their head. Pressure sores are painful and can quickly become infected.
- Helping your dog maintain his optimal weight helps prevent pressure sores.

- Use dog wipes or unscented, hypoallergenic baby wipes (and keep them in a wipe warmer) to help spot-clean areas when needed.
- Avoid "quarantining" your dog if possible—isolation leads to emotional stress for your dog and for you. Help your dog stay in the areas close to you and other members of the household.

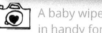
A baby wipe warmer comes in handy for messy pets, too.

PRODUCT RECOMMENDATIONS

- Nose Butter (The Blissful Dog)
  https://theblissfuldog.com/collections/nose-butter
- Elbow Butter (The Blissful Dog)
  https://theblissfuldog.com/products/elbow-butter
- Snout Soother, Paw Soother, Skin Soother (The Natural Dog Company)
  https://naturaldogcompany.com/
- Vet-Aid wound care spray or foam – great for all wounds including bed sores
  vetaidproducts.com

CHAPTER 12:

Heart:
Keeping the beat strong

"The best and most beautiful things in the world cannot be seen
nor even touched, but just felt in the heart."

— Helen Keller

Some dog breeds are prone to heart problems, and Doberman pinschers, like my dog Duncan, are on that list. So I made it a habit to take him to see a veterinary cardiologist yearly. He got a special examination and full workup with all the diagnostic bells and whistles.

FUN FACT

Dogs help our heart health!
Studies show that pet ownership
may protect us against heart
disease and help lower blood
pressure and cholesterol.
(Cardiovascular health/HABRI)

I wanted to catch any hint of heart trouble as early as possible. Every year he got an "A+" on his cardiac exam—no signs of heartache for him or for me!

On Duncan's 12th birthday, I listened to his chest with my stethoscope (yes, I do a physical exam on all my fur kids as one of their birthday gifts, whether they like it or not!). I heard a faint heart murmur! Murmurs occur when blood doesn't flow normally through the heart. In older dogs, this altered blood flow typically happens because one of the heart valves doesn't close completely. (In a young dog, a murmur may occur because the dog is born with a small hole inside the heart chambers.)

Heart murmurs are graded on a sound scale of 1 to 6, with 6 being the loudest. Duncan's murmur was barely audible, a grade 1. Instead of hearing the clear, two-part "lub-dub" of each heartbeat (the sounds of the heart valves closing), his first heart sound was faintly whooshy. His heartbeat sounded like "whluh-dub." This was a yellow flag to me, so I was on alert for heart disease!

Duncan's heart rhythm sounded normal, he was peppy, his appetite was hearty, and he had no other signs of trouble like coughing or abnormal gum color. We celebrated his birthday (he also got doggie ice cream and cake) and I temporarily pushed his murmur to the back of my mind. But I scheduled his annual cardiology exam to be done sooner than normal that year.

FUN FACT

Having spent so much time in the ocean, I learned that a yellow flag on a ship stands for the letter Q (for quarantine), but when it's flown alone, it means that the ship is healthy! On a beach, a yellow flag means the ocean waves or undertow may be rough but not life-threatening.

Not long after his birthday but before his cardiac exam, Duncan started to cough. Two years earlier, Duncan had had laryngeal tieback surgery to help hold his airway open because he had a condition called *geriatric-onset laryngeal paralysis* (the larynx, or voice box, guards entry to the trachea, or windpipe, and with this condition the larynx doesn't open normally). So at first I focused on checking Duncan for aspiration pneumonia—lung inflammation caused by accidentally inhaling things that would normally be swallowed, such as food, water, and saliva. It occurs more easily in dogs after tieback surgery. But when I listened to his chest, his heart murmur was louder than it had been on his birthday. And Duncan's chest radiographs showed that he didn't have pneumonia, but the left side of his heart and one of the major blood vessels in his lungs looked bigger than normal. So I switched to red-flag alert mode about the condition of his heart.

I knew that Duncan's slightly increased breathing effort, mild coughing, decreased energy level, heart murmur, and the changes on his radiographs probably indicated the heartbreak I was afraid of. I loaded him into his minivan (yes, I bought a used one just to shuttle my dog to his appointments, because he was my baby) and off we went to see his cardiologist right away.

During that visit, Duncan got a "D+" on his exam. His echocardiogram (an ultrasound exam that shows heart structure and blood flow) showed that he had dilated cardiomyopathy (DCM), which meant his heart muscle was thinner than normal and weakened. His heart had to work harder to pump blood, so one of his heart chambers was slightly enlarged. Duncan also had abnormally thickened heart valves (which explained the murmur) and an arrhythmia (irregular heartbeat).

DCM was the problem I had been worried about for Duncan because it's a common heart disease in large-breed dogs and is thought to be hereditary in Dobermans (and Great Danes, boxers, and Irish wolfhounds). In some dogs, a deficiency of taurine or carnitine (amino acids that make up protein) can lead to DCM.

I wasn't shocked by the news, but I was astounded by how quickly his signs had seemed to progress—and I was incredibly sad.

Duncan was already receiving a handful of medications to treat his laryngeal paralysis and mobility issues, and now he needed three heart medications to control his signs of heart failure. I bought the largest size pill box available to organize and hold his daily supplies. I needed to give him his medications five different times every day, which meant I had to rearrange my work schedule. But it was all worth it for my big angel. Within a week after starting his heart medications, Duncan felt loads better! A contented, normal life was once again restored for my gentle giant.

Duncan had stolen my heart, and I realized that eventually his heart disease would steal him away from me. I promised myself that until then, we would enjoy every day!

Near and dear to the heart

The heart is the engine that pumps blood to the lungs to pick up oxygen and travel around the body. Blood ends up back in the heart to be pushed to the lungs again. The heart is basically one big muscle with four chambers: the right atrium and left atrium sit on top, and the right ventricle and left ventricle are the larger chambers beneath them. Four valves within the heart act as doorways (like old-time saloon doors, but they normally swing only one way) to direct blood flow through the heart and into two of the major blood vessels.

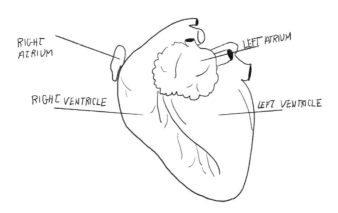

Inhaling brings oxygen into the lungs to be transferred to the blood. This oxygenated blood from the lungs travels to the left atrium, where it is pumped through the mitral valve into the left ventricle. The left ventricle pumps the oxygenated blood out through the aortic valve into the aorta (the body's largest blood vessel) where the blood travels and branches off into other blood vessels (called arteries) to the organs and tissues. Blood circulation is an amazing oxygen, nutrient, hormone, and immune cell delivery system! In addition, byproducts from cell metabolism are picked up and shuttled to organs such as the kidney and liver, and also back to the lungs to clear up.

When cells use oxygen, they produce carbon dioxide, which travels back with the blood through vessels (called veins) to the heart. This deoxygenated blood enters the right atrium and is pumped through the tricuspid valve to the right ventricle, then through the pulmonary valve into the pulmonary artery, which is like a one-way "highway" to the lungs. The carbon dioxide is expelled by exhaling, and oxygen is picked up again during inhalation.

The oxygenated blood in the lungs again travels to the left atrium and left ventricle and the process repeats—about 70 to 120 times a minute; in other words, at the speed of a dog's heartbeat, or heart rate. Dogs' heart rates vary. Larger dogs and those who are more physically fit have lower heart rates. Many nerves and specialized heart muscle cells control this rate. They send electrical impulses that choreograph the rhythm and speed of the heart's pumping action.

The heart sits in a delicate but tough sac called the pericardium. It contains a small amount of fluid and is like a pillowcase for the heart. It helps lubricate the heart and protects it from injury and infection.

Some heartbreaks

Unlike people, dogs rarely have heart attacks. The blood vessels within their heart muscles typically don't become hardened and narrowed with cholesterol deposits like ours can as we age. Such narrowing can cut off blood supply to portions of the heart muscle and cause a heart attack, also known as a *myocardial infarction*.

FUN HEART RATE FACTS

Normal heart rates at rest (beats per minute): (Fielder 2015)
- Cat 120 to 140
- Dog 70 to 120
- Guinea pig 200 to 300
- Elephant 25 to 35
- Dairy cow 48 to 84
- Baby chick 350 to 450
- Goat 70 to 80
- Rabbit 180 to 350

Manatees' heart rates drop by half during long dives!
Octopuses have three hearts!
(Bartel 2018)

Instead, many other types of heart disease can affect dogs, and they result from the usual suspects that cause trouble elsewhere in the body, including infection, inflammation, degenerative changes, nutritional deficiencies, and tumors. Heart tumors can be benign or malignant (cancerous) and are fairly uncommon in dogs. Dogs who have a heart tumor may need to be evaluated by three veterinary specialists—a cardiologist, an oncologist, and a surgeon.

Heart trouble can stem from a problem with the heart's electrical system, which disturbs the nerves and signals that coordinate the heart's rhythm and rate. Trouble also stems from structural problems that involve the heart chamber walls and muscle, the valves, or the pericardial sac. Structural issues can in turn lead to electrical issues, and electrical issues can lead to structural issues.

Duncan had a structural problem that primarily involved the muscle of his left ventricle, the strongest of all four heart chambers. It became dilated, like an overstretched, weak bag, and it could not pump blood properly or relay coordinated electrical signals.

Young at heart with an aging heart

A leaky mitral valve is the most common cause of heart disease in dogs. Degenerative changes in the valve tissue especially affect middle-aged and older small- and toy-breed dogs. Most adult dogs experience some degenerative mitral valve changes as they age, (Fox 2012) but age doesn't seem to be the only factor involved. Dogs also likely inherit the changes that contribute to leaky valves. (Connell 2012)

These degenerative changes cause thickening or slight curling of the one-way heart valves, so they no longer close tightly. This allows blood to flow backward through the valve into the chamber (and is heard as a heart murmur). The chamber overfills with blood, so the heart muscle works harder to pump it out. Ultimately, the muscle of the chamber hypertrophies (thickens) or dilates (stretches or thins), which further weakens the chamber's pumping ability.

When the heart's pumping ability is diminished, blood flow through blood vessels throughout the body is altered. This eventually leads to fluid buildup (congestion) in the lungs or in the abdomen and other parts of the body. This is called *congestive heart failure*. Heart failure is classified based on whether the left or right side of the heart is affected.

Does a dog's diet play a role in DCM?

An increase in reports of dogs (dogs of all ages, not only seniors) who have developed DCM has occurred since 2018. (FDA Investigation 2019) Breeds not known to be genetically predisposed to DCM have developed the disease. So far, the condition is thought to be associated with the diets that these dogs had been receiving. However, no specific diet component or nutrient deficiency has yet been identified as the cause. Reports of diet-associated DCM are still being monitored and investigated.

Heartworms

Heartworms are parasites that can infect dogs of all ages. I mention them here because I often see dog parents who have stopped giving heartworm preventive medications to their senior dogs because they think older dogs no longer need them. But dogs need heartworm (and flea, tick, and intestinal parasite) prevention starting when they are puppies and throughout their entire lives. Parasite prevention protects not only the dog, it protects other dogs in the household and neighborhood, and human family members, too.

Mosquitoes transmit heartworms to dogs. Young heartworms (called *heartworm larvae*) develop in a dog's bloodstream, and the adult worms live in the heart, lungs, and large blood vessels associated with the heart. These parasites are super creepy (they can be a foot long!) and can cause serious lung and heart disease and death in dogs.

Once dogs are infected, the heartworm treatment is lengthy, costly, and associated with side effects from the death of the worms, which in itself can result in a dog's death.

So please continue heartworm preventive medication regardless of your dog's age! It's less costly and safer to prevent heartworm disease than to treat it. And when you adopt a dog—no matter his age—talk with your veterinarian about heartworm testing and starting a preventive medication.

When the heart is not content

Left-sided congestive heart failure is the most common type of heart failure in dogs. This was the case for Duncan. When oxygenated blood that comes from the lungs is not properly pumped from the left ventricle (because of a structural or electrical heart problem), it eventually strains the left atrium. Then the left atrial blood pressure rises, which in turn leads to fluid buildup in the lungs (called *pulmonary edema*). The fluid buildup makes dogs cough and have trouble breathing. Chronic left-sided heart failure often leads to right-sided heart failure.

Right-sided heart failure means that the blood returning from the body to the heart (to be pumped to the lungs to release carbon dioxide) does not adequately flow into the right side of the heart and on into the lungs. This leads to fluid buildup in the veins, which leaks out into the abdomen (called *ascites*) and in the limbs (called *peripheral edema*). So some dogs develop a swollen abdomen and swelling in the legs.

Heart disease differs from heart failure. Your dog could have heart disease and you might not know it. The heart itself and many other mechanisms in the body compensate for altered heart function, so some dogs with heart disease have no signs. Many dog parents are surprised to learn that their dog has a heart problem because veterinarians often discover heart issues brewing during a dog's yearly physical examination or before a dog's surgical procedure or professional dental cleaning.

But as heart disease progresses, dogs have signs that range from subtle to severe, and you'll know that your dog needs to be evaluated. More severe signs and heart failure occur when the heart can no longer efficiently pump blood. Heart disease and heart failure can be managed—to a point—with diet changes, medications, and activity adjustments.

See your veterinarian if your dog:

- Tires easily or sooner than is typical for her with normal activity
- Breathes faster or harder than normal with mild exercise or at rest
- Coughs
- Pants or paces more than normal
- Has a reduced appetite
- Has unintentional weight loss
- Vomits frequently or has diarrhea
- Has pale or bluish gums or a bluish tongue
- Has a swollen belly or legs
- Cries in pain
- Seems weak
- Faints or collapses

Getting a diagnosis

Depending on your dog's signs and physical examination findings, your veterinarian may want to perform standard blood tests (complete blood count and serum chemistry profile) as well as blood tests to check for specific markers of heart disease (called *nT-pro-BNP* and *cardiac troponin-1*). Additional diagnostic testing may include chest and belly radio-graphs, an electrocardiogram (ECG) to evaluate the electrical signals that spark the heart's rhythm and rate, blood pressure measurement, and an echocardiogram. Dogs may need referral to a veterinary cardiologist for advanced testing such as echocardiography or Holter monitoring (a portable ECG that a dog wears to identify whether arrhythmias occur during routine daily activities).

Doing your dog's heart good

Most heart diseases in dogs can be man-aged well with medications that help the heart muscle pump better, dilate blood vessels to reduce resistance so the heart can more easily push blood through the

 My dog Duncan, wearing a Holter monitor on his way to visit his cardiologist.

body, and reduce congestion in the lungs and other parts of the body.

A veterinary therapeutic diet formulated specifically for dogs who have heart disease is also beneficial. These diets are low-salt and contain other nutrients at optimal levels for dogs with heart disease. It's important to have a conversation about diet with your veterinarian, especially if your dog has another condition (e.g. kidney disease, obesity, thyroid disease) that requires dietary adjustments.

Because dental disease may contribute to heart problems and heart disease progression, veterinarians may also recommend a professional dental cleaning and treatment of gum disease, or tooth extractions for dogs who may not have received regular dental care.

Surgery may be an option to treat some types of heart disease. In some cases, a pacemaker can be placed to regulate the heart rate and rhythm, just like in people with arrhythmias! Advanced treatments like these require referral to a vet-erinary cardiologist and may also require help from other veterinary specialists.

Dogs with heart disease can often maintain a great quality of life for several months or many years if we manage their signs, and they can continue to enjoy most activities and even undergo anesthesia when necessary. It's crucial to con-tinue to give dogs their heart medications as directed, even when they seem like they feel normal, because treatment is lifelong.

Dogs who have congestive heart failure—that buildup of fluid in the lungs, abdomen, or elsewhere—often develop cardiac cachexia, a loss of lean muscle mass. This can cause weakness, a decreased ability to fight infection, and a reduced survival time. It can occur even in overweight animals, and veterinarians can help monitor for muscle loss and help prevent its progression. Cardiac cachexia may occur in dogs in spite of a good appetite, or cachexia may cause a reduced appetite. Changing your dog's diet to more palatable foods and making a few feeding schedule adjustments (smaller amounts more frequently) may be needed. Diet supplements such as fish oil (omega-3 fatty acids) or certain amino acids (taurine or L-carnitine, depending on the type of heart disease) may help. An appetite stimulant or anti-nausea medication may be needed at times. If those interventions aren't successful, veterinarians may suggest placing a feeding tube, which allows you to provide the calories your dog needs without worrying whether he'll eat enough. A feeding tube can also make medication administration easier. Dogs tolerate feeding tubes well, and using a feeding tube can reduce your and your dog's stress associated with their care.

During the later stages of heart failure, veterinarians can drain the fluid buildup in a dog's abdomen or chest with a special needle and catheter as needed (sometimes every two to four weeks) to help the dog stay comfortable. But when the heart can no longer pump blood effectively even with our best efforts, the disease becomes life-threatening. Congestion in the lungs from left-sided heart failure causes coughing, respiratory distress, and, eventually, death. Congestion in other parts of the body from right-sided heart failure leads to uncomfortable pressure on the abdominal organs and the diaphragm—a muscle that helps with breathing.

Any disease that affects a pet's ability to breathe comfortably is a major cause of concern for me. I cannot imagine any harder form of suffering than the inability to breathe well and the intense anxiety and discomfort it causes.

Duncan will always be in my heart

After Duncan's heart disease diagnosis, my focus on his care and comfort intensified as his disease progressed. I knew I could manage his dietary changes, adjust his activity schedule, and reduce his stress and any temptations of overexcitement (no more doorbells ringing [even on TV!] or squirrel-viewing from the window). I also knew that I never wanted to allow him to experience prolonged respiratory distress related to his heart failure.

After a few months passed, Duncan needed an appetite stimulant because he had become a picky eater (and he was still receiving all his other medications). I also stopped taking vacations and kept my time traveling for work to a minimum. But about eight months after his DCM diagnosis, I was on the other side of the country taking a course in veterinary physical rehabilitation when I received a distressing phone call. The person caring for Duncan told me Duncan was not doing well, and then quietly asked me which veterinarian I would suggest to euthanize Duncan.

My heart pounded with anxiety. "WHAT?!" I blurted. "Excuse me! What do you mean, *which* veterinarian?!"

The veterinarian would be me, of course. I quickly booked a red-eye flight home and left my continuing education course half finished. I was so happy I did. I was able to adjust Duncan's medications and environment to make him more comfortable, which gave me time to better prepare to say goodbye.

Duncan was breathing a wee bit better, but I knew that soon I would not be able to make enough adjustments to alleviate the fluid buildup in his lungs. And I had promised Duncan and myself that I would never make him suffer because it was too hard for me to let him go.

So after two great days of checking off all the remaining items on Duncan's bucket list, I let my big red gentle warrior receive his angel wings. His heart was tired. He was tired. And honestly, I was tired of worrying about him. But I would have done so for 20 more years to have that blessed time with him, if I knew he wouldn't suffer.

When I heard Duncan's last heartbeat, the anxiety I carried washed away instantly. All I felt was gratitude for having his heart love me so much for as long as it did.

Questions to ask your veterinarian

- What tests will my dog need to evaluate his heart?
- What caused my dog's heart disease?
- Does my dog need a referral to a veterinary cardiologist? If so, can we schedule an appointment right away?
- What medications will help?
- What are the possible side effects of my dog's medications?
- Are the medications a lifelong treatment?
- What is my dog's prognosis?
- How often does my dog need rechecks?
- What will be done during the rechecks?
- Does my dog need a special diet?
- Will my dog benefit from specific dietary supplements?
- What kinds of treats can I give my dog?
- Does my dog have exercise restrictions?
- What are the signs of distress I should look out for?
- What is the normal heart rate for my dog while resting? (Ask your veterinarian to show you how to feel your dog's heartbeat.)

CAREGIVER TIPS AND HOME HACKS

- Help your dog maintain a healthy weight and feed the appropriate diet for your dog's condition.
- Avoid high-salt treats and most of the food that people eat, especially potato chips, pretzels, cheese, and processed meats. Low-sodium drinking water may be needed if your tap water contains a high level of sodium.
- Continue providing parasite prevention, routine vaccinations, and dental care.
- Use a pill organizer to help keep track of your dog's daily medications. Giving heart medications at the correct dosages and on time each day is important. Be mindful of when medication refills will be needed. Plan to request and pick them up or have them delivered before the medication is gone.
- Keep a dog health journal to routinely note your dog's respiratory rate, activity level, appetite, and the timing of any dosage changes that your veterinarian prescribes. This helps your veterinarian determine whether medications need to be added or otherwise adjusted.
- To count your dog's respiratory rate, wait until your dog is quietly resting or sleeping. Count the number of breaths your dog takes in 20 seconds and multiply it by three. This equals your dog's respiratory rate per minute. It should be less than 30 breaths per minute. If the number increases by 20% or more over two or three days (for example, from 25 breaths per minute to 30 breaths per minute or more) it may mean that fluid is accumulating in the lungs and a medication adjustment or other therapy is needed, so call your veterinarian.
- Schedule and keep all your dog's veterinary recheck appointments. Dogs with heart disease need more frequent monitoring and checkups. Take your dog's health journal with you to each appointment.
- Keep dogs calm and shield them from things that can get them worked up, like the doorbell ringing or children playing.
- Allow easy access to quiet places so your dog can "get away from it all" if needed.
- Dogs who are well managed with medications and diet can still enjoy their regular mild to moderate levels of activity. Just avoid allowing them to overdo it and become short of breath, pant excessively, or exhibit weakness.
- If your dog loves to swim, try wading. If your dog normally runs with you, take walks instead. If your dog loves to walk, slow the pace or reduce the duration of the walk, or go every other day instead if needed.

- Engage dogs in quiet, low-stress activities like food puzzles and other interactive, low-key toys. Use a variety of toys and rotate them to prevent boredom. Passive range-of-motion exercises or massage may be helpful and provide mental stimulation for your dog as well.
- Maintain the environmental temperature and humidity at comfortable levels and take care to avoid heat or cold stress when outdoors.
- Keep food and water bowls and potty areas easily accessible.
- Place non-slip rugs or yoga mats on slippery floors, and keep your dog's toenails trimmed.
- Place ramps or stairs where needed to discourage jumping.
- Use a harness to avoid putting pressure on your dog's neck.
- Use a support sling if needed to help your dog get up and to posture to urinate or defecate.
- Place nightlights where needed.
- Direct a fan toward your dog's bed. The increased airflow on dogs' faces and in their noses helps them breathe easier.
- Massage limbs lightly to help alleviate pressure from fluid retention.

 PRODUCT RECOMMENDATIONS

- Joyride Harness: **https://joyrideharness.com/**
- Harnesses, support slings, and booties: **www.handicappedpets.com** and **www.Helpemup.com**
- Music: iCalmPet™ (BioAcoustic Research) **https://icalmpet.com/**
- Cooling mats: **www.arfpets.com**
- Do not ring or knock signs: **https://www.amazon.com/dp/B01BL4MP3I/?ref=exp_drmarygardner_dp_vv_d**
- To alleviate anxiety in dogs: Calmer Canine device **https://www.calmerk9.com/**
- Calming pheromones: Adaptil (Ceva) **www.adaptil.com**
- If home oxygen treatment is needed: Oxygen for pets (Pawprint) **https://pawprintoxygen.com/**
- Pillbox organizers (available at many pharmacies, online retailers, and pet retailers)

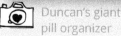
Duncan's giant pill organizer

READING RECOMMENDATIONS

- More information about pets with heart disease: **https://heartsmart.vet.tufts.edu/**
- Heartworm information: American Heartworm Society: **https://www.heartwormsociety.org/pet-owner-resources**
- Parasite information: **https://www.petsandparasites.org/**
- Information about veterinary specialists in cardiology, oncology, and surgery: **https://vetspecialists.com**

CHAPTER 13:

The kidneys: Little wonders

"It has long been an axiom of mine that the little things are infinitely the most important."

— SHERLOCK HOLMES (FROM "A CASE OF IDENTITY" BY SIR ARTHUR CONAN DOYLE)

The first dog I ever treated for chronic kidney disease was Cali, a light-brown mixed breed from … California! During the year of her treatment, Cali had to be hospitalized a few times for two days to receive intravenous (also called *IV*) fluid therapy. I became attached to Cali and good friends with her pet parent, Grace. Cali was a great hospital guest—she gave lots of love to all veterinary team members.

Grace eagerly learned how to give Cali fluids subcutaneously (under the skin) every day at home. Cali was fairly tolerant of it, and she also learned that after each treatment, she got a tasty treat!

When the time came for Grace to say goodbye to Cali, Grace asked me to come to her home for Cali's euthanasia. I didn't hesitate. Cali was the first pet I ever delivered angel wings to at home.

I've helped many senior dogs like Cali deal with kidney issues. These organs are little wonders that perform multiple key activities.

 Me and Cali during one of Cali's visits to the veterinary hospital.

Kidney duties and design

Most mammals, including ourselves and our dear canines, have two kidneys that sit in the upper part of the abdomen—one on each side. They are part of the urinary system (also called the *renal system*), which also includes the ureters, bladder, and urethra. Renal is another term that refers to the kidneys—you've no doubt heard the twin name for kidney disease: *renal disease*. Like our kidneys, dogs' kidneys perform vital functions:

- They filter toxins from the blood and send water-soluble waste out of the body through the urine.
- They stabilize electro-lytes and other blood-stream components.
- They help regulate blood pressure and blood pH (pH relates to acid-base balance, a chemical harmony in fluid that allows cells to function normally).

FUN FOOD FACT

The kidney bean derives its name from the shape and color of the kidneys!

- They produce certain hormones, including one that helps make red blood cells.

The kidney's structure is pretty cool. Its outer protective shell is a fibrous capsule embedded in fat. Inside are the renal cortex, medulla, and pelvis. Hundreds of thousands of nephrons run through the cortex and medulla.

The nephrons are amazing, teeny, blood-filtering systems that shuttle nutrients, sort electrolytes, and help pass waste products. The little powerhouses in the kidneys vary in numbers among different dog breeds, because even people, with our many body organ similarities, are estimated to have a wide number—between 210,000 and 2,000,000 nephrons! Beagles are estimated to have between 445,000 and 589,000 nephrons per kidney.(Cianciolo 2016)

The renal pelvis is the funnel-shaped, innermost section of the kidney. It provides the pathway for urine to flow into the ureter—a muscular tube that runs from each kidney to carry urine to the bladder. The urine is stored in the bladder until urination occurs, and then the urine travels through another muscular tube, the urethra, to exit the body.

CORTEX

NEPHRON

MEDULLA

Get to know your electrolytes!

Sodium, potassium, phosphorus, and calcium are a few of the electrically charged essential minerals present in blood, urine, tissues, and other liquids that the kidneys are hard at work stabilizing. These electrolytes maintain hydration and proper blood pH. When electrolyte concentrations are imbalanced in the body, lethargy, vomiting, irregular heart rate, seizures, and many more symptoms occur.

Testing for kidney disorders

Urinary system troubles include acute (sudden) and chronic (long-term) kidney disease, kidney failure, cancer, urine crystals, stones, cysts, strictures, infections, and inflammation. If your dog's symptoms point to the urinary tract, your veterinarian may use blood and urine tests, x-rays, and ultrasound to identify the cause. Blood and urine tests done as part of your dog's routine yearly or twice yearly checkups allow your veterinarian to monitor for changes in kidney function as your dog ages, before symptoms occur. If reduced kidney function is detected, supportive measures can be started to slow disease progression.

Two wastes that can be measured with blood tests to check kidney function are blood urea nitrogen (also called BUN; medical savvy tip—say each letter separately (B-U-N)) and creatinine. A different substance in the blood that indicates early kidney disease is called symmetric dimethylarginine, or SDMA.

Blood concentrations of these substances correlate with kidney damage and increase as kidney disease progresses. When both BUN and creatinine levels are too high, it's called *azotemia*. Azotemia occurs when the kidneys have trouble filtering blood for one of three major reasons:

1. Blood circulation through the kidneys is reduced, possibly because of dehydration or blood loss;
2. Kidney function itself is badly compromised; or
3. Urine can't be expelled from the body (because of blockage from a urinary stone, for example), so waste products in the urine are reabsorbed and build up improperly in the blood.

Urine tests give additional clues about kidney function. Veterinarians can check whether protein, glucose, ketones (chemicals the liver creates for energy if there is not enough glucose around), or blood cells are improperly leaking into your dog's urine. And because the kidneys conserve water and concentrate urine, they also check urine concentration by measuring its specific gravity. This test compares urine density to the density of water. The lower the urine specific gravity, the less concentrated the urine is, which may indicate kidney damage—or indicate that your dog drinks a lot of water. With urine and blood tests, veterinarians can detect whether your dog has one of the three types of azotemia.

X-rays and ultrasound allow veterinarians to look at the size and shape of the kidneys and bladder and to check whether bladder stones, kidney stones, tumors, or other abnormalities are present.

Your veterinarian should also check your dog's blood pressure. High blood pressure (hypertension) can be a silent killer which can lead to renal hypertension, blindness, heart failure, and even dementia.

The International Renal Interest Society is a non-profit organization that was established to help veterinary practitioners better diagnose, understand and treat renal disease in cats and dogs. They have established an internationally recognized set of guidelines on the diagnosis and assessment of renal disease in dogs and cats. Plus they have also created guidelines on the management if renal disease. For more information and education – visit their website: **http://www.iris-kidney.com/**

Chronic kidney disease

I'll focus on chronic kidney disease here because it's a common urinary system problem in senior dogs. A single, precise cause of chronic kidney disease in dogs has not yet been found. Several factors probably play a role in sparking kidney disease and allowing it to progress: age-associated changes in kidney cell function and tissue structure, environmental influences such as diet and stress, and damage from intermittent insults that reduce oxygen or induce inflammation in some parts of the kidneys. (Brown 2016 Cianciolo 2016) Kidney damage can stem from:

- Bacterial diseases, such as canine leptospirosis
- Genetics (some dog breeds are predisposed to kidney problems)
- Medications that can compromise kidney function, such as nonsteroidal anti-inflammatory drugs
- Medical conditions such as high blood pressure, heart disease, diabetes, or immune system dysfunction
- Severe dehydration or blood loss
- Blockages in the urinary tract
- Parasites (uncommon unless dogs eat earthworms, raw fish, or frogs)

Damaged kidneys allow waste products to build up in the blood. Less water is reabsorbed and electrolyte balance is disrupted, so dehydration occurs. And electrolyte imbalances, such as excess phosphorus, can cause further kidney damage. If too much potassium is lost in the urine, muscle weakness or weight loss (from lack of appetite or nausea) can occur. If too much potassium is retained, heart rhythm problems occur. Damaged kidneys allow protein and glucose to leak into the urine (called *proteinuria* and *glucosuria*, respectively) and don't reabsorb them properly for the body to use.

With blood and urine tests, blood pressure measurement, and other tests if needed, along with your dog's history and signs, your veterinarian can evaluate whether another condition is affecting your dog's kidney function. Veterinarians can also determine what stage of kidney disease a dog has, which allows us to recommend the best course of treatment for each stage.

Stages of kidney disease in dogs

Stage I   no azotemia is present; urine tests may show proteinuria and decreased specific gravity; blood creatinine concentrations may show a progressive increase; the kidneys may be abnormal in size or shape; the dog shows no obvious outward signs

Stage II   mild azotemia; the dog may have no signs or mild signs

Stage III   moderate azotemia; the dog may have no signs or mild or moderate signs

Stage IV   severe azotemia with a range of clinical signs

See your veterinarian if your dog:

- Drinks more water
- Urinates more often
- Urinates in odd locations
- Strains to urinate
- Is weak
- Has unintended weight loss
- Has a loss of appetite
- Has nausea
- Salivates or drools excessively
- Has bad breath
- Has sores in her mouth
- Vomits
- Has diarrhea

- Is dehydrated (signs include decreased skin elasticity, dry or sticky gums, weakness)
- Is lethargic
- Sleeps in odd locations

Managing kidney disease—and your expectations

Pet parents have told me they think kidney disease is a death sentence. But it isn't, especially when it's caught early enough. It's true that chronic kidney disease is not easily reversible and rarely disappears. (Brown 2016) But kidney disease progression in dogs can be slowed with diet, fluid therapy, and supportive medications, which also alleviate dogs' symptoms. Many dogs who have kidney disease can live several more happy, active years.

In the early stages of kidney disease your dog may not experience discomfort. Dogs whose kidney disease is being well managed can be likened to being on a sailboat in calm seas for long periods. As the disease progresses, their sailboat may be intermittently caught in bad storms, so rechecking the dog's blood and urine test results and addressing the dog's symptoms is paramount. Dogs can feel quite sick and develop oral ulcers (because of toxin build up in the blood). They can become dehydrated and have mobility issues from weakness related to electrolyte imbalances. But with treatment adjustments, the calm seas return.

Eventually, worse storms arrive that make you wonder whether the boat will sink and it's time to jump ship. But, with further treatment tweaks, calm weather arrives again! Recognizing when the storm will not abate while carefully evaluating your dog's quality of life are key.

Dietary therapy

Feeding veterinary therapeutic diets designed for pets with kidney disease reduces kidney disease progression and increases survival time. (Polzin 2019) These diets are highly recommended because they address many mechanisms at work in kidney disease. They typically have lower phosphorus, sodium, and protein content and include more omega-3 fatty acids. They may also contain more fat (which makes the food taste better and increases calories), additional antioxidants such as vitamins C and E (to reduce oxidative stress in the kidney), and more fiber. Bacteria in the colon like fiber, so feeding specific types of dietary fiber helps the bacteria do their job to reduce wastes that might otherwise build up in the blood of pets who have kidney disease. (Cline 2016, Hall 2020) Many therapeutic diets designed for dogs with kidney disease are available, and your veterinarian will discuss these with you.

What's oxidative stress?

As cells generate energy, they produce oxygen-containing molecules that can damage tissue (called *free radicals)* and repair tissue (called *antioxidants*). This production is normal and necessary. But when too many free radicals are running about, an imbalance between free radicals and antioxidants occurs, which damages cells, and cell damage leads to tissue and organ damage. Disease, a poor diet, and environmental pollution can also cause excess free radical production. Antioxidants can be supplied in the diet to help cells vanquish excess free radicals and restore balance.

The dietary protein debate

One characteristic of veterinary therapeutic diets for pets with kidney disease is that they contain a reduced amount of protein. Yet veterinarians debate whether protein restriction is necessary in pets with kidney disease, or at which stage of kidney disease protein restriction should be started. The debate continues because the benefits of feeding therapeutic diets for kidney disease can only be attributed to the diets as a whole, and not to an individual component of the diets such as reduced protein. Evidence that dietary protein intake plays a role in kidney disease progression is lacking. (Brown 2016)

Restricting dietary protein in pets with kidney disease may be beneficial because it reduces buildup of nitrogen wastes in the blood, and these wastes cause many of the signs of illness. On the other hand, veterinarians worry that protein restriction leads to protein malnutrition and loss of lean muscle. Loss of lean body mass is common in pets with chronic kidney disease, and it may contribute to weakness, hamper immune function, reduce wound healing, and decrease overall survival time. (Freeman 2012) But studies that evaluate feeding a higher protein diet (a diet that is not protein-restricted) to pets with chronic kidney disease have not been done. (Polzin 2019)

The bottom line is that your veterinarian should assess your dog to determine whether dietary protein restriction would be beneficial or potentially harmful. Your veterinarian will consider your dog's protein intake in light of the amount of protein loss in your dog's urine, the degree of toxin buildup in the blood and your dog's clinical signs, and whether your dog has muscle wasting. (Cline 2016)

How (and how not) to switch to a therapeutic diet

Introduce your dog to his new diet gradually, replacing his old diet with the new diet in 25% increments over a two-week period. Avoid starting the switch while your dog feels unwell, because he may associate the new diet with his illness and develop an aversion to the food. This is why veterinarians try to avoid introducing pets to therapeutic foods while they are hospitalized and will instead send samples with you to feed after your dog feels better at home.

Keep your dog hydrated and interested in mealtimes

Because dogs with kidney disease are unable to drink enough water to keep up with the amount of fluid they lose through the urine, veterinarians often suggest giving affected dogs subcutaneous fluids a few days a week and up to once a day. Fluid therapy helps keep your dog hydrated and feeling good when their kidneys lose their concentrating abilities.

Dogs are usually tolerant of subcutaneous fluid therapy, and even if they're hesitant at first, they tend to grow accepting of it with time. And once pet parents get the hang of it, it can be done quickly. Your veterinarian will show you how to do this and tell you how much fluid to give your dog. Videos are also available on YouTube that demonstrate this technique, so ask your veterinarian to point out a few. Once kidney disease reaches the late stage, like Cali, your dog may need to be hospitalized for IV fluid therapy and other supportive treatments from time to time. Typically dogs return home feeling good again and do well with continued subcutaneous fluid treatments at home.

Eventually some dogs seem to tire of their therapeutic diets—usually when they have nausea associated with their disease and lose their appetite. So talk with your veterinarian about whether your dog needs additional fluid therapy, anti-nausea medication, and an appetite stimulant. These treatments can make dogs with kidney disease feel better and eat more.

If treatment adjustments still don't entice them to eat their therapeutic diet, you may need to switch back to feeding their regular diet or switch to an even tastier diet to ensure they eat enough. Consuming sufficient calories to preserve body functions and provide energy is more important than insisting that your dog continue to eat the therapeutic diet.

Also talk with your veterinarian about whether placing a feeding tube may be needed. A feeding tube can support dogs through an illness setback that they might otherwise succumb to. Feeding tubes can be used long-term or removed once dogs eat enough on their own. Dogs tend to tolerate feeding tubes well, and the tube allows easier medication administration.

Many people ask me if kidney disease hurts and the answer is 'it depends'. It depends on the stage of the disease and what side effects your dog is experiencing. Often times early stages of kidney disease has no apparently effect on a dog's quality of life – it usually is not noticed until annual bloodwork is taken where a hint of kidney disease is seen. But as the disease progresses, your dog may experience dehydration, nausea, oral ulcers and other side effects that are not comfortable. And that to me, is living with pain, discomfort or dis-ease and it should be addressed.

Questions to ask your veterinarian

- What stage of kidney disease does my dog have?
- Is treatment needed if my dog does not have outward signs of kidney disease?
- What is my dog's prognosis with and without treatment?
- What treatments will be needed, how will they be given, how often, and for how long?
- Does my dog need to be treated for high blood pressure?
- Does my dog need a special diet, nutritional supplements, or an oral hydration supplement?
- Will my dog need fluid therapy at home? If so, how do I do that?
- Will my dog benefit from a feeding tube?
- What follow-up tests and exams will be needed to monitor my dog and how often? What are the costs?
- Are there side effects of treatment?
- What problems do I need to watch out for?
- What do I do if problems occur after regular business hours?

 CAREGIVER TIPS AND HOME HACKS

- Always provide clean, fresh water. Consider providing filtered water. Drinking fountains designed for dogs may help entice your dog to drink more than with her normal water bowl.
- Flavored broths and nutrient-enriched water supplements (oral hydration supplements) are available for dogs—ask your veterinarian.
- Feed a veterinary therapeutic diet formulated for dogs with kidney disease.
- Feed primarily canned or moist foods, or add water to dry kibble.
- Warm foods slightly or add low- or no-sodium chicken broth or tuna juice to enhance palatability (the yum! factor).
- Keep several varieties of extra tasty, "special" canned dog food on hand for the days when your dog's appetite needs a boost. Your dog may get to a point where you need to rotate these and offer a different flavor or formulation (gravy, chunky, slices, pâté) every day, or even at each meal to keep your dog interested.
- If your dog has oral ulcers, your veterinarian can prescribe a special mouthwash used often in human medicine which they call "magic mouthwash." It has to be made at a compounding pharmacy and contains lidocaine, diphenhydramine, and sucralfate and is used as a

soothing and protective mouth rinse. This is not to be confused with other over-the-counter trademarked dental rinse products with similar names.

- Remember that dogs who are receiving fluid therapy will also urinate more and need longer and more frequent potty breaks.
- When giving subcutaneous fluids, warm the bag (but not the injection port or injection set) in hot water for 5 or 10 minutes. Before giving the fluids, test the temperature of the water by dripping a few drops on your wrist, similar to testing the temperature of milk in a baby's bottle. After each treatment, give your dog a treat and lots of praise or kisses!
- Frequently launder your dog's bedding, and rotate different types of blankets to different spots to increase their comfort and keep them clean.
- Provide heated dog beds, especially for underweight dogs and those with decreased lean muscle mass who have trouble regulating their body temperature and are susceptible to hypothermia.
- Provide a calm environment to reduce stress. For example, if your dog doesn't adapt well to boarding, have a family member or dog sitter care for your dog if you have to travel. Reduce contact with other visiting family members' dogs if they tend to make your dog anxious.
- Watch for mobility difficulties and place rugs, small stairs, or ramps where needed; consider providing booties if needed.

PRODUCT RECOMMENDATION

- Veterinarian-prescribed appetite stimulant:
  Entyce (made by Elanco) or others

SUPPORT RECOMMENDATION

- Facebook group for dogs with renal failure and kidney disease:
  https://www.facebook.com/groups/582094775463298

CHAPTER 14:

Incontinence: Squish squash

"I don't need you to remind me of my age. I have a bladder to do that for me."

—STEPHEN FRY, ACTOR/COMEDIAN/WRITER

I always considered urinary incontinence to be worse than fecal incontinence. It makes sense, right? A poop ball is easy to pick up and toss out! But with urine, you deal with sopping up a puddle and possibly tackling rug damage.

I reconsidered my preference early one morning (4 a.m.!) when I got up to take aspirin for a headache. I opened my bedroom door, and that unmistakable poop odor triggered the dread alarms in my head. I knew instantly that my dog Sam had had an accident. She had spinal cancer, and it affected her mobility and the nerves to her rear end. I had noticed this new weakness a few weeks earlier when I had taken her for a walk, and plop! A ball of poop fell onto the sidewalk and she didn't even seem to know it.

So I began my wee hours poop hunt! Light from the full moon illuminated the living room, but not enough for me to spot my prey. I crossed the room to turn on a light when… smoosh! I felt the full impact of the squashy poop that oozed between my toes! NOOOOOO!!!! I lifted my foot and stood there like a (stinky) flamingo. I knew I was in the middle of a hazard zone, with another possible pileup ahead!

I gingerly placed my heel back on the floor to avoid spreading the dung that had stuck to the ball of my foot. I hobbled my way to the kitchen to clean it off. When I went back to the living room to inspect the damage and flicked on the light, I flinched.

I felt a quick burst of emotions. Disgust. Fear. Anger. Guilt. Sadness. Sam hadn't simply had one accident, she was sick with diarrhea. It was splattered all over the carpet. And that wasn't the worst thing. She had fallen in it, so it was smeared on her beautiful long white hair, on her bed, and in other spots around the room.

UH-OH!

Poo Patrol

161

At that point I would've traded the mess for pee puddles if I could! The diarrhea disgusted me. As a veterinarian, I routinely see and smell gross things, but my living room carpet-bombed with diarrhea earned one of my top prizes in ickiness.

Then I felt afraid that someone else would wake up and see it. The last thing I needed at that moment was to hear, "Sam is getting really bad. Who lives like this?" Or, "It isn't fair to make her sit in her own feces." Of course I would never allow my dog to stay soiled. But Sam's dad has strong feelings about fecal incontinence. He likens it to how he would feel if it happened to him, and he didn't want that for Sam. I hoped I'd be the sole witness to this disaster.

Then anger crept in. In my thoughts I yelled, "It's 4 a.m., Sam! We went for a walk at midnight! Couldn't you have done this then?! I have to get up in two hours and it'll take me an hour to clean this up!"

I immediately felt guilty for feeling angry. This wasn't Sam's fault. She was a great dog who was sick, and she simply couldn't hold it. She'd never done anything wrong in her life (literally, not one thing!), so she had a few hundred "oops passes" to use up during her geriatric years. I had to be honest with myself and wonder whether her diarrhea was my fault. I gave her lots of snacks and too much table food (which many people do toward the end of their dog's life). "Treat overdose" often doesn't sit well with the belly!

Then sadness hit. I knew the lymphoma in Sam's spine was like a weed growing, invading her spinal cord and doing more damage with each passing day.

So before I could cry, I took my aspirin and a few deep breaths (through my mouth, NOT my nose), cleaned Sam up, and took her outside (she pooped again!). Then I headed to the garage to get the best investment I ever made: the carpet cleaning machine. This ick-extractor should come with every dog. It's a lifesaver!

And I knew it would wake up the house. (Someone, please design a rug shampooer muffler!)

I do ick extraction at my house about once a week!

Oops, my dog did it again!

Young and old dogs alike can lose urine or bowel control, and sometimes dogs lose both. Several conditions, many of which are more likely to affect senior dogs, can cause or contribute to these problems. Whether a dog is incontinent and can't control peeing or pooping or is having "accidents" for another reason must be sorted out. Veterinary evaluation to find the underlying medical cause or behavioral reason is always warranted so the condition can be corrected or managed.

When the "wee" hours add up

Urinary incontinence means that the dog has involuntary urine leakage at rest or during sleep—or may dribble urine while walking—but otherwise urinates normally during waking hours. A weak urinary sphincter is the cause, and it occurs most often in spayed female dogs related to decreased hormones. In affected dogs, it typically occurs three or more years after spay surgery. It's rare in neutered male dogs. Affected dogs also void urine normally, but leakage occurs at different times because a weak or overwhelmed sphincter lets urine seep from the bladder.

If a dog is lifting a leg or squatting to urinate in the house, the dog is having urine accidents. This is known as *inappropriate urination*. How appropriate! This is distinct from urinary incontinence. Inappropriate urination results from medical problems such as diabetes, cognitive dysfunction, cancer, or a behavior issue. Behavior issues include dogs who aren't housetrained, dogs showing submission, or dogs with separation anxiety.

> ### Separation anxiety?
>
> You might be thinking, well, of course my dog is anxious when I'm not with him! But separation anxiety is a behavioral condition diagnosed in dogs who react to being left alone by barking or howling excessively, having urine or fecal accidents, or destroying household items.

To determine whether your dog has incontinence or is having accidents for other reasons, your veterinarian will ask several questions, such as:

- Does your dog—
  - leak urine while sleeping but hold it normally during waking hours?
  - lick his urogenital area frequently?
  - lift his leg or squat normally to urinate?
  - potty in multiple small spots around the house, or do you find one large puddle on the floor?
  - dribble urine immediately after urinating normally?
  - drink more water than usual and want to go outside more often to urinate?
  - urinate in the house right in front of you?
  - leave urine puddles only while you're out of the house?

Your veterinarian might also ask about medications and supplements your dog is receiving, because some can make dogs urinate more frequently. My dog Duncan received a diuretic to help treat his heart failure, and it did what it was supposed to do—help his body get rid of excess water. So it made him urinate A LOT! Sometimes he'd even urinate during the night without seeming to realize it. I'd wake to find him urine-soaked and snoring.

If your dog urinates in little spots indoors throughout the day even though she is well trained to potty outside, it may be a sign of a urinary tract infection, bladder stones, cancer, urethral irritation, or urinary tract blockage. If your dog urinates on the floor in one big spot, then diabetes, kidney disease, Cushing's disease (an adrenal hormone disorder), or another condition may be the cause. These problems can be sorted out by your veterinarian with blood and urine tests, including a culture to check for bacterial growth in the urine, and with x-rays and ultrasound, if needed.

Nerve dysfunction from spinal problems such as intervertebral disk disease, degenerative myelopathy, or cancer can also cause urinary incontinence. Your veterinarian can check your dog's reflexes and sensation by doing a neurologic exam, and, if needed, radiographs, a computed tomography (CT) scan, or magnetic resonance imaging (MRI) will help pinpoint the affected part of the spinal cord.

Cognitive dysfunction can cause loss of housetraining. Affected dogs seemingly forget where they are supposed to potty, which might mimic incontinence. These dogs typically posture to eliminate rather than leak urine during sleep, but I have seen dogs with cognitive dysfunction and no identifiable urinary sphincter problem do both. Treatment for cognitive dysfunction and a housetraining refresher course can help.

Depending on the cause of a dog's urinary incontinence, veterinarians may prescribe antibiotics, phenylpropanolamine, specific hormones, or other medications that affect the urinary sphincter tone or bladder muscle. Or they may suggest bladder surgery or collagen injection into the urethra. (Martinoli 2014, Banks 2017, Chen 2020) Veterinarians who are certified in acupuncture or chiropractic techniques may also be able to help manage dogs who have urinary incontinence. (Tang 2009, Cimons 2013, Thude 2015, Banks 2017)

When dogs are (more than) pooped

Dogs who have fecal incontinence can't properly control defecation. They may not posture to poop and may not be aware that they are having a bowel movement. If your dog has fecal incontinence or his feces are unformed, liquid, or contain blood or mucus, schedule a veterinary examination. Your veterinarian will take a careful history to help identify the cause and ask questions such as:

• Do you find feces next to the door to the outside? In your dog's bed?

- What is the color and the consistency of your dog's feces? (It's helpful to bring a fresh stool sample with you to the examination.)
- Does your dog posture normally to defecate?
- Does your dog sometimes seem to be unaware when stool comes out?
- Does stool come out when your dog is barking or excited or when he gets up?
- How often does your dog defecate?
- Have you changed your dog's diet recently?
- Does your dog lick her hind end frequently or scoot on her rear?

Your veterinarian may also do fecal, rectal, and neurologic examinations along with blood tests and x-rays.

A dog who has normal feces (formed and a bit moist) but has fecal incontinece may have a nerve-related disease that causes anal sphincter malfunction. In affected dogs, poop is evacuated and the dog isn't aware of it. When dogs with mobility disorders struggle to get up, fecal balls may fall out. Dogs with severe arthritis may have trouble getting to their potty location in time or posturing to defecate. Dogs with cognitive dysfunction may also defecate in inappropriate places or seem to be unaware of defecation.

Depending on the cause of a dog's fecal incontinence, veterinarians may prescribe drugs that slow gastrointestinal motility or an analgesic (for dogs with arthritis), along with a change in diet to a low-fiber, more highly digestible diet. In some cases, they may suggest adding a dietary supplement such as pumpkin or other

sources to boost dietary fiber. Some dogs may benefit from surgery if a tumor is found to affect the colon or anal sphincter.

Dogs with fecal incontinence also have a higher risk of urinary tract infections, so help them keep their heinies clean and watch for additional signs of discomfort. Dogs with urinary tract infections may have urine accidents in the house, make numerous trips outside or to their potty location, or urinate small amounts frequently.

Regaining control

No matter the cause, urine or fecal incontinence is tough to manage, and I empathize with caregivers of affected dogs. In Sam's case, I determined that one of the medications she receives to

 I spy a poop ball, do you? Sam doesn't even realize she did it! (Pro-tip: buy a carpet that hides stains and poop balls well)

treat her cancer causes her diarrhea. It's not an easy side effect to manage, and I get frustrated. But I remind myself it's temporary and should resolve when this treatment is complete. I'll need to continue to manage her fecal incontinence that's likely caused by her spinal tumor.

Managing a dog with incontinence requires a considerable degree of ongoing dedicated care. So it's important to seek veterinary evaluation to identify the reason for a dog's urine or fecal incontinence. Many causes of incontinence respond to appropriate treatment or can be well managed. With medications, surgical treatment (if needed), changes to the dog's diet (if applicable), and environmental adjustments, pet parents and their incontinent dogs can live contentedly together. Next up are tips to help you keep the peace!

Should my dog wear diapers?

In general, diapers are more practical for small-breed dogs than for larger breeds. For diaper-clad dogs or those resting on potty pads, be on alert and prevent painful skin rashes and infections. They commonly develop and if they do, require additional time, attention, treatment, and cost. I usually reserve recommending diapers until we are at our wits' end or if it is absolutely necessary due to the dangerous side effect of increased chances of urinary tract infections. So please use them carefully and under your veterinarian's guidance. With that said, I have used them on my own dog Serissa as I had no other option because her urinary incontinence was so severe and I was renting a house with rugs all over.

For medium- or long-haired dogs, do a "sanitary trim." Beard trimmers work great for this. Carefully clip the fur (also avoid clipper burn) around the areas where urine or feces may cling and not be easy to clean. I did this for my dog Sam and also clipped the fur on the back of her legs where feces became trapped. Check diapers and potty pads frequently and change them regularly to

Serissa wore pretty pee-panties

keep your dog's fur and skin clean and dry. If needed, use wipes made specifically for dogs or unscented, hypoallergenic baby wipes.

Dogs with urinary incontinence can suffer from urine scalding—inflammation caused by urine sitting on the skin. If your dog's skin is mildly irritated, this is a warning sign, so wash the area with a mild dog shampoo and thoroughly dry it. Your veterinarian can prescribe specific skin care products to support healing as needed. After the skin is completely dry, you may apply a thin layer of a pet-safe skin ointment or baby diaper rash ointment to relieve irritation and leave a moisture barrier. Some ointments contain zinc oxide, which can be toxic to dogs, so avoid those or be sure your dog doesn't ingest a substantial amount by chewing on the tube or repeatedly licking the applied area.

If your dog tends to gobble strange things, supervise them so they don't pull off their diapers to snack on or chew up their potty pads. Keep incontinent outdoor dogs clean and dry too, to avoid maggot infestation.

The cotton swab secret for pooping on demand

Sam's fecal incontinence had been bad for a few weeks. I would let her outside or take her for a walk, but she wouldn't reliably poop. And when she didn't, I'd wake up to find poop squished into the rug, smeared in her fur, on her harness, or in the tile grout. Or I would leave for a few hours and return home to the same ugly scenario.

Then I learned a trick from pet parents who show their dogs and need their dog to defecate before stepping into the ring. Insert the tip of a cotton swab or unlit wooden matchstick to stimulate the anal sphincter, and the dog will defecate. Now when we go out to the backyard or for a walk and Sam doesn't poop, I stick the cotton swab tip just inside her anus and gently move it in small circles. She poops right away! The first time I did this, I stuck the cotton tip too far into her rectum, beyond the anal sphincter, and it didn't work. After I got the hang of it, I was a poop master! With this trick I can stimulate Sam to poop right before bed or before I leave for a few hours. It works like a charm. This trick has saved me from hours of arguing with Sam's dad and given me more precious time with Sam and less time with the rug shampooer!

I was so impressed by how well the cotton swab trick worked, I took a picture! (Remember to clean up after your dog, even outdoors! Always clean up in public spaces, and don't leave swabs in your yard, either, in case your dog has poop-snacking tendencies.)

CAREGIVER TIPS AND HOME HACKS

- Keep consistent feeding and potty schedules. Learn your dog's usual pee and poop schedule, and add potty times accordingly to give them more opportunities to eliminate.
- Consider adding a dog door for easy outdoor access. (I removed the door's locking mechanism on our screened porch so Sam can push the door to go out when she wants. She barks when she's ready to come back in.)
- Reduce your dog's access to the house. When you're away, confine them to a non-carpeted room. When you're home, use baby gates, tension rods, dog playpens, or exercise pens where possible so dogs can remain near family.
- Place motion-sensor lights in designated elimination areas for visually impaired dogs who have reduced night vision.
- Place easy-to-clean rubber mats, rubber-backed bath mats, or water-resistant picnic tablecloths over cushioned surfaces.
- Use washable, reusable potty pads to protect furniture, car upholstery, dog beds, or kennels.
- Use disposable potty pads where needed.
- Cover duvets and couches with washable, water-proof covers.
- Use easy-to-clean dog beds or baby crib mattresses.
- Cover dog beds with water-proof mattress covers (crib mattress covers are the best!). A shower curtain under a

 I covered Duncan's bed with a crib mattress protector.

blanket also works and is less likely to tear or bunch up. In a pinch, cover dog beds with trash bags and place old blankets or towels on top.
- Some dog beds are "water resistant" and not waterproof, so they may not stand up to leakage that isn't immediately cleaned up. Or some are designed with waterproof liners that sit between the bed cover and the bedding material. So if your dog is consistently incontinent, consider adding an absorbent layer of protection on top that's disposable or easier to remove and launder than the dog bed cover or liner.
- Organize your dog's grooming supplies and skin care products in a tote kept in a handy spot for quick cleanups.
- Consider keeping dog wipes or baby wipes in a wipe warmer for your dog's added comfort.

- On frequently wiped areas of skin, apply diaper rash ointment to prevent or relieve irritation (be sure your dog doesn't ingest the ointment).
- Prevent sores and infections from urine scalding by placing absorbent pads under your bedridden dog, or use diapers if needed for incontinent dogs and change them right away when they become soiled.

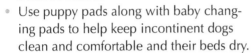
Who wouldn't like a warm wipe?

- Use puppy pads along with baby changing pads to help keep incontinent dogs clean and comfortable and their beds dry.
- Invest in a carpet cleaner and keep the machine, rug cleaning solution, and pet stain and odor remover products in a readily accessible location.
- Use a black-light flashlight in a dark room to help you find urine spots you missed.
- Avoid disciplining or punishing your dog for incontinence or accidents in the house.
- See the cotton swab secret section above!
- Put an inflatable peanut ball under your dog's abdomen for support while you clean them off.

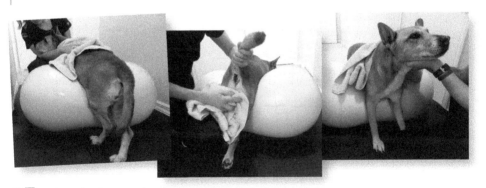

Angel gets a wash on a peanut ball to comfortably support her.

⁇ Questions to ask your veterinarian

- If pain from mobility problems or muscle weakness may be preventing my dog from eliminating appropriately, will my dog benefit from receiving pain management? And will my dog benefit from treatments that support muscle strength or joint function?

- Will my dog with fecal incontinence benefit from a diet change to a more highly digestible food? Or to a food with higher fiber content?
- What is the cause of my dog's urine or fecal elimination issue and what is the expected outcome with treatment?
- Will acupuncture or physical rehabilitation help my dog?
- Do you offer special grooming for "sanitary cuts" (shaving around the rear end and groin —like a bikini trim—to help keep those areas clean)?

 PRODUCT RECOMMENDATIONS

Dog diapers and related supplies

- Barkertime **https://barkertime.com/**
- Pet Parents **https://petparentsbrand.com/**
- Senye Pet diapers (**www.amazon.com**)< **https://www.amazon.com/SENYEPETS-Senye-Disposable-Diaper-12Pcs/dp/B074C5ZMZF?**
- Escape-proof dog diaper (for use with feminine hygiene pad or incontinence pad): PeeKeeper **www.peekeeper.com**
- For use with baby diapers or incontinence pads: TinkleTrousers (Tamashii Co.) **www.tinkletrousers.com** and Belly Bands **www.bellybands.net**
- Diaper rash cream: A+D Original Ointment (Bayer)
- Skin irritation cream: Calmoseptine Ointment (Calmoseptine Inc)

Beds for incontinent dogs

- SleePee Time Bed (Handicapped Pets) **https://www.handicappeddogs.com/sleepee-time-bed-for-incontinent-dogs/**
- Komfy K9 Beds **komfyk9.com/**

Washable, reusable potty pads

- Trendy Den Pet Mat (Trendy Den Creations) **https://thetrendyden.com/product-1-trendy-pet-mat/**

Washable duvet and couch covers

- Floppy Ears Design **www.floppyearsdesign.com/**

READING RECOMMENDATIONS

Bowel management for incontinent dogs

- https://www.handicappeddogs.com/blog/
  bowel-management-incontinent-dogs/

Diaper selection guide

- Dog Quality **https://dogquality.com/blogs/senior-dog-blog/
  ultimate-guide-choosing-dog-diaper-senior-dog**

Veterinary acupuncture and chiropractic

- American Holistic Veterinary Medical Association
  https://www.ahvma.org/find-a-holistic-veterinarian/
- International Veterinary Acupuncture Society **https://www.ivas.org/**
- American Veterinary Chiropractic Association
  https://www.animalchiropractic.org/
- Acupuncture, rehabilitation therapy and medical massage
  www.curacore.org

CHAPTER 15:

The lungs: Keeping the wind in their sails

Movie night! I had my favorite snack, a fluffy blanket, and pants with an elastic waist. The lights were low. My favorite human moviegoer was with me to share the experience. Our dogs had full bellies and were resting comfortably on their beds. The setup for a perfect evening!

Then, 15 minutes into the movie, my dog Sam propped herself up on her elbows, looked over at us, and started panting. Dogs sometimes pant, right? Well, she didn't stop. And it was LOUD. I had to turn the volume up so we could catch the dialogue in the movie.

While she was receiving prednisone, Sam would stare and pant heavily at rest for hours!

I pride myself on having phenomenal patience with dogs, especially the older ones. But Sam's panting started to annoy even me! And our other dog didn't seem bothered by anything or worried about her; he continued snoozing quietly. I paused the movie and quickly checked her out for discomfort or distress. I found no obvious problems. Sam didn't ask to go outside, and she seemed content on her bed.

She simply stared at me and kept panting. I secretly hoped maybe it was because her belly was a little too full and that she would soon start snoozing, too.

I climbed back under my blanket and restarted the movie. But at minute 28, I was at the end of my tolerance rope. Sam was still panting. I stared back at her, willing her to settle down and fall back asleep. But my wishful-thinking powers did not win out.

Then from the other end of the couch came the dreaded questions:

- "Why is she doing that?"
- "Can't you do something about it?"

Now my movie buddy was frustrated with Sam, too.

I explained, "She's receiving medication and one of its side effects is excessive panting." (I had sassier thoughts to share, but I knew that would not help the situation!)

So no, there was nothing I could do because Sam needed that drug. And we didn't want to move her to another room because all her life she had shared the living room with us. We both took deep breaths and focused on the movie, and Sam finally fell asleep.

When I became a veterinarian, I never considered that a dog's panting would cause problems in a household, including mine. But I fully understand and empathize with this issue. And as much as I want Sam to STOP panting so much, I know one day, after she earns her angel wings, I will yearn to hear that old girl's breath just one more time.

So, other than certain medications, what causes some dogs to pant more than other dogs? How do dogs' lungs and breathing change with age?

Breathing basics

Inhaled room air—made up of about 78% nitrogen, 21% oxygen, 0.04% carbon dioxide, and tiny fractions of other gases, plus water vapor—begins its journey through the breathing passageway in the upper respiratory tract: the nose, mouth, and *larynx* (voice box—part of the throat that connects to the windpipe). It then travels through the lower respiratory tract: down the windpipe (*trachea*) and into the lungs, which are made up of large and small airway tubes (called *bronchi* and *bronchioles*) and millions of air sacs (called *alveoli*). Each air sac is surrounded by tiny blood vessels (*capillaries*).

Oxygen crosses the air sac membranes into the capillaries, where red blood cells pick it up for delivery to all the body's tissues. After delivering the oxygen, the red blood cells return with the byproduct—carbon dioxide—which is transferred back through the air sacs and up and out of the respiratory tract. Exhaled air contains about 4% carbon dioxide, 16% oxygen, 78% nitrogen, and a small amount of moisture.

The flow of oxygen in and carbon dioxide out is choreographed by brain signals that produce a rhythmic dance of alternating contraction and relaxation of muscles that assist breathing, including the diaphragm, intercostal muscles (the muscles between the ribs), and a few accessory muscles. Air flows into the lungs when the diaphragm contracts downward, the intercostal muscles expand the chest wall outward, and pressure in the lungs decreases. During exhalation, the muscles return to their resting places.

Some cells that line the respiratory tract produce mucus, and other cells have tiny hair-like projections called *cilia*. The cilia move together in rhythm (called *beat frequency*) to transport mucus-trapped invaders such as bacteria, viruses, and pollen back up and out of the respiratory tract, banishing as many as they can before they reach the delicate air sacs.

Reasons to pant

The biggest reason dogs pant is to cool off, because they can't sweat like we do (though they do have a small number of sweat glands in their paw pads). This rapid, shallow, relaxed, open-mouth breathing is generally nothing to worry about. Panting allows quick exchange of hot air from the lungs with cooler external air, and that speeds water evaporation from a dog's mouth (especially from their tongue), nose, and upper respiratory tract. This process effectively and efficiently regulates body temperature. Dogs can't cool down properly if they can't pant effectively. This is why we must take extra precautions to prevent dogs with airway issues from overheating.

Dogs also pant when they're happy and excited or, on the flip side, when stressed and anxious. Anxious dogs give other subtle cues of distress as well, such as yawning, licking their lips, and turning away from the source of the anxiety. If the source remains or approaches, dogs may show more obvious signs like whining and hiding, or growling, snapping, and biting. Common driving forces of anxiety in dogs include car rides, thunderstorms, fireworks, or being approached by people or animals they're not familiar or comfortable with.

Pain is another factor in the panting equation. Dogs don't always show signs of pain that are obvious to us, but panting can be one, especially when they wouldn't normally pant—like when they're resting or cooled down.

Some medical conditions (such as Cushing's disease, where excess cortisol, a stress hormone, is present in the bloodstream) make a dog pant more than normal. And, as in Sam's case, some medications, such as prednisone (which works like cortisol), also stimulate panting in dogs. I've been unable to find studies that explain WHY prednisone makes dogs pant! Maybe dogs pant because prednisone can weaken the breathing muscles, as can occur in people, (Wan 2018) or because prednisone can make dogs more restless or anxious. (Levine 2015)

When taking a breath isn't as easy as breathing

Dyspnea means labored or difficult breathing. Dyspnea massively adversely impacts a dog's quality of life. Human hospice patients equate the suffering associated with being breathless to the suffering associated with uncontrolled pain. I have seen many dogs with dyspnea, and although they can't tell me whether they are suffering, I believe that they are. It's important for pet parents to understand the causes of respiratory system changes and the ways to help alleviate any stress and discomfort associated with their dog's dyspnea.

Some dogs have physical abnormalities that make breathing a challenge. Brachycephalic (meaning a broad, short head) or "smooshed-face" dogs (such as pugs and boxers) are born with airway disadvantages. They may have narrow nostrils, an overlong soft palate (the area just behind the roof of the mouth), tissue in the larynx (voice box) that blocks air flow, and an underdeveloped trachea. Some dogs are severely affected and require surgery to correct these problems. For example, I have seen an internet video of a tiny bulldog puppy whose owners mistakenly think their puppy is "adorably" fighting sleep. The puppy tries to stay upright but repeatedly falls over as it falls asleep from exhaustion. Sadly, the puppy's owners don't realize the puppy jolts awake each time because it can't get enough air when it lies down.

Even brachycephalic dogs with mild to moderate physical abnormalities and who may not have needed surgery earlier in life may still have more breathing problems as they age than other breeds do.

Age-related breathing challenges

Age-related changes in the spine (decreased space between the vertebrae can adversely affect the intercostal muscles), the ribs (hardening of rib cartilage decreases flexibility of the chest wall), and the breathing muscles (weakening) can hamper breathing. Weak contraction or diminished strength of the breathing muscles—the diaphragm and intercostal and accessory muscles—makes them less efficient. So as dogs age, they may cough less effectively.

Cough strength can be measured in people and it indicates whether we can properly clear secretions from our respiratory tract and whether we have a high risk of aspirating food. We can't ask our dogs to cough on demand to check their cough strength, but veterinarians presume that senior dogs who do have weak cough strength can't effectively clear mucus and other particles from their breathing passageway.

With age, lung tissue becomes stiffer and less elastic. During regular day-to-day activities, geriatric dogs usually compensate for this. But when they are faced with other respiratory system stressors, it becomes difficult for them to recover. Scar tissue can replace normal lung tissue. This is called *fibrosis* and it makes breathing more difficult. Fibrosis can occur for unknown reasons, as a result of various airway diseases, or because of long-term exposure to airway irritants (like secondhand smoke—yes, dogs are at risk, too!). Even the little cilia deep in the lungs can develop a diminished beat frequency rhythm with age, or they can be hampered by secondhand smoke exposure or other airway insults.

Disturbances anywhere along the respiratory pathway can impair breathing. Such changes increase dogs' risk of developing serious breathing issues.

Common respiratory problems in senior dogs

A progressive, irreversible condition called tracheal collapse is common in small-breed dogs such as Chihuahuas and Yorkshire terriers. The trachea contains rings of cartilage that support it and keep it open. If the cartilage is weak, the trachea narrows during breathing and limits air flow. This condition is typically identified when an affected dog is young, but as the dog ages, becomes obese, or lives with someone who smokes, it can become life-threatening. Affected dogs have a "goose-honk" cough that gets worse during exercise or when they pull against their collars. Affected dogs may sometimes even faint.

Tracheal damage can also occur in dogs who have worn choke collars, pulled hard against a regular collar, or been yanked by a leash while wearing a collar.

Paralysis of the larynx occurs most often in geriatric large- and giant-breed dogs. The larynx protects the entrance to the trachea. It's made up of cartilage flaps controlled by muscles that keep the flaps open during breathing and closed during swallowing. For more about this condition, see Chapter 16 "Laryngeal paralysis: GOLPPing for air"

Heart disease can occur for various reasons at any point in a dog's life but is more common in older dogs. It, too, can result in breathing problems and is managed with medications. (See Chapter 12 "Heart: Keeping the beat strong.")

Senior dogs can develop inflammation in the airways that leads to chronic bronchitis, and they can catch infectious causes of lung disease such as bacteria, viruses, fungi, and parasites—especially heartworms. Vaccinations and parasite preventives remain important protective measures throughout dogs' lives.

I mention cancer here as well because cancer is so common, especially in senior dogs. Cancer can start in the lungs or other places in the respiratory tract, or it can travel there from a tumor that develops elsewhere in the body. (See Chapter 20 "Cancer: Things that go bump in senior dogs.") According to the American College of Veterinary Surgeons, about one in four dogs who have a lung tumor will not show any signs, and veterinarians instead find it when they take chest x-rays for other reasons. (ACVS 2020)

Help keep the wind in your dog's sails

- Keep your dog up to date on vaccinations and parasite preventives to reduce the risk or severity of infectious diseases that can affect the respiratory system. The vaccinations dogs receive protect against common viruses and bacteria that cause many problems, including those that damage the respiratory tract. Also protect your dog against heartworms by giving a heartworm preventive, because these mosquito-borne parasites cause severe lung disease.

- Help your dog maintain a healthy weight and body condition by feeding the right amount of high-quality food and promoting physical activity. Obesity can exacerbate respiratory distress from any cause.
- Make your dog quit being a secondhand smoker. Now *that's* a good reason for people to stop an unhealthy habit if they need another convincing argument—their dog's health. Your dog wants you to be well as well! Secondhand smoke can cause chronic respiratory problems and cancer in dogs.

See your veterinarian if your dog

- Exhibits unexplained weight loss or lethargy, which can be signs of lung cancer, among many other conditions
- Has a breathing rate consistently over 30 breaths per minute while he is relaxed and resting or sleeping
- Coughs or gags frequently
- Pants excessively (at rest, or more than expected after exercise or in warm weather)
- Has noisy breathing
- Exhibits distress or anxiety, is restless, or can't rest comfortably
- Has flared nostrils during breathing
- Breathes with an open mouth
- Uses her abdominal muscles to help her breathe
- Needs to stay upright or extend his neck to breathe; or stands with his head down and elbows out
- Has pale, bluish, or gray gums
- Faints or collapses
- Has voice changes, such as an odd, husky bark

 CAREGIVER TIPS AND HOME HACKS

Managing a dog's respiratory issues can be distressing for the family. But a simple rule applies: do everything to keep the dog calm and comfortable. These suggestions have worked for my patients and my dogs:

- Walk your dog during cooler times of the day to help prevent heat exhaustion.
- Use a high-quality harness to prevent putting pressure on her throat.
- Play relaxing music, place "do not disturb" signs on your front door, and use dog pheromone sprays.
- Run a fan next to your dog's bed to promote more air flow into his nose. This helps alleviate distress in people with dyspnea and works well in my

pet hospice practice. The cool airflow may trigger nerve receptors in the nose to send signals that "trick" the brain into thinking enough airflow is present. (Morélot-Panzini 2017) This can really help calm a dog in respiratory distress. Also make sure your dog is otherwise comfortable with the fan and not cold—drape a lightweight towel or blanket up to his shoulders if needed, because a heavy blanket may be too restrictive.

A TIP JUST FOR YOU: Caregiver fatigue can be a huge issue while managing an aging dog. For example, after helping thousands of families navigate their dogs' end of life, I know that ceaseless loud panting, especially throughout the night, can lead to many disputes and exhausted pet parents. To help yourself breathe easier, see Chapter 30 "Caregiver stress, burden and burnout: When loving hurts."

 Questions to ask your veterinarian

- Will my dog benefit from receiving canine influenza and canine bordetella vaccinations in addition to other routine vaccinations against respiratory illnesses?
- What tests will my dog need to evaluate her breathing problem?
- What medications will help?
- What are the possible side effects of my dog's medications?
- Will my dog's condition resolve with treatment?
- How can I help my dog breathe easier at home?
- Does my dog need oxygen therapy?

 PRODUCT RECOMMENDATIONS

- Joyride Harness for dogs **https://joyrideharness.com/**
- Music for dogs iCalmPet (BioAcoustic Research) **https://icalmpet.com/**
- Cooling mats for dogs **www.arfdogs.com**
- Calmer Canine device **https://www.calmerk9.com/**
- Pheromones: Adaptil for dogs (Ceva) **www.adaptil.com**
- "Do not ring or knock" signs **https://amzn.to/3GiJgNE**
- Oxygen for dogs (Pawprint) **https://pawprintoxygen.com/**

CHAPTER 16:

Laryngeal paralysis: GOLPPing for air

"That breath that you just took, that's a gift!"

— THE INTERNET ATTRIBUTES THIS QUOTE TO ROB BELL, AMERICAN AUTHOR AND FORMER PASTOR

When my dog Duncan was 10 years old, he started clearing his throat more often. It was a loud, quick "AAA-CK!" sound combined with a quick, blunt cough. At first I figured he had bits of grass or dirt caught in the back of his throat. But over a few weeks' time, I heard him do it at least once or twice a day. It reminded me of my grandmother, who had post-nasal drip!

Because Doberman pinschers are prone to heart disease, my mind went down a dark path wondering whether his cough was an early sign of heart failure.

I listened to Duncan's chest with my stethoscope, and his ticker and lungs sounded great. But I wanted reassurance, so I took him to see a veterinary cardiologist. Duncan's examination and heart test results came back PER-FECT! Whew!

But his throat clearing continued. After Duncan had a few more tests and I talked with colleagues about his results, I determined that Duncan was showing early signs of *geriatric-onset laryngeal*

 Me with Duncan when he was 10 years old, the age at which he started "coughing."

paralysis and polyneuropathy. That's a mouthful! So veterinarians and pet parents call it "GOLPP" or "LarPar" for short.

GOLPP is most common in geriatric large-breed dogs. It's a non-painful disease of many nerves (polyneuropathy) that weakens the larynx (the voice box and part of the throat that connects to the windpipe), the esophagus (food pipe), and the legs.

How the voice box relates to breathing, eating, and walking

The nose, mouth, pharynx (part of the throat that connects to the esophagus), and larynx make up the upper respiratory tract, or breathing passageway. The larynx protects the entrance to the trachea (windpipe) with flaps (called laryngeal folds) made of cartilage (flexible, tough connective tissue) that are controlled by muscles. The muscles keep the flaps open for breathing but close the flaps during swallowing to prevent food and water from going down the windpipe into the lungs.

The muscle in the larynx that holds the flaps open is called the *cricoarytenoideus dorsalis* (that's a tough one to pronounce—"crick-oh-arit-noyd-ee-us door-sal-iss"). It receives signals from the right and left recurrent laryngeal nerves.

GOLPP is a degenerative peripheral nerve disease. Degenerative diseases typically get worse with time, and peripheral nerves are the nerves that run outside the brain and spinal cord and send signals to the rest of the body. Similar to some peripheral nerve diseases in people, GOLPP more severely affects longer nerves. (Sample 2020) And in dogs, the nerves to the larynx and esophagus (recurrent laryngeal nerves) and to the hindlimbs (sciatic nerve and its branches) are among the longest. (Sample 2020) In fact, with GOLPP, the left side of the larynx is paralyzed first, possibly because the left recurrent laryngeal nerve is longer than the right recurrent laryngeal nerve. Nerve degeneration weakens and ultimately paralyzes the laryngeal muscles, and the laryngeal flaps don't stay open properly for breathing.

I like to use an analogy that the laryngeal folds are like heavy window curtains that you pull back from an open window to let air into the house. If the curtains stay closed, air doesn't easily flow through. And when an affected dog tries to breathe in lots of air during hot weather, exercise, or excitement, the laryngeal folds or "curtains" can be sucked inward and completely close, so no air can get through to the lungs, leading to asphyxiation and death.

The larynx also contains the vocal cords, so when the laryngeal muscles malfunction, the dog's bark begins to change, which is technically called *dysphonia*.

FUN FACT

The recurrent laryngeal nerves branch from Cranial Nerve X (ten), also called the vagus nerve. The vagus nerve is the longest of the 12 cranial nerves and is pretty powerful because it helps control many bodily functions besides how the laryngeal muscles move. Swallowing, esophagus movement, stomach emptying, bile release in the gallbladder, sneezing, heart rate, and even some anti-inflammatory responses are also under the vagus nerve's domain.

Pet parents often think nothing of a change in their old dog's bark, but that can be an early warning sign I tell owners to be on the lookout for! However, not all dogs with GOLPP will have a change in their bark so it is important to look for other signs as well.

As the disease progresses

As the recurrent laryngeal nerves degenerate, not only does the larynx malfunction, esophagus function also declines. Food moves more slowly through the esophagus on its way to the stomach, or it stalls out for prolonged periods. So dogs who have GOLPP may gag or regurgitate food when eating, or they may seemingly "out of the blue" gag and regurgitate food several hours *after* eating. They may also have discomfort from stomach acid reflux (heartburn). How can you spot a dog with heartburn? They may seem restless, suddenly sit up and pant after lying down, or urgently eat grass. (Rasmussen 2018)

Because other nerves are involved as GOLPP progresses, neurologic deterioration eventually occurs in the front and rear legs. You may notice that your dog has trouble getting up onto the bed or into the car, and these may be signs of front or hind limb weakness. But it's the hindlimb weakness that tends to be most noticeable. The dog may "sink" in the hind end, walk unsteadily, drag one or more toes, or walk or stand on the top of their foot (called knuckling).

What causes laryngeal paralysis?

In dogs with GOLPP, the condition is idiopathic, which means that we don't know the underlying cause. It affects middle-age and older large- and giant-breed dogs—especially Labrador retrievers—as well as greyhounds, Newfoundlands, German shepherds, Australian shepherds, borzois, golden retrievers, Saint Bernards, Irish setters, and English setters. It also affects a medium-size breed—Brittany spaniels. GOLPP is uncommon in small- and toy-breed dogs; those breeds tend to have upper airway problems related to their head conformation.

Other than GOLPP, laryngeal paralysis can be congenital. In these dogs, the nerves involved do not function normally at birth, and the dog shows signs of laryngeal paralysis at a young age.

Throat trauma can also damage the larynx, trachea, and associated nerves and cause laryngeal paralysis. Neck injury tends to occur in small dogs who are attacked by another dog and grabbed by the throat during a fight. Laryngeal paralysis from bite wounds affects both sides of the larynx.

Choke collars, prong collars, or a sudden, hard jerk on a standard collar have been speculated to contribute to injuries that lead to laryngeal paralysis, but collar type is not a contributing factor in this disease. (Side note: To prevent dogs from pulling on their leashes, veterinarians recommend using head halters or body halters instead.) Furthermore, this type of injury would not be expected to cause the nerve degeneration and progressive esophageal or limb mobility problems seen in dogs with GOLPP.

The endocrine (hormonal) disorders hypothyroidism (inadequate thyroid hormone production) and hyperadrenocorticism (excess cortisol production) have been implicated as causes of laryngeal paralysis in dogs, so veterinarians may check for these diseases as well. Tumors of the neck and chest can also cause recurrent laryngeal nerves dysfunction and signs of laryngeal paralysis, so it's important to check for thyroid gland and other nearby tumors, because they affect the type of treatment needed and a dog's prognosis.

When to see your veterinarian: Signs of GOLPP

- Throat clearing or hacking
- Coughing
- Gagging with or without regurgitation
- Harsh, increased noise when breathing (called *stridor*) or when panting
- Panting when the dog is otherwise comfortable and calm
- Bark changes—voice may sound gruff, croaky, or husky
- Exercise intolerance—tiring easily and possibly having trouble breathing after normal activity, or after getting mildly excited about something. Pet parents sometimes attribute this to their dog "getting old and slowing down," when the true cause is lack of air.

 Duncan's sand pawprints highlight his toe drag—it's the straight line "drawn" by one of his toenails.

- Difficulty breathing—dogs have a wide-eyed, anxious facial expression, or appear to "smile" when panting because their lips are pulled back in an effort to draw in more air. They may also have more pronounced chest expansion because the abdominal muscles work harder to draw air in.

- Pale, blue, or dark-red gums or tongue
- Front or hind end weakness
- Loss of muscle mass
- Unsteady or wobbly when walking
- Dragging rear toes or knuckling

 Duncan started to show hind end weakness.

Tests your veterinarian may recommend

Depending on your dog's symptoms—whether it's voice change, throat clearing, coughing, breathing difficulty, gagging, or limb weakness—your veterinarian will check for conditions that might cause them. Physical and neurologic examinations, blood tests, and radiographs of the chest and hindlimbs are usually the first diagnostic steps. To confirm whether your dog has GOLPP, your veterinarian will sedate or lightly anesthetize your dog and look in the back of his throat with a laryngoscope to watch laryngeal fold (the "curtains") movements during breathing. If a dog is too heavily sedated or anesthetized, the laryngeal muscles relax too much and give misleading findings.

Your veterinarian may refer you to a board-certified veterinary surgeon for your dog's evaluation and diagnostic tests or to discuss treatment options. If your veterinarian doesn't offer a referral to explore treatment options, don't hesitate to ask for one. (I expand on the reason why later in this chapter!)

Can laryngeal paralysis be treated?

The most common treatment is the laryngeal "tie-back" surgery (technically called *unilateral arytenoid lateralization*). The surgeon makes a small incision on the side of the dog's neck and places a permanent suture in one of the laryngeal folds to hold the fold open and allow air to more freely flow

185

through. It's a little like using a curtain tieback to permanently hold a curtain open so air can flow through the window. The suture must be tied with just the right amount of tension to avoid pulling the fold back too far and leaving the windpipe overly exposed. When done by a veterinary surgical specialist, the surgery itself takes about 30 minutes, and dogs can often go home the same day of the surgery.

Veterinarians have also explored surgically placing a stent to hold the larynx open, but this technique is not widely available. (Ricart 2020, Cabano 2011)

How well does surgery work?

Most laryngeal tie-back surgeries are successful and the dogs have great outcomes. In one study of 76 Labrador retrievers with GOLPP, pet parents of dogs who underwent tie-back surgery gave their dogs significantly higher quality-of-life scores than did the pet parents of dogs who did not have surgery. Of the 33 pet parents whose dogs had surgery, 32 were happy with their decision to have surgery, and one was neutral. (Sample 2020)

After surgery, dogs can more easily inhale food and water while eating and drinking, so *aspiration pneumonia* is a potential complication. Aspiration pneumonia involves inhaled material reaching the lungs and causing serious inflammation and infection. This risk is the reason why many veterinarians and pet parents hesitate to go ahead with laryngeal tie-back surgery. But medications and special eating, drinking, and activity precautions can reduce the risk. Omeprazole, an antacid, is prescribed to reduce stomach acidity in case reflux or regurgitation occurs, (Rasmussen 2018) and cisapride, a gastric motility stimulant, is given so food leaves the stomach sooner.

Pet parents often report that their dogs seem young again after the surgery (because they can breathe easier!). Dogs may still clear their throats for a few months after the surgery, and this is probably caused by small amounts of saliva or fluid dripping into the trachea. Another postoperative side effect that is not harmful, but one that pet parents may not anticipate, is that dogs lose their normal voices afterward. Dogs will still try to bark, but a weird sound escapes and their fearsome woof will be tamed.

Is my dog a good candidate for surgery?

Dogs who are otherwise healthy or have chronic diseases that are well-managed should be eligible for laryngeal tieback surgery. If a dog with GOLPP already has moderately reduced esophageal function, his chance of developing aspiration pneumonia after tie-back surgery increases. In that case, the surgeon may use a slightly different, more complex laryngeal surgery technique. But if a dog has severely reduced esophageal function or has megaesophagus, laryngeal surgery may not be an option at all. (With megaesophagus, the esophagus is so overly enlarged and distended that food doesn't move to the stomach.) In addition, dogs who already have severe mobility problems or can't get up on their own are not candidates for this surgery.

To check esophageal function before surgery, your dog will have x-rays taken of his esophagus while he swallows (called an *esophagram*). These radiographs show how fast food and liquid move through the esophagus and whether any of it moves backward, which helps us decide whether laryngeal surgery is a good option.

Veterinary surgeons also recommend that dogs have a computed tomography (CT) scan to check for thyroid, lung, or heart tumors before laryngeal surgery. Tumors of the neck and chest can also cause signs of laryngeal dysfunction and change a dog's treatment options and prognosis. If a tumor is found elsewhere (nose, spleen, adrenal glands, liver), it also affects a dog's prognosis and may need to be treated first if possible.

For dogs with megaesophagus who aren't candidates for laryngeal tieback surgery, a tracheostomy (surgically creating a permanent opening in the windpipe) may be an option.

What if my dog doesn't have tie-back surgery?

In a study of pet Labrador retrievers with laryngeal paralysis who had not had surgery, a drug called doxepin was explored as a potential treatment and compared to placebo. (Rishniw 2021) The results showed that doxepin was no better than placebo in improving the dogs' quality of life, according to their pet parents. This mirrors my experience with doxepin in dogs with laryngeal paralysis—it doesn't seem to help.

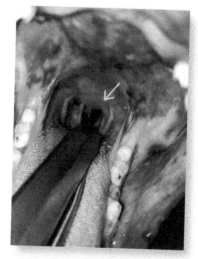

Duncan't throat a few months after his laryngeal tie-back surgery. The left side of his larynx has been tied back (arrow) and is more open than the right side. (A laryngoscope blade is pressing down on Duncan's tongue to hold it out of the way)

If surgery isn't an option, no medical cure exists for GOLPP. Dogs can be managed with anti-inflammatory medications, antihistamines, antacids, gastric motility enhancers, and measures to limit activity and assist swallowing. But without surgery, dogs with laryngeal paralysis have a greater chance of experiencing severe breathing problems. So continue to focus on home care and monitoring your dog's quality of life. Pay special attention to preventing aspiration and to keeping your dog calm and on steady footing.

With or without surgery, veterinary rehabilitation therapy and exercises to help your dog maintain her balance and strength are recommended.

Why talk with a veterinary surgeon about treatment options?

Once when I taught at a veterinary conference for primary care veterinarians, I discussed Duncan's case during my lecture, but I didn't share with the audience members that the patient was my dog. I described a 10-year-old large-breed dog with laryngeal paralysis who had no other health problems, but who was showing signs of breathing struggles because of laryngeal paralysis. When I started talking about treatment, I took a poll and asked the audience to raise their hand if they would discuss the option of laryngeal tie-back surgery with the dog's owner. Only two veterinarians (out of more than 100 attendees in the room) raised their hands, which surprised me!

I asked a few of my colleagues to share why they wouldn't discuss tie-back surgery with the dog's owner. They told me that the patient was old, and that there were too many post-surgery complications. It made me sad to hear this, because it meant that the owners of so many dogs who may be helped by tie-back surgery were probably not being offered the treatment, nor even being given the information. So I decided to explore this scenario further and ask for feedback from pet owners whose dogs had this disease.

I created a survey and invited members of a canine laryngeal paralysis support group on Facebook to participate. Of the 422 dog owners who responded, 206 chose to have laryngeal tie-back surgery for their dogs, and 216 chose not to have the surgery. Here are highlights of the survey results:

- About half of both groups didn't receive information about the laryngeal tieback surgery from their primary care veterinarian.
- 62% of the dogs who didn't have surgery died or were euthanized because of complications from their disease (either pneumonia or mobility problems), compared with 32% of the dogs who had surgery.
- 76% of the dogs who didn't have surgery had difficulty breathing as a current concern, compared with 15% of the dogs who had surgery.

- 42% of the owners whose dogs didn't have surgery decided against it because of the risk of post-surgery complications.
- 95% of the dogs who had surgery survived, and of those the average survival time after surgery was 19 months (the range was one month to more than two years).
- 87% of the dogs who had surgery had more energy after the surgery than before the surgery.
- 92% of the owners whose dogs had surgery said they would elect to have the surgery again.
- The dogs who had surgery ranged in age from 9 years to 15 years:
  - 6% = 9 years
  - 11% = 10 years
  - 19% = 11 years
  - 33% = 12 years
  - 14% = 13 years
  - 5% = 14 years
  - 2% = 15 years
- 68% of owners who elected surgery for their dogs said they wish they had done it sooner.

Based on my informal surveys of pet parents and my colleagues, I encourage you to talk with a board-certified veterinary surgeon to get all the facts about your dog's treatment options and risks before making a decision.

Home care necessities and tips

Whether or not dogs with GOLPP have had tieback surgery, they have special dining needs and cautious exercise considerations. You can help them gobble their meals and watch their steps while staying strong.

Eating and drinking

One of the problems to watch for in all dogs with GOLPP is aspiration pneumonia. Food and water may not move normally through the esophagus regardless of whether the dog has had tie-back surgery. And dogs who have had tie-back surgery have a slightly greater risk of aspiration pneumonia because the airway is more exposed. Veterinarians recommend feeding solid food over soft food because solid food moves better through the esophagus, which should reduce the likelihood of regurgitation. (Rasmussen 2018) By studying dogs who have laryngeal paralysis, we know that large, dry kibble moves faster through their esophagus than does canned food or a liquid diet. (Stanley 2010) But also keep in mind that it's more important to ensure dogs are getting sufficient calories, rather than struggling to get them to eat a food they're not fond of. So if your dog will eat only canned dog food meatballs, that's OK, too (but perhaps first test whether they'll eat a canned food meatball that contains dry kibble).

We also know that allowing dogs with laryngeal paralysis to eat quickly is better than encouraging them to eat slowly. So contrary to popular advice, we no longer recommend using slow-feeder bowls for dogs with laryngeal paralysis.

When it comes to drinking water, the opposite is true. To prevent regurgitation and aspiration, encourage your dog to drink water slowly and intermittently. Don't let him drink large amounts of water at one time—for example, when your dog wants to drink a lot after he's been outside. Water bowls with special floats are available to slow drinking. You don't want to limit your dog's total daily water intake, just help him go slower and drink smaller amounts at one time.

Aspiration pneumonia can occur if your dog inhales food, water, vomit, or other foreign material. So it's also important to keep your dog from chewing up items they might inadvertently inhale. Also avoid overfeeding your dog or giving treats or table food he's not accustomed to that might make him vomit.

Eating position

Many dogs can continue to eat from their bowl on the floor. Food doesn't move differently through the esophagus in dogs who are fed from a standard elevated feeder compared with dogs fed from bowls on the floor. (Stanley 2010) So contrary to popular advice, standard platform feeders aren't needed because the dog's head, esophagus, and stomach stay parallel to the floor.

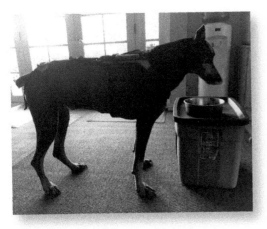

This type of platform feeding isn't necessary to prevent aspiration or speed food through the esophagus, and Duncan's surgeon told me I could feed Duncan with his bowl on the floor. But Duncan seemed more comfortable and stayed steadier while eating in this position, so because I knew it wouldn't harm him, I let him eat from the platform. (Duncan is also wearing a Help 'Em Up Harness.)

However, some dogs benefit from being fed with their head and front end elevated. For example, you can feed your dog on steps, or feed your dog while she's sitting. These positions harness the power of gravity to help move food into the stomach and prevent aspiration pneumonia. To feed on stairs, your dog needs to stand on a 30- to 45-degree incline plane with her front legs higher than her hind end and her head higher than her front legs. (Michigan State University Website)

So according to veterinary surgeons, you can feed your dog with her bowl on the floor, while your dog is standing on an incline, or while she's sitting, whichever position works best for your dog.

Dogs who have severe megaesophagus may need to use a Bailey Chair, which is a little like a specially built high chair for dogs that keeps them vertical while they eat and drink to help prevent aspiration pneumonia.

Clues that signal aspiration pneumonia

The first signs of aspiration pneumonia are that your dog has less energy, less or no interest in food, and a fever. Keep a thermometer handy (that's solely for your dog) so you can take his temperature. A temperature of 103 F (39.4 C) or higher means he has a fever. Coughing and nasal discharge may occur later. It's crucial to take your dog to the veterinarian at the very first signs of aspiration pneumonia. Your veterinarian may take chest x-rays and do blood tests. Antibiotics and other treatments such as coupage (gently hitting the chest wall with cupped hands) and nebulization (delivering moist air with or without medications through the airways) to resolve the lung infection and reduce inflammation can be used to treat aspiration pneumonia.

Activity

Replace your dog's collar with a harness to reduce stress on the trachea, larynx, neck muscles, and nerves, especially during walks. Harnesses also help dogs with hindlimb weakness.

Non-slip flooring is imperative for weak and wobbly dogs who have hindlimb unsteadiness. Use a variety of tactics to help dogs get around easier (see Chapter 17 "Mobility: The weak, wobbly, and unsteady"), as this vastly improves their quality of life—and yours!

In my experience, dogs who have had tie-back surgery recover their pre-disease activity level and are hard to keep up with because they can breathe again! An exception to this is agility dogs, who tend to need to retire from competition after surgery. But if tie-back surgery is not done, then the dog often experiences exercise intolerance. Dogs with restricted airflow can't cool off sufficiently by panting even in mildly warm or humid conditions, and they rapidly become overheated and suffer from heat exhaustion or life-threatening heatstroke. So exercise your dog only during the cool hours of the day and for short periods, as well as in the shade whenever possible. Also limit your dog's exposure to secondhand smoke to avoid irritating her airways.

Keep your dog at an ideal body weight—obesity hinders mobility and breathing, and underweight dogs may be weak and have decreased immune responses.

Dogs who have breathing issues must be kept calm. Veterinarians sometimes prescribe sedatives for dog parents to keep on hand to give to dogs in specific stressful situations. Limit taxing interactions, and use low-key activities for exercise and engagement.

Keep in mind it isn't healthy for dogs with GOLPP to be couch potatoes, either, so find a good balance according to their limitations and help keep them as active as possible. Activity promotes strength, keeps those nerves firing, and boosts dogs' mental health. A veterinary rehabilitation therapy program that uses strength training, balance exercises, and helping dogs stay attuned to where their limbs are positioned brings all those benefits.

Many of the large dog breeds who have this disease also love to swim. Because of the risk of aspiration pneumonia, especially after a tie-back surgery, swimming is generally not recommended, but surgeons differ in their opinions on this activity after surgery. Some surgeons allow wading and swimming, especially because these dogs love it and it's a great physical rehabilitation activity. In addition, dog life vests can be specially altered! These help keep the dog's head above water and decrease the chance of aspiration. Of course you wouldn't want them to swim in choppy water where a wave can overwhelm them, but with careful monitoring in calm waters, smooth sailing is possible! Remember that NO diving is allowed, for example, to jump in or to fetch objects from the water.

Note that dogs who have a tracheostomy can't be allowed to swim at all; in fact, extra special care must be taken to protect their airway even during baths.

Follow-up healthcare

Dogs who've had laryngeal tieback surgery can still undergo anesthesia afterward for dental cleanings and other procedures such as tumor removal. GOLPP and laryngeal tieback surgery are both important components of your dog's medical history, so keep track in your dog's health journal, and remind your dog's ongoing and new healthcare providers of these facts.

Duncan's surgery

About six months after Duncan's GOLPP diagnosis, he started having trouble breathing, even at rest. And although he was a large-breed, nearly 11-year-old boy and surgery and postsurgical complications were not without risk, I booked the tie-back surgery for him. I could not bear watching him get worse. I wanted to give him some relief and a shot at a longer, happy life.

I was a nervous wreck about the surgery even though I knew better. I didn't have the experience to perform a tie-back technique successfully. So I took him to one of the best veterinary surgeons in Southern California (shout out to Veterinary Surgical Specialists and Dr. Diane Craig!). Fortunately, it's not a difficult surgery for the patient because it involves only a small incision in the neck. Duncan's surgery went great and he recovered like a champ. About a month later, he was running around like a pup! Duncan did lose his bark, and I sure missed his deep bellow of protection. But to see him full of vitality again was heartwarming.

About eight months after Duncan's surgery, the disease's progressive nerve degeneration started to rear its ugly head. Duncan began to get a little wobbly in the hind end. So he received weekly acupuncture treatments, physical rehabilitation, moderate exercise, and even massages—all of which really seemed to help slow the disease and keep him as strong and steady as he could be.

I didn't expect Duncan to make it into his teenage years. But at age 13, he was living proof that old age was not a disease, nor was his "tween" age of 11 a reason for me to not have allowed him the surgery that helped him live longer and so well.

Questions to ask your veterinarian

- My dog seems normal but his voice has changed. Is this caused by laryngeal paralysis?
- Does my dog need laryngeal tie-back surgery now or will my dog need it later?
- Is it necessary to wait for my dog's signs to get worse? Are there benefits of having the surgery earlier?
- Should we consult with a veterinary surgeon?
- Does my dog need a special diet or feeding technique?
- Does my dog have exercise restrictions or special recommendations?
- Will veterinary rehabilitation therapy, massage, or acupuncture help?

PRODUCT RECOMMENDATIONS

- Toenail grips for slippery floors: Dr. Buzby's Toe Grips **https://toegrips.com/**

- Stairs for access to the couch or the bed, and potentially to feed your dog on if you don't otherwise have access to stairs (available at pet retailers)

- A harness to help you help your dog get up off the floor, get in and out of the car, and walk up and down stairs: Help 'Em Up Harness — Blue Dog Designs **https://helpemup.com/**

 Maple is getting toenail grips applied.

- UPSKY Slow Water Dog Bowl available at **www.amazon.com**

- Purchase a fan to keep next to your dog's bed or resting spot to promote more air flow into his nose, which can help calm him if he has mild difficulty breathing. (see Chapter 15: The lungs: Keeping the wind in their sails)

 Xander has a fan next to his favorite spot on the couch.

 READING AND VIEWING RECOMMENDATIONS

- Educational video. Dr. Mary: Helping Dogs with GOLPP (Feat. Dr. Bryden Stanley)
- American College of Veterinary Surgeons website:
  - Find a veterinarian near you who specializes in surgery: **https://online.acvs.org/acvsssa/rflssareferral.query_page?P_VENDOR_TY=VETS**

- o And information about laryngeal paralysis: **https://www.acvs.org/ small-animal/laryngeal-paralysis**
- Michigan State University College of Veterinary Medicine website. How to modify a life jacket for swim-loving dogs who have GOLPP
- Information about megaesophagus and Bailey Chairs: **https://www.k9megaesophagus.com/home.html**

SUPPORT RECOMMENDATION

- Laryngeal Paralysis (LP) GOLPP Support Group (Dogs):
- **www.facebook.com/groups/larpar**

CHAPTER 17:

Mobility: The weak, wobbly, and unsteady

After over a decade of offering in-home end-of-life care, I can confidently say that my most common patients are dogs with mobility issues. They simply cannot get up and get around as well anymore and their owners have trouble getting them to the veterinary clinic.

Mobility issues affect dogs of all shapes and sizes, but I typically see large dogs who weigh 60 pounds or more. As a veterinarian, I have grown to more fully appreciate the impact that mobility problems have in my patients. And as a pet parent of three dogs with impaired mobility, I even more deeply understand these daily struggles. Each one of my patients and pets has taught me so much.

Serissa's painful hip

Serissa, my Samoyed, was pure joy! She brightened my life after I lost my dog Snow White. Samoyeds have a huge, heartwarming grin. It's even listed as a defining trait in the American Kennel Club standard for their breed! It states, "Lips - Should be black for preference and slightly curved up at the corners of the mouth, giving the 'Samoyed smile.'" (AKC) Serissa had a million-dollar Samoyed smile, along with the characteristic Samoyed "roo," which is a sweet-sounding howl.

Serissa started having mobility problems when she was 8 years old. Instead of readily settling down to rest, she would repeatedly circle the spot where she wanted to lie

Serissa rooing!

down, then finally ease into her descent. During walks, she started favoring her right side, especially when she jumped over a small obstacle such as a parking curb. She never whined, yipped, or snipped, even when I palpated her limbs and spine. But radiographs of her hips showed signs of arthritis and hip dysplasia—an inherited deformity that's more common in large-breed dogs. The top of the femur (thigh bone), called the *femoral head*, should be a smooth ball that fits into the hip socket. Serissa's right femoral head looked like a cauliflower.

Surgery was an option, but I decided to try medical therapy first. I gave her medications to alleviate her hip pain and inflammation, and they seemed to help for a while. But her signs of discomfort grew. She started to hesitate when I asked her to "sit," which had previously been easy for her. She favored her left side even more, so the muscles in her right leg shrank from disuse. Then she sometimes yelped when she got up. I realized that medications alone would not stop her pain.

I knew surgery could help Serissa, and I regret waiting so long to schedule it. Her yelps finally convinced me, and by then a year had passed! I took her to a veterinary orthopedic surgeon who removed the top of her femur (a procedure called *femoral head ostectomy*, or *FHO*) and along with it, her pain! Another surgical option might have been a total hip replacement (similar to the surgery people undergo), but her hip joint was not a good candidate for that procedure.

After an FHO, dogs do well because the soft tissues and muscles around the hip act as a false joint. Serissa took a bit longer than usual to regain her strength because her right side was already quite weak. Her walk was also a little off afterward (she had a hitch in her giddyup), which can sometimes happen after FHO surgery. But after she fully recovered, she sat, lay down, got up, walked, and ran without hesitation, and her right hip didn't hurt her again!

 Serissa recovering from hip surgery at the veterinary hospital.

Duncan's hindlimb weakness

Duncan, one of my Doberman pinschers, had geriatric-onset laryngeal paralysis and polyneuropathy (GOLPP). Before he turned 11 years old, he had larynx (voice box) surgery to prevent breathing problems. But as it occurs with this odd disease as it progresses, his hind legs weakened.

Duncan weighed 110 pounds, but he was easy for me to manage because he was tall! I'm tall, too, so our physiques worked well together. I bought him a fitted lifting harness and took him to weekly acupuncture treatments. He also got a minivan! Yes, I bought my dog a pre-owned, beat up minivan, and it was perfect. I removed the seats in the back and placed large rubber mats so he could more easily get in and out of the car for his frequent medical appointments.

Sam's tremor

Now I have Sam, my senior Anatolian shepherd. One day I detected a slight tremor in her hind leg while she was standing. It was barely noticeable, but I took a video. As months passed, her tremor became more noticeable. Then on one of our walks, I heard it. The dreaded toenail scrape on the cement. I knew that sound all too well because of my experience with Duncan. It meant Sam wasn't picking up one of her feet normally. I heard it about once every 10 minutes. I desperately wanted to pretend I didn't hear it, but I knew something was seriously wrong.

Typically a toenail scrape occurs because of a nerve problem that reduces the dog's awareness of foot placement. But not all diseases play by the rules, and if Sam had to have a problem, I was hoping for arthritis. Sam's radiographs showed that the tops of her thigh bones fit beautifully in her hip sockets (no hip dysplasia, hurrah!) and only minimal arthritis in her spine. Her neurologic examination results confirmed that she had delayed ability to correctly place her hind paws. I worried that she had degenerative myelopathy, a progressive spinal cord disease that tends to affect large-breed dogs.

Not long after, I heard Sam's toenail scrape once every minute during our walks, and periodically she would "knuckle over"— briefly walk on the top of one of her hind paws and not seem to notice it. She also started to "sink" in her hind end when she stood at her food or water bowl.

I explored Sam's condition further to identify what we were dealing with and to better set my expectations for what was to come. Magnetic resonance imaging (MRI) showed two abnormal spots within her spinal cord,

Sam's hindlegs. She doesn't sense that she's standing with her left paw knuckled over.

 Sam's hind end would "sink" as she stood at her bowl.

which affected her nerve function and explained her hindlimb weakness and mobility problems. Analysis of her cerebrospinal fluid (the fluid that surrounds the spinal cord and brain to provide protection and nutrients) showed no infection, so the next possibility was that she had cancer in her spinal cord. Spinal cord cancer is rare, but it can occur as a tumor that starts in the spinal cord or as cancer cells that have spread from elsewhere in the body (called *metastasis*). Cancer cells don't always show up in the spinal fluid.

To check other places where cancer may be hiding, Sam's next stop was the ultrasonography room. She had an abdominal ultrasound exam and needle biopsies of her spleen, liver, and a few lymph nodes to check for cancer cells. We found that Sam had lymphoma (cancer involving lymphocytes, one of the white blood cells involved in immunity) in her liver and spleen. This meant that the abnormal spots in her spinal cord were most likely lymphoma. Lymphoma can't be cured, but the cancer's progression can be slowed with chemotherapy and possibly with radiation therapy. So off to the veterinary oncologist we went!

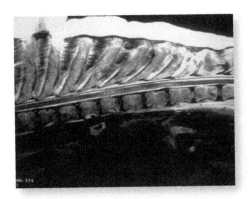

Sam's MRI revealed two lesions in her spinal cord (red arrows) that were likely cancer.

 Sam and I on the way to the veterinary speciality hospital, and Sam waiting patiently to see the oncologist.

When to see your veterinarian

Limping is an obvious sign of a mobility problem, but a dog's signs can be subtle, such as taking a little longer to get up from lying down or having a slight muscle tremor. Dogs may easily slip on a tile or wood floor when they rarely did before, not jump onto the bed or couch with the same energy (or stop jumping altogether), scrape a toenail while walking (like Sam!), or struggle to walk up stairs. Dogs who become grumpier or lash out may have pain associated with mobility troubles, or they may be afraid of not being able to move away as quickly. (Horwitz [1] 2020)

Keep an eye out for signs of weakness or wobbliness as your dog ages. The earlier you spot mobility issues, the sooner your veterinarian can find the cause and have a better opportunity to provide effective treatments to keep your dog strong and stable. Dogs with mobility issues may:

- Walk or run slower to greet you
- Climb or descend stairs slower
- "Bunny hop" while walking or running
- Be less enthusiastic about going on walks or playing
- Be less enthusiastic about social interactions with human or pet family members
- Spend more time sleeping

- Have decreased range of motion (are less flexible and show more stiffness)
- Hesitate to get up or lie down
- Be reluctant to walk on slippery surfaces
- Stop getting up to greet you
- Have trouble squatting or lifting their leg to eliminate
- "Freeze" when they see or stand on a surface that seems unsafe to them ("scary floor syndrome") (Robertson [1]) 2020)
- Pant excessively
- Circle more before lying down
- Favor one side (or the front limbs vs. the back limbs) while walking or sitting
- Eat or drink less because of pain or because their bowls are inconveniently located (e.g. dog must use stairs to access food or water)
- Repeatedly lick their front legs or tops of their paws (arthritis pain in the shoulder, elbow, or neck can be "referred" to the front paws, and dogs lick to soothe themselves) or a painful joint
- Have difficulty getting into the car, or on or off the couch or the bed
- Vocalize (yelp or growl) with certain movements
- Limp
- Be more irritable, aggressive, or fearful in response to certain stimuli or situations
- Stand in a sawhorse stance
- Exhibit leg or muscle tremors
- Drag toenails
- Knuckle over on paws while standing or walking
- Stumble or be otherwise unsteady
- Exhibit sinking in the hind end
- Have fecal incontinence (this is a sign of a nerve problem that may also affect mobility)
- Have difficulty keeping up on slow walks

Angel (a relative's dog who was later adopted by Dr. Sheilah Robertson as a geriatric when her care became intense) became progressively slower on walks.

It helps to take short video clips that demonstrate your dog's mobility troubles at home and share them with your veterinarian. Dogs often behave differently in an exam room, so their signs of discomfort may be less evident during a veterinary visit. (Robertson [3] 2020) If you are a gadget fan, Fitbit-like activity monitors are available for dogs that allow you to track changes in your dog's movement habits and objectively gauge their response to various treatments.

Common causes of mobility issues in senior dogs

Dozens of diseases or conditions cause mobility trouble. A broken leg or torn knee ligament not only causes short-term incapacity, it can lead to joint changes that result in long-term lameness. Fungal infections or disease-carrying ticks can also cause lameness. The mobility issues that most often affect geriatric dogs include broken or overgrown toenails, arthritis, obesity, degenerative myelopathy, intervertebral disk disease, other types of neuropathies (nerve diseases), cancer, and sarcopenia (muscle loss with aging).

Toenail troubles

Broken or overgrown toenails are painful and cause lameness. Regularly trim your dog's toenails to help prevent a toenail from catching on something and tearing or breaking. Overgrown toenails can also reduce your dog's traction on slippery floors, which could lead to a fall and further injury.

Arthritis

Arthritis (also called *osteoarthritis* and *degenerative joint disease*) means joint inflammation. It not only causes mobility problems, it is painful and can make dogs irritable. Arthritis is the number one cause of chronic pain in dogs. (Dowgray 2020) At least one out of five (20%) dogs will have arthritis in their lifetime. (Johnston 1997) Recent statistics suggest that up to 40% of dogs have arthritis. (Kirkby Shaw 2021) In people, 23% of adults age 18 and older have arthritis, and it is expected to increase to about 26% of the projected population by the year 2040. (CDC)

Joints are areas where two (or three) bones meet or join together, and most joints allow movement. Dogs have hundreds of joints, and there are three types:

- Fibrous joints are made of thick fibrous tissue; they don't allow movement and occur where bones of the skull meet.
- Cartilaginous joints contain cartilage and allow some movement between bones in the spine.

- Synovial joints (e.g. knee, hip, elbow, shoulder) are surrounded by a capsule that contains a lubricant called synovial fluid. These joints allow the most movement, and the ends of the bones that meet in synovial joints are covered in thin cartilage.

Changes that lead to arthritis

People and cats most often develop what's known as *primary arthritis*—arthritis that develops because of degenerative, wear-and-tear changes in the joints that occur with advanced age. Dogs are different, because they typically develop *secondary arthritis*—arthritis that stems from an underlying insult. (Kirkby Shaw 2021)

Regardless of the cause—whether it's injury, infection, overload, hereditary conditions, or degenerative changes—inflammation and other changes in the joints trigger thinning of the cartilage. Then the joint capsule, ligaments, and tissues around the joint may thicken to help stabilize the joint, and swelling from fluid buildup in the joint occurs. At this point, stiffness and pain enter the scene. Cartilage contains no nerves, so as more cartilage wears away, pain results from bone-on-bone friction.

Joint instability from inherited growth deformities, like hip or elbow dysplasia, and from knee problems, like cranial cruciate ligament injury (called an *anterior cruciate ligament* [or *ACL*] tear in people) or patella luxation (kneecap dislocation), are common problems that lead to arthritis in dogs. Being overweight is a big risk factor for arthritis in dogs. (Anderson 2020) At least 50% of dogs are obese, and most obese dogs have arthritis. (Kirkby Shaw 2021) That's a lot of dogs walking around with arthritis!

Identifying arthritis

To diagnose arthritis, veterinarians usually do physical and neurologic examinations and take radiographs. Dogs may also need blood tests or joint fluid evaluation. A test for a biomarker called lubricin may be available in the future to help veterinarians predict whether dogs will develop osteoarthritis. Lubricin is a protein that lubricates joint cartilage, and it increases in knee joint fluid after a cranial cruciate ligament rupture, but before signs of arthritis develop. (Wang 2020)

Hip and elbow dysplasia occur most commonly in large- or giant-breed dogs and can affect both elbows or both hips. Mobility issues especially develop if these young, large-breed dogs rapidly gain weight and grow too quickly, are over-active or underactive, or experience joint trauma. Even though these hereditary conditions are present at a young age, signs of mobility problems may not be seen until later in life when arthritis develops, such as happened with my dog Serissa. However, some veterinarians can perform special examinations—palpating for an Ortolani sign or obtaining PennHip radiographs—in puppies and young dogs to check for these conditions. Finding these problems early in life allows opportunity for the best corrective treatments.

Dogs who have joint instability from dysplasia, a knee injury, or a fracture that involves a joint, can develop arthritis in that joint if the instability is not treated in a timely manner with surgery and postoperative rehabilitation therapy. Infections that lead to arthritis can be treated with medications to clear the offending bug and stop ongoing joint damage, but initial joint damage will remain.

Treating arthritis

Sadly, no cure exists for arthritis once it's established, so earlier diagnosis and earlier intervention is best. But arthritis is very manageable. Veterinarians often recommend management options that work best together, such as weight control—which means staying on the skinny side of normal body condition—along with anti-inflammatory and pain medications, low-impact exercises such as walking and swimming (special note: no jumping down is allowed!), omega-3 fatty acids from fish oil, supplements such as polysulfated glycosaminoglycan (Adequan Canine) or others (including cannabidiol, or CBD), physical rehabilitation exercises, underwater treadmill therapy, massage, surgery, laser therapy, and acupuncture. Whew! Bottom line: For overweight or obese dogs who have arthritis, weight loss with a lifelong nutritional plan to maintain a lean body condition is the single most important therapy. For more information on how to tell if your dog is portly, see Chapter 9 "Body condition and nutrition: Helping senior dogs eat better and feel better."

Activity is key for all dogs with arthritis. So if dogs don't have another medical condition that precludes activity, no couch potatoes are allowed! Daily walks of 60 minutes or more provide more benefit than 20-minute walks a day. But work up to these long walks gradually if your dog isn't already accustomed to them, or you'll trigger stiffness and soreness.

A caveat: In general, playing fetch isn't recommended for dogs with arthritis. Racing out to the object, hard stops when reaching it, or landing after jumping up and catching the object are high-impact activities that overtax even healthy joints. But if your arthritic dog lives to retrieve, you may still gently play if you dial back your dog's duration of participation and level of joint exertion. Also talk with your veterinarian about whether increasing pain medications would help.

Joint support supplements that contain glucosamine abound, but studies reveal that glucosamine doesn't help dogs with arthritis much. If you'd like to give a joint supplement, talk with your veterinarian about their recommendations, and look for supplements that follow National Animal Supplement Council (NASC) and Current Good Manufacturing Practice (CGMP) guidelines. Two supplements that one veterinary surgeon recommended to me are MovoFlex (made by Virbac) and Flexadin Advanced (made by Vetoquinol).

In the future, treatment with anti-nerve growth factor monoclonal antibodies may be available to help manage osteoarthritis in dogs. (Enomoto 2019, Lascelles 2015) Nerve growth factor plays a role in painful conditions in adult animals, and monoclonal antibodies are molecules that mimic some of the body's natural disease-fighting abilities.

Obesity: Less food for thought

Being overweight can contribute to not only arthritis, but to mobility issues of all types and to other health problems in pets.

Dogs with limited mobility who are also overweight are more reluctant to exercise. So you'll need to gradually introduce a new or enhanced exercise regimen, and ask your veterinarian about supplements or medications to reduce your dog's discomfort so he can be more active and reach his target weight faster. (Lobprise [1] 2020) Pain-free exercise, along with environmental enrichment activities that promote appropriate food intake such as food puzzles or foraging activities also benefit your dog's overall attitude and general health.

Exercise is beneficial to boost weight loss and improve mobility, yet an obese dog's path to a healthy weight begins with her family dishing out less food and treats, or with serving a veterinary-prescribed food for weight loss. About 90% of weight control involves the amount of calories consumed, and about 10% involves calories burned through increased activity. Dog parents and other family members are completely in charge of helping their dogs get lean by limiting calories and helping them burn calories by staying active.

Degenerative myelopathy

As I mentioned earlier, initially I thought my dog Sam had degenerative myelopathy, a slowly progressive spinal cord disease of older dogs that leads to hind end weakness and paralysis. The cause is unknown, but a genetic mutation is suspected. Certain dog breeds are predisposed, including German shepherds, Siberian huskies, and collies, and several other breeds have a high risk of developing degenerative myelopathy. The disease has been compared to amyotrophic lateral sclerosis (ALS), a progressive degenerative nerve disease of the spinal cord and brain in people.

Many people confuse the signs of degenerative myelopathy in dogs with osteoarthritis or intervertebral disk disease (a spinal cord disease). The signs in large-breed dogs typically start at around 9 years of age (Coates 2010), and the early stage may cause only mild weakness. Pet parents often think their dogs simply get tired while standing.

The disease slowly progresses to far worse signs, including swaying when walking or standing, toe dragging and toenail scraping, toe knuckling, falling over easily, difficulty rising from lying down, severe hindlimb weakness and inability to walk, urinary and fecal incontinence, and, eventually, weakness of the front limbs. The disease does not appear to be painful, so if a dog shows signs of pain, he may have a different condition or an additional problem.

Diagnosing degenerative myelopathy can be challenging. It's based on the dog's breed, age, history, physical and neurologic examination findings, and results of diagnostic tests. Radiographs, MRI, tissue biopsies, DNA testing, and cerebrospinal fluid analysis may be recommended. The only way to confirm the diagnosis is by looking at a sample of the spinal cord under a microscope, which can only be done after the affected dog has died. Therefore, degenerative myelopathy is diagnosed by ruling out other diseases.

 Visual evidence of a dog's toe drag in the snow.

No cure exists for degenerative myelopathy, so slowing the disease progression is key. Weight loss, physical rehabilitation exercises, walking, and swimming are all vital components. Massage may also be helpful and can be incorporated into a physical rehabilitation program. Physical rehabilitation therapy may slow the disease progression. In a study, dogs with degenerative myelopathy who received intensive physical rehabilitation lived longer (255 days) compared with dogs who had moderate physical rehabilitation (130 days) or no physical rehabilitation (55 days). (Kathmann 2006) New research indicates that physical rehabilitation coupled with laser therapy also holds promise for slowing the disease progression. (Miller 2020)

Medications or supplements have been studied as potential treatments for degenerative myelopathy, including corticosteroids, aminocaproic acid (inhibits

 Part of Duncan's physical rehabilitation therapy included this home cavaletti setup, which are elevated poles that dogs must step over to pass.

the breakdown of a protein called fibrin and potentially slows inflammation), N-acetylcysteine (an antioxidant that may protect nerve cells), methionine (an amino acid), and vitamins B, C, and E. Unfortunately, none of these have shown benefit. (Coates 2007, Polizopoulou 2008)

For now it seems that dogs with degenerative myelopathy should be kept as active as possible, because staying active appears to be the best way to slow the disease. To avoid overexertion or injury, it's crucial to follow a veterinary rehabilitation program tailored to the individual dog's abilities. After nerve injury in people, evidence backs using a combination of rehabilitation therapies to promote quicker and better recoveries. (Frank 2018) A general recommendation for managing dogs recovering from many types of neurologic disorders suggests that a combination of therapies may be most beneficial, such as combining a physical rehabilitation program with neuromuscular electrical stimulation (using a low-frequency current to trigger a nerve to induce muscle contraction) and acupuncture. (Frank 2018)

The main focus of treatment is on slowing the progression of degenerative myelopathy because, sadly, this disease results in complete paralysis. Pressure sores and fecal and urinary incontinence may become an issue in the later stages of the disease, and dog parents often elect euthanasia for their pets related to quality-of-life concerns.

Intervertebral disk disease

Sitting between the bones in the spine (called *vertebrae*) are "shock absorbers" made of cartilage called *intervertebral disks*. As dogs age, the disks may degenerate and lose their cushioning capacity. They become stiff and may slip out of position (herniate) and put pressure on the spinal cord. Depending on the amount or force of the pressure, a sudden or gradual onset of back or neck pain, limb weakness, and paralysis occurs.

Intervertebral disk disease is the most common spinal cord disease in dogs. It occurs most often in middle-aged dogs, especially in French bulldogs, dachshunds, basset hounds, shih tzus, Pekingese, and American cocker spaniels. (Shores 2014) Older large-breed dogs may also be affected.

The earlier the problem is identified and treatment is started, the better the chances of recovery. Diagnosis involves physical and neurologic examinations plus radiographs or a computed tomography (CT) scan or MRI. It may be necessary to inject dye into the space around the spinal cord (called a *myelogram*) to identify the precise location of the diseased disk or disks.

Depending on the disease severity, medical treatment (strict activity restriction for up to four weeks, pain medications, a muscle relaxant, and possibly acupuncture) or surgery (performed by a veterinary neurosurgeon) is needed.

Most dogs will need help urinating during their recovery process, so pet parents must express their dog's bladder at least three times a day. (Shores 2014)

Physical rehabilitation is also highly recommended. Depending on the dog's needs and pet parent's abilities, it may entail simple exercises to do at home, floor or swimming activities at a veterinary physical rehabilitation center, massage therapy, laser therapy, or acupuncture. (Shores 2014)

Other neuropathies

A disease or injury that affects the nerves outside the spinal cord and brain is referred to as *peripheral neuropathy*. And depending on whether the damaged nerves control sensory, motor, or autonomic (involuntary) processes, an affected dog will have sensation, movement, or gland or organ dysfunction that results in a variety of symptoms. If more than one type of peripheral nerve is affected, it's called *polyneuropathy*.

Because this chapter focuses on weak and wobbly dogs, I'll mention the nerve problems that affect mobility. They're called *motor neuropathies*. These disorders may be acute (sudden onset and short-term) or chronic (slowly progressive and long-term). Dogs with peripheral motor neuropathy may have muscle atrophy, weakness, reduced or absent muscle reflexes, little to no muscle tone, or paralysis. Often the rear legs are affected.

Some peripheral motor neuropathies are caused by genetic abnormalities, such as dancing Doberman disease (an uncommon disorder that causes muscles in the hind legs to flex involuntarily). Lyme disease, a bacterial infection spread through tick bites, can cause peripheral motor neuropathy. Chronic diseases such as diabetes or geriatric-onset laryngeal paralysis and polyneuropathy (GOLPP) are among other causes.

If the underlying cause is curable, such as an infection, then the nerve dysfunction may be reversible. But often with geriatric-onset neuropathies, no cure exists. The pet's signs can be managed while attempting to slow the disease progression, as is done for dogs who have degenerative myelopathy.

Cancer

When an older large-breed dog suddenly develops lameness that affects only one leg, my mind jumps to osteosarcoma. It's the most common bone cancer in large dogs that typically affects their long bones. Radiographs and biopsy help confirm the diagnosis. No cure exists for osteosarcoma, but amputation is suggested to remove the source of pain and give dogs a better quality of life. Dogs with three legs do well and can be active and happy!

Spinal tumors and brain tumors can also cause mobility problems. Cancer in the lymph nodes (lymphoma) creates mobility issues if it spreads to the spinal cord (as it did in my dog Sam) or causes greatly enlarged lymph nodes that interfere with movement.

Sarcopenia and cachexia

As I discuss in the chapter on body condition and nutrition, sarcopenia is muscle loss that occurs with aging, while cachexia is muscle loss caused by diseases such as congestive heart failure or cancer. Muscle loss hinders strength and contributes to mobility problems. Geriatric dogs who have chronic diseases may have both sarcopenia and cachexia. Remember that muscle loss is not as easy to spot in dogs who are overweight.

My clients who have dogs with mobility issues often ask me to prescribe medications to alleviate their dogs' pain. In some cases I find that the dog doesn't appear to be in pain or have arthritis, but they do have sarcopenia.

In dogs with cachexia, the most effective way to help them is to treat the underlying illness and provide supportive care.

Supportive care for dogs with sarcopenia or cachexia helps them stay strong, and may include:

- Exercise! Increasing activity through exercise that includes resistance training may slow or reverse muscle loss. (Freeman 2018) Resistance exercises increase strength and muscle mass, and endurance exercises build aerobic power generated by the heart and lungs. A three-day-a-week balanced resistance and endurance exercise program is physically and mentally beneficial for dogs. (Perkins Johnson 2017)
- Myostatin blockers (myostatin is a protein that muscle cells make to limit their growth). Two different myostatin-reducing agents have been evaluated in dogs (Freeman 2015) (White 2020); one is available as MYOS Canine Muscle Formula (a fertilized egg yolk product). I gave my dog Sam this product.
- Capromorelin, an appetite stimulant approved for use in dogs (called Entyce). It's a ghrelin receptor enhancer. Ghrelin is the "hunger hormone" and ghrelin also increases two other hormones that can affect muscle mass: growth hormone and insulin-like growth factor-1. (Freeman 2018)
- Omega-3 fatty acids, which may help reduce inflammation, decrease muscle loss, and improve appetite. (Freeman 2018)
- Optimal nutrition that is formulated for the animal's life stage, or feeding a therapeutic diet to manage a chronic disease, if indicated, along with using assisted feeding techniques such as placing a feeding tube, if needed. (Freeman 2018)

Until veterinarians know more about the optimal approach to combating or reversing sarcopenia and cachexia, it appears that an exercise program tailored to an individual dog's needs and limitations, along with diet changes or supplements, if needed, are excellent options. Your veterinarian can suggest an appropriate exercise program and determine whether your dog may benefit from additional therapies.

Helping senior dogs move along

I could dedicate an entire book to mobility issues in dogs, so the diseases and conditions I outline above are the most common ones I encounter in senior dogs. Regardless of the cause, managing these dogs, whether they're large or small, can be a challenge.

In one study, pet parents of dogs with osteoarthritis in the United Kingdom reported that their dogs' mobility limitations and treatment needs gradually limited their own lifestyles. But owners expressed that they were strongly bonded with their dogs and dedicated to giving ongoing care. Owners also indicated they were highly motivated to improve their dogs' mobility and reduce the effects of their dogs' condition on their own lives—but many pet parents were unsure how to do this. (Belshaw 2020) Sound familiar? These findings mirror my experiences with my clients and my personal experiences with my dogs. In the remaining sections of this chapter, I am grateful to be able to share with you what I have learned about managing dogs' mobility issues.

Pain medications

Relieving pain that often accompanies short- or long-term mobility problems in dogs is a big component of managing these dogs, along with managing their underlying disease. Pain relief not only helps dogs want to stay active, it improves their quality of life. Chronic, unrelieved pain causes emotional distress, along with physical changes in the spinal cord that heighten pain sensation, making pain more difficult to treat.

It's important to be able to recognize signs of pain in your dog so you can let your veterinarian know to make appropriate treatment adjustments. For a closer look at signs of pain, see Chapter 21 "Pain: If only our dogs could talk about discomfort, malaise, anxiety, and suffering". Keep in mind that arthritis and other types of mobility-associated pain may flare up periodically, so adjustments in pain medications will likely often be needed.

A sneak peek at a critical take-home from the chapter on pain: Never give your own pain medication to your dog, keep on schedule with the medications your veterinarian prescribes, and tell your veterinarian about any other medications or supplements your dog is receiving.

Physical rehabilitation

Veterinary physical rehabilitation has become an important component of helping dogs who have a wide range of mobility issues. Through a variety of exercises, treatments, and massage, rehabilitation works to improve dogs' flexibility, range of motion, muscle strength, balance, and endurance. The goals of veterinary physical rehabilitation are to stabilize, renew, and support a dog's optimal function and quality of life in relation to mobility, while minimizing the signs and limitations caused by their condition, disease, or injury. (Perkins Johnson 2017)

I cannot say enough about physical rehabilitation exercises, underwater treadmill therapy, laser therapy, massage, and acupuncture to help dogs who have mobility issues. Starting treatments sooner rather than later is advisable. As Dick Van Dyke has advised people of all ages, the secret to keeping moving is to keep moving! I believe this is true for dogs as well. While trying these therapies is worthwhile at any stage, waiting until mobility is badly compromised makes managing it more difficult. I've included resources at the end of this chapter to find people to help you develop just the right physical rehabilitation program for your dog.

 Sam's rehabilitation therapy included balance balls, which help muscle strength and limb position awareness.

CAREGIVER TIPS AND HOME HACKS

Altering the environment and using mobility aids as needed so that dogs with mobility issues can more easily navigate their home (and their routine excursions) go a long way in improving their quality of life (and yours). It also keeps dogs safer by helping to prevent injuries and extra veterinary visits.

SLIP SLIDING AWAY

I cringe when I visit someone's home and see a dog lying in the middle of a tile or wood floor who then anxiously and repeatedly tries and miserably fails to get up. It reminds me of when I was 5 years old and trying to ice skate. And once the dog stands up, they slip, slide, wobble, and sway as they make their way to me. And this reminds me of when I was 15 years old and trying to walk in tall heels for the first time—something I have yet to master!

Slippery surfaces are a huge downfall for all dogs with mobility issues. The more slippery the floor is, the more afraid your dog will be to walk on it. And this means they get less exercise, and they have a higher risk of falling or sliding awkwardly and tweaking a muscle or ligament in the process.

Make 'em stick

The best way to handle a slippery surface is to pave a path that helps dogs get a grip, walk confidently, and remain safe.

FLOORING

- **Yoga mats.** I love yoga mats, but not for yoga, of course! Lining slippery floors with yoga mats provides wonderful support for dogs. Bonus: They are easy to clean! You can purchase large rolls and cut the mats to fit your needs. Also place yoga mats in showers and tubs to keep dogs surefooted during baths.

 Serissa can't get traction on the tile floor and has splayed out while enjoying her treat (my cat Lilu stands steady).

- **Bath mats/rugs.** Because most bathroom floors have nonporous surfaces like tile, bath mats usually have a non-skid rubber underside. Like yoga mats, you can place them on slippery pathways throughout your home, but the topside is fluffy and comfy for dogs to lie on. Also place bath mats in the back of your car or wherever your dog rides to help keep him stable during drives.

 Murdog's mom put bath mats in many areas of their house.

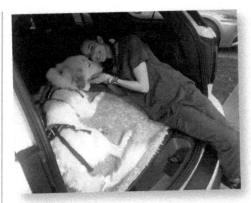

Sam had a sturdy, comfy grip on a bath mat during her frequent car rides to see Gillian for rehabilitation therapy.

- **Ruggable.com.** This website has beautiful, water-resistant, stain-resistant rugs in all different sizes and colors that feature a non-slip rubber bottom and a machine-washable rug top. They keep dogs steady and protect hardwood floors!
- **Gym flooring.** These interlocking, square rubber floor tiles fit together like a puzzle and are popular in gyms and children's play areas. They're squishy and comfortable to lie on. **https://www.greatmats.com**
- **Gritty stickers.** Similar to those '70s era, non-slip, flower-power stickers for the shower, non-slip stickers are great for your outdoor steps. Sticker strips are also available online.

Remember to place a mat at your dog's food and water bowls so she can stay steady on all four (or three!) feet while she eats and drinks. For slippery stairs and landings, place a carpet runner on a staircase and a non-slip mat at the top and bottom.

When it comes to flooring, the key is to buy heavier products. If a bath mat or area rug is flimsy, you may trip over it. It must also have high-quality

Sam at her bowl before I placed a yoga mat.

Sam at her bowl after I placed a yoga mat.

 Norrin and Sam benefit from non-slip mats and area rugs placed over the slippery tile.

rubber backing so it stays put. And you need to cover all your slippery floors. Let's face it, your house may not look exquisitely decorated while you're making accommodations for your geriatric dog, but who cares?!

FOOTWEAR

- **Nail grips.** One of my veterinarian friends created Dr. Buzby's ToeGrips for Dogs. Place these ingenious little rubber rings over the tips of your dog's nails. When dogs bear weight, their toenails naturally extend outward to contact the ground, and these grippers provide traction! They are inexpensive and easy to apply! Check out the website for great information and videos: **https://toegrips.com/**

 This geriatric pug sports Dr. Buzby's ToeGrips on all toenails.

- **Paw pad coating.** PawFriction was co-developed by a veterinarian to improve dogs' mobility on slick surfaces. The product includes a nontoxic adhesive you apply to your dog's foot pads. Then you gently press the paw into a tray of nontoxic granules or sprinkle the granules onto the foot pads. The granules create a gritty coating on the bottom of dogs' paws to provide traction wherever they go. **https://pawfriction.com/**

- **Adhesive foot pads.** Type "adhesive pads dogs" into an internet search engine, and you will find many options for helping dogs get a grip about the house. I have tried these temporary stick-on traction pads, and they have helped Sam. They only last about a day, are very easy to apply, and, once they get wet, tend to roll up so you can gently peel them off.

- **Grooming.** Trim your dog's nails and keep them short! This can be the least expensive (but not always the easiest) measure to help keep your dog steady. And trim any long fur between their foot pads and toes, because otherwise it's like they're wearing slippery socks!

 Maple is receiving a PawFriction application.

 Sam getting adhesive foot pads applied (they can also be trimmed to fit).

 These nails need a good trim!

 Sam gets a wee shave of her foot fur.

 Serissa's boots were comfy enough for her to snooze in.

Two boots were sufficient for Serissa to stay on track.

- **Boots, booties and socks.** I have become a bootie connoisseur! (I want to say "bootie queen" but that just sounds wrong!) I LOVE booties for dogs, but they are not all designed the same, and some work better for particular problems. Depending on your dog's mobility issue, your dog may need one, two, or four booties or socks.

  o **Boots.** If your dog slips on your floors but does not have muscle weakness or toe dragging or knuckling, I recommend Ruffwear dog boots (**https://ruffwear.com**). They're available in different sizes and colors and are made for various types of weather conditions and activities. My dog Serissa wore these and, after a few initial "donkey

 Reggie needed 4-wheel-drive boots.

 Sam's first boots became too heavy as her hindlimb weakness progressed.

kicks," she adapted well to wearing them. My dog Sam can't wear these because they are too heavy for her and she drags her toes, so these boots trip her up.

- o **Booties and socks.** Many options are available, so choose booties or socks that securely stay on your dog's feet, are not too heavy, and can breathe a little. For indoor use, I recommend OrthoPets Slip Grip Slippers: **https://orthopets.com/product/orthopets-slip-grip-slippers/**

Remember to take these along when you visit a friend's home, the veterinary clinic, or a pet store so your dog can stride with added confidence.

Does the shoe fit?

Always be careful not to strap booties or socks on too tightly. I have seen dogs with tissue damage caused by their pet parents pulling or wrapping the hook-and-loop fastener (Velcro) straps too tight. Also remove booties or socks at least twice a day to let your dog's feet breathe.

SPECIAL FOOTWEAR: FOR DOGS WITH TOE DRAGGING OR PAW KNUCKLING

Toe dragging or paw knuckling usually occurs because of a nerve problem, and incoordination and weakness are likely to eventually follow. My dog Sam has these issues now. My suggestions are:

 Sam gets her paw measured, which should be done while she's standing.

- **Nail caps.** Products such as Soft-Paws are applied to completely cover each toenail. They help prevent the grinding down of the nail against the pavement. I wish I had applied these caps to Sam's toenails sooner! Sam's two middle toenails on each hind paw have been worn too short to apply the caps now. Many products are available and you can select the size that best fits your dog. You can easily trim the caps before you put them on, too. Heed my warning and use these

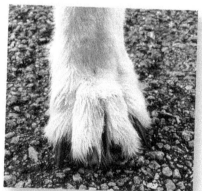 Sam's knuckling, or "toe flip" progressed to both hindlimbs as her spinal cord cancer progressed.

 Sam's middle two toenails on her hind feet were reduced to a bloody pulp because of her toe dragging and knuckling over. Not good!

 Sam models her no-knuckling sock.

sooner rather than later! Dr. Buzby's ToeGrips for Dogs also protect the nails.

- **Training equipment.** Before purchasing these products, talk with your veterinarian or rehabilitation specialist about whether they are appropriate for your dog and how best to use them. If used inappropriately, they can cause more damage. The Rear No-knuckling Training Sock (**https://www.handicappedpets.com/no-knuckling-training-sock/**) is primarily used during physical rehabilitation exercises or for two- to five-minute sessions at home as prescribed by a veterinarian or rehabilitation specialist. The OrthoPets Toe-Up Device with Boot is another option: **https://orthopets.com/product/orthopets-toe-up-device/**

  o Another trick that Sam's physical rehabilitation specialist suggested was to occasionally put a hair scrunchie (an elastic band covered with gathered fabric) around each hind foot, which would send signals to stimulate her brain to be more aware of her feet.

HARNESSES

- In general, wearing a harness is more comfortable and safer for a geriatric dog than wearing a collar. A harness helps you assist a geriatric dog with mobility issues, is safer for a dog who has laryngeal paralysis, and shields

 Sam with scrunchies on her back feet.

dogs from the potential adverse effects of pulling against a collar, such as increases in internal eye pressure and neck pain related to osteoarthritis. (Robertson [1] 2020)

I have tried many different harnesses for my dogs, and I recommend only one, the Help 'Em Up Harness: **https://helpemup.com/**. It is by far the best harness and worth every penny. (Remember, I don't receive monetary or other compensation from companies whose products I recommend in this book!) For dogs with mobility issues, it's best to use a harness that stays on your dog for the majority of the day or night so you can quickly assist them, and this harness allows that. Sling-type harnesses work only for temporary situations.

The Help 'Em Up Harness is wonderful for front and hind end mobility issues. It's built with high-quality materials, is thoughtfully designed, and comes in a configuration that fits both female and male dogs so they can urinate without soiling the harness. They even make a special version for male dogs whose penis is located farther back on the abdomen. The harness also has optional walking accessories and a shoulder strap to help distribute the dog's weight and make lifting easier for the owner. With this harness, I can easily lift Sam, who is 70 pounds, into the back of my SUV without additional assistance.

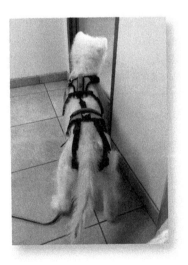

 Serissa, and Smudge modeling their Help 'Em Up Harnesses.

WHEELCHAIRS

A dog may need a wheelchair or cart when their mobility is so badly affected that they can barely walk or are completely paralyzed. Dogs may also benefit from using a wheelchair so they can take longer walks with you as they did before. It can help keep up their strength and improve their quality of life—and help you maintain yours!

Wheelchair manufacturers that I suggest include Eddie's Wheels for Pets (**https://www.eddieswheels.com/**) (where I bought Sam's wheelchair), Walkin' Pets Walkin' Wheels (**https://handicappedpets.com**), and K9 Carts (**https://k9carts.com**).

It's extremely important that you work with the manufacturer or veterinary rehabilitation therapist to get the best fit possible. They will also walk you through how to get your dog accustomed to the chair so she isn't anxious in it. Sam's rehabilitation therapist fit her for her chair, and it's perfect!

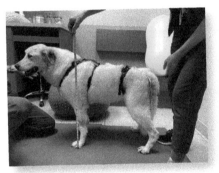

Sam being measured for, then raring to go in her stylin' new wheels!

STROLLERS AND WAGONS

It's not uncommon to see small dogs in baby strollers, usually because they simply cannot walk the same distance as their owner or at the same speed. But larger dogs with limited mobility can take advantage of strollers or wagons so that they can continue to enjoy the scents in the air and the wind in their fur, even if their owner does all the work!

Walking strollers, jogging strollers, wagons, and bike trailers are all great options so you can stay active and not have to leave your workout buddy behind when you get out to exercise. Big sturdy wheels and the ability to lower one side of the "cabin" (so the dog can easily get in and out or have a better view) are recommended.

Me and my client and friend Grace, who uses a stroller for her two little ones.

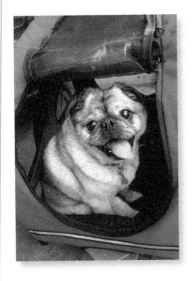

 Reggie loves taking rides in his bike trailer.

Angel's wagon is a garden cart from the hardware store.

Angel gets out periodically to walk next to her wagon.

 These two senior friends have a bike trailer all their own!

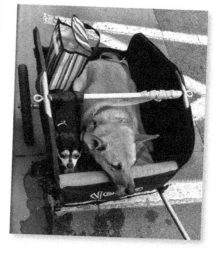

Good options include:

- West Marine Folding Wagon with Tailgate **https://www.westmarine.com/buy/west-marine--folding-wagon-with-tailgate--19290220**
- Dutch Dog Design Doggyride Novel Dog Stroller **https://www.dutchdogdesign.com/**
- Pet Safe Happy Ride Aluminum Dog Bike Trailer **https://store.petsafe.net/happy-ride-aluminum-dog-bicycle-trailer**
- Garden Carts (available at Tractor Supply or Home Depot). Be sure to add cushioning to make it a comfy ride!
- Radio Flyer Build-A-Wagon **https://www.radioflyer.com/build-a-wagon.html**

STEPS AND RAMPS

A wide variety of pet steps and dog ramps are available to help your dog reach the bed, couch, or car—or you can build your own! Ramps can also be used as an alternative to the stairs around your home. The key is to make sure the ramp or steps are not too steep, so keep in mind that a more gradual incline takes up more room. Alpha Paw offers sturdy, adjustable dog ramps: **https://www.alphapaw.com**

Also make sure your dog does not struggle to walk up or down any of the steps you have in or near your home. Dogs with mobility issues can severely injure themselves, even on only one step. For example, if the step down from your front or back door is steep, place a short slip-resistant bath

step in front of the door as a "transition" step. These have rubber feet and a rubber top to provide stability and good traction.

If your steps are too steep for your dog, consider a ramp instead, placed next to or over the steps. Ramps with raised edges along the sides are especially helpful to keep your dog on the correct path and discourage him from jumping off.

 A slip-resistant bath step like this one can be used in various places around the home to help dogs get to where they need to be. Angel uses hers to get out on the patio.

 Reggie's ramp with artificial turf and side walls keeps him safe, comfortable, and independent.

Dog ramps for the car can be tricky because not all dogs appreciate these, especially if they've been accustomed to simply jumping in and out of the car their entire lives. Sam taught me that hard lesson! I have an SUV, and the ramps I tried were too steep for her liking, so she simply jumped off of them. I even tried backing up my car to the curb to reduce the ramp's incline angle, and she still gave me the stink eye! I wish I had started training her to use a ramp when she still had confident mobility.

Unfortunately, Sam was so uninclined to use the car ramp that I scrapped the training efforts as soon as I bought her a Help 'Em Up Harness!

Keep in mind the physics of going uphill and downhill for our four-legged friends (or three-legged!). As they walk uphill, most of their weight shifts to their hind end. And when they walk downhill, their weight shifts to the front end. Weakness or pain in either area can still make it difficult for a dog to use a ramp, so help them with a harness if needed.

 One of Sam's pet peeves was the ramp to my car!

Ramp and step training

To train a dog to use a ramp, start by placing it flat on the ground and use treats or toys to entice them to walk on it—like a wide balance beam. Do this for one week. Then create a slight incline by placing a brick under one end. Teach them to walk on the raised ramp until they are comfortable. Then prop one end on stairs to increase the incline and teach them to use that. Continue to increase the incline until your dog is using the ramp to get where they need to be or to enter and exit your car.

Similarly, use treats or another of your dog's favorite enticements to train them to use dog stairs. Place a treat at the base of the stairs, and when your dog takes that, place a treat on the first step. Repeat this until your dog comfortably takes a treat off the first step. Then place a treat on the first and the second step. Practice until your dog comfortably stands on or walks up each step and takes the treats from each one. Provide support or position them correctly on the steps as needed. Remember to reward at

 A short step stool covered with a bath mat can help your dog get in and out of the car.

the top—your dog should get a treat for standing fully on the bed or couch. Repeat this process to train your dog to comfortably walk back down each step. You can gradually decrease the treats and reward only at the top or bottom of the stairs. Once your dog is fully comfortable, reward them at random intervals for using the steps to help hold their interest.

MISCELLANEOUS MOBILITY CONSIDERATIONS

- **Bedding.** Cushy or fluffy dog beds are comfy but can be difficult to walk on. If a dog bed is too soft, a dog with mobility issues may struggle to get in and out of it. Orthopedic dog beds and mattresses need to be comfy yet provide adequate support. Heated dog beds may also be helpful for some. Just be sure your dog can freely move off of it and has another comfy sleep option if they prefer. Water-resistant baby "nests" are appropriate for some small dogs.

- o If your dog is bedridden, be vigilant about warding off pressure sores—these can develop on your dog's elbows, shoulders, hocks, knees, hips, and head. Help your dog turn over—from one side, then to the middle, then to the other side—so they can rest in a different position every two or three hours. Use memory foam pads under bony contact points. Pressure sores are uncomfortable and can become irritated and infected.

- **Access.** If your dog likes to look out windows but is unable to do so, make a safe perch for them to get up to so they can still enjoy scouting their territory!

 After Andy had spinal surgery, his family made him a special bed with a view (they called it Andy's deck) and wide, low, carpeted platforms that he could easily climb.

- **Safety.** Sometimes dogs with mobility issues can get into difficult situations. Create a safe spot where you can leave them unattended when

 Sam sometimes even gets stuck on her bed. It's crucial that she can wear her harness at all times so we can quickly fix her position.

necessary and where they won't get hurt if they fall or get stuck.

- **Food and water bowls.** Elevating a dog's bowls can reduce neck and back pressure and strain.

 Sam seems more comfortable eating from an elevated bowl, and a peanut ball gives her extra stability and comfy support.

For dogs who sink in the hind end while eating, a peanut ball helps keep them steady.

- **Pheromones.** These calming chemical messengers delivered via room diffusers, sprays, and collars can help alleviate anxiety in dogs (e.g. Adaptil). (Robertson [4] 2020)
- **Emergency pit stops.** Consider training your dog to use puppy pads, or place them near or en route to the door or doggie litter box in case they can no longer hold it as long to make it to their toileting area. Magic Pee Pads by Alpha Paw (**https://alphapaw.com**) are one option, and many pet retailers carry others.
- **Ice packs.** Icing arthritic joints is great after activity such as playing a gentle game of fetch. Use the blue flexible type and keep them in place (NEVER place them directly on the skin; wrap them in a dish towel or pillowcase) for at least five minutes and ideally for 15 to 20 minutes. You can also wrap an ACE bandage around an elbow to provide additional compression. You can make your own flexible ice pack by mixing two parts water and one part rubbing alcohol in a freezer bag, and place it inside another freezer bag and then in the freezer. Don't use bags of frozen corn or peas because they contain too much air and aren't cold enough to penetrate the tissues.
- **Hygiene.** Inevitably, dogs with mobility issues will have hygiene issues, especially if they have fecal or urinary incontinence or if they cannot posture properly to eliminate. My dog Sam can posture, but she quickly tires and stumbles or falls and sometimes lands in her poop!

To help reduce the mess, give a sanitary haircut by trimming the fur around the areas where urine or feces can linger, especially for medium- or long-haired dogs.

Use a peanut ball (peanut-shaped stability or exercise balls often used in physical rehabilitation) inflated to the appropriate size to support your dog during clean-ups and baths (but do not use a peanut ball if your dog is recovering from abdominal surgery). Place a yoga mat beneath your dog and the peanut ball to provide extra paw traction. (Robertson [1] 2020)

Keep pet wipes or unscented hypoallergenic baby wipes handy.

Use puppy pads, perhaps along with baby changing pads, to help keep incontinent dogs clean and comfortable and their beds dry.

 Sam's tail eventually became paralyzed, so after she peed, it would drag in the puddle. We needed wet wipes all the time!

Dogs with fecal incontinence are more susceptible to urinary tract infections. Help them keep their rear end clean and keep an eye out for signs of a urinary tract infection, such as urine accidents in the house, asking to go out more often, or urinating small amounts frequently.

Ending on a good note

End-of-life decisions for dogs struggling with mobility issues are especially hard, because oftentimes dogs are still happy and enjoying some aspects of life and eating well. I fully empathize with you if you are in this position because I'm in the same spot with my dog Sam. Sometimes I wish my decision to euthanize her will be easier and clear-cut because she will be obviously sicker. But that is me selfishly not wanting to have to grapple with the decision. I don't really want Sam to be sick.

I know that when I say goodbye, Sam will get the biggest pancakes and cupcakes meal she ever dreamt of. And I'll know that I'm sending my girl to heaven where she'll run around in the clouds without any trouble! She may even bump into Duncan and Serissa!

Questions for your veterinarian

- What examinations or tests will my dog need?
- What can I expect to happen with my dog's condition? Will my dog regain normal mobility or activity levels again?
- Will my dog benefit from surgery?
- Is my dog overweight or obese? (Take no offense if the answer is "yes.")
- Has my dog lost muscle mass?
- Will diet adjustments help my dog?
- What types of environmental alterations will my dog need?
- What types of exercise or environmental enrichment activities will help my dog?
- Will my dog benefit from pain medications?
- How will I know whether my dog's pain medications are working?
- Will nutritional or other types of supplements help my dog?
- Will my dog benefit from veterinary physical rehabilitation?
- Do you offer physical rehabilitation services? If not, will you refer me to a veterinary physical rehabilitation practice or telemedicine service?
- Do you provide special padded bedding for my dog who has arthritis or mobility issues while my dog stays here?
- If my dog will be anesthetized for a procedure (for example, a professional dental cleaning), how can you ensure her position will be comfortable so she's not stiff and sore when she recovers?
- Can my dog be scheduled on a day when he can have a morning appointment and be discharged soon after? (So he doesn't have to stay in the clinic all day.)

 RESOURCES AND READING RECOMMENDATIONS

- Canine Arthritis Resources & Education website: **https://caninearthritis.org/**
- Assessing muscle condition in dogs and cats: **https://vetnutrition.tufts.edu/2017/11/mcs/**
- Assessing body condition, muscle condition, and nutrition in dogs and cats: World Small Animal Veterinary Association Nutrition Toolkit **https://wsava.org/wp-content/uploads/2020/05/WSAVA-Global -Nutrition-Toolkit-English.pdf**
- Pet amputation information: Tripawds **https://tripawds.com/**
- American Association of Rehabilitation Veterinarians **https://rehabvets.org/**

- American College of Veterinary Sports Medicine and Rehabilitation — Search for a specialist: **https://vsmr.site-ym.com/search/custom.asp?id=5595**
- Canine Arthritis Management website: **https://caninearthritis.co.uk/**
- Facebook group for families with dogs that have disabilities: **https://www.facebook.com/groups/LivingwithDogswithDisabilities**

CHAPTER 18:

Balance:
Is the room spinning?

"As long as the world is turning and spinning, we're gonna be dizzy and we're gonna make mistakes."

— MEL BROOKS

My furry niece Kalick, a senior Labrador retriever, had the life! She held reign in my sister's house, and the lounge chairs by the swimming pool were always covered in her golden fur. One morning my sister, Sharon, called me in a calm panic. "Kalick can barely get up, and she has a head tilt! What's going on?"

I knew that Kalick sometimes had mobility troubles because she had arthritis in her hips and elbows, but this sudden episode plus her head tilt led me down a different diagnostic path. I suspected Kalick had vestibular disease—a problem

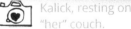
Kalick, resting on "her" couch.

with her balance system. My first inquiry: "When Kalick gets up, does she stumble like she's drunk?" Sharon said yes. I followed up with, "Are her eyes moving back and forth quickly?" Sharon said no. I headed to my sister's house to evaluate Kalick.

Kalick was conscious but not her normal jovial self. She seemed more comfortable lying down and didn't want to lift her head. When I finally got her to stand, she acted like a drunken pirate and she held

231

her head tilted to the right. Her right upper eyelid drooped. I briefly discussed vestibular disease with Sharon and encouraged her to take Kalick to my veterinary hospital for tests to check whether anything else might explain her signs.

We have *rocks* in our heads?

The balance system, otherwise known as the vestibular system, tells our dogs (and us!) which way is up. It senses head position and coordinates eye and body movements. It allows the brain and body to respond to gravity and positional changes to maintain posture, keep balance, and move steadily. This complex system has two main segments: peripheral and central.

The *peripheral vestibular system* sits within the inner ear and contains canals (called *semicircular canals*) and tiny organs (known as the *utricle* and *saccule*) that together are called the *vestibular apparatus*. This apparatus senses motion and sends signals to the brain by way of a nerve called *cranial nerve VIII*, or the *vestibulocochlear nerve*.

The vestibular apparatus senses rotational motion because fluid (called *endolymph*) within the semicircular canals shifts and triggers special receptors called *hair cells* that send nerve impulses to the brain. It also senses linear motion and forces of gravity because the utricle and saccule contain tiny crystals made of calcium and protein called *otoconia* or *otoliths* ("ear stones"). These "rocks" are attached to a membrane (called an *otolithic membrane)* that puts pressure on the special hair cells to send signals to the brain. (Casale 2020, Rouse 1984)

The *central vestibular system* is associated with the cerebellum (the hind portion of the brain) and the brainstem (which sits at the base of the brain and connects the cerebellum to the spinal cord). This system receives the inner ear's signals and sends information back to the body to coordinate the movements that maintain posture, position, and balance.

Not knowing which way is up

Vestibular disease is a disorder of the vestibular system and it most often affects older dogs. It's also known as *old dog vestibular disease* and *vertigo* in our canine friends, and in people it's called *benign paroxysmal positional vertigo* (which means self-limiting, sudden dizziness that's triggered by certain head positions). In people it's most common in women over age 50.

If vestibular disease stems from a problem in the brain such as cancer, an infection, trauma, or a stroke, it's called *central vestibular disease*. A stroke can be caused by problems such as high blood pressure, brain bleeding or blood clots, or kidney, thyroid, or adrenal gland diseases. Hypothyroidism (a thyroid gland disease in which insufficient thyroid hormones are produced) has been associated with both central and peripheral vestibular disease in dogs. (Higgins 2006, Orlandi 2020, Jaggy 1994)

Peripheral vestibular disease is more common than central vestibular disease. It stems most often from an unknown cause (this is called *idiopathic*) and is associated with advanced age. (Orlandi 2020)

Peripheral vestibular disease can also result from anything that inflames or otherwise disturbs the inner ear, like an ear infection (the second most common cause of peripheral vestibular disease), a benign polyp, a tumor, or trauma. Certain medications given orally or by injection (e.g. some antibiotics, anti-cancer drugs, and diuretics) can also be toxic to the ear and the vestibular system. (Oishi 2012) In addition, sometimes using an ear cleaning solution or otic medication inside an ear with a ruptured eardrum can cause vestibular disease. (Carnes 2018) So if your dog has signs of an ear infection (scratching, ear rubbing, head shaking, pain), let your veterinarian check whether your dog's eardrums are intact before you squirt cleansers or medications into their ears.

In people who have benign paroxysmal positional vertigo (that really is a mouthful), it is thought that our otoliths ("rocks") or fragments of the otolithic membrane degenerate or dislodge and get stuck in the wrong spots within the inner ear. (Kao 2017) This sends mixed signals to the brain about the body's position, and we get dizzy. The room seems to spin or turn upside down, which makes it difficult to sit upright or to walk in a straight line without support. It also causes motion sickness. We don't know whether this same type of "rocks in the head" disturbance occurs in dogs with vestibular disease, but many of the signs that dogs have are similar to those in people who have vertigo!

When that head tilt is not a quizzical look

Similar to vertigo in people, vestibular disease in dogs can vary from mild to incapacitating. Dogs can have signs that range from a minor head tilt to incoordination, nausea, circling, an inability to stay upright, and even repeated rolling. The signs tend to appear suddenly and can be quite alarming to pet parents.

See your veterinarian if your dog:

- Has a head tilt—the head is cocked to one side, usually toward the affected side.
- Has nystagmus—an involuntary, jerky, rapid eye movement back and forth or up and down (nystagmus has two phases: a *fast phase* in which the eyes move rapidly away from the affected side, and a *slow phase* return toward the affected side).
- Tilts to one side, or leans against the wall to walk.

- Stumbles or staggers ("drunken sailor walk").
- Walks in circles.
- Repeatedly falls over.
- "Alligator rolls" (repeatedly, uncontrollably rolling over).
- Has facial weakness or paralysis.
- Has strabismus, an abnormal eye position in which both eyes do not look in the same direction.
- Vomits repeatedly.
- Has Horner's syndrome (the eye droops on one side or appears sunken, the pupil is abnormally small, and the third eyelid is raised).

Serissa had a bout of Horner's syndrome that affected her left eye. That eye appears sunken and her upper eyelid is droopy. This condition resolved on its own in about two weeks.

Detecting the cause of topsy-turviness

In many cases, idiopathic peripheral vestibular disease is the most likely culprit. But it's helpful for veterinarians to determine whether affected dogs have central or peripheral vestibular disease in order to take the correct course of action and give a prognosis for recovery. Peripheral vestibular disease that is idiopathic or that results from an ear infection usually has a better outcome than central vestibular disease.

To identify the cause, at a minimum your veterinarian will perform a physical examination that includes looking in your dog's ears and checking some nerve functions. On a case-by-case basis, blood and urine tests, an eye exam, and blood pressure measurement may be done. Radiography, magnetic resonance imaging (MRI), or computed tomography (CT) can also help pinpoint the cause if your veterinarian suspects central vestibular disease. Not all of these tests may be needed.

Setting the world right again

The treatment for vestibular disease varies depending on the underlying cause. Addressing the conditions that cause high blood pressure, stopping drugs that are harmful to the ears, or, in some dogs, performing surgery (e.g. to remove a tumor or polyp) is needed. Ear infections of the middle or inner ear may be treated with systemic antibiotics. Sometimes flushing the ear canal while the dog is anesthetized is helpful. Resolving an ear infection produces a good outcome and the tilt usually goes away.

As I mentioned earlier, idiopathic vestibular disease is the most common cause. The great news is that it usually gets better on its own within a few days. Veterinarians sometimes prescribe "tincture of time," and dogs can resume their normal lives after recovery. So even if diagnostic tests to pinpoint the cause aren't financially feasible, it's worthwhile to wait and see how a dog does and treat the dog's signs as needed.

Occasionally, it takes affected dogs a few weeks to recover. Managing their care during recovery can be challenging. Medication to alleviate nausea or to treat motion sickness can be prescribed. Sometimes dogs need to be hospitalized to be sedated and receive supportive therapy such as intravenous fluids. Some treatments can be given at home if hospitalization isn't an option. Veterinarians will need to carefully select a sedative to use in these dogs, because one sedative, midazolam, was reported to worsen the signs of idiopathic vestibular disease in two geriatric dogs. (Jang 2020) The bottom line is that providing supportive care and keeping your dog comfortable and safe at home or in the hospital is crucial.

In people with benign paroxysmal positional vertigo, physicians guide patients through a series of physical positioning maneuvers to try to move the displaced otoliths out of the semicircular canals, which, if successful, alleviates the symptoms. A modified version of this maneuver for dogs was proposed by a physical therapist and found to be successful in 12 dogs with vestibular disease. (Kraeling 2014) Because canine ear structure differs from human ear structure and also differs a bit by breed, the expected response to this therapy is unknown and probably varies. This type of therapy may be available on a limited basis in some veterinary practices.

You may also want to consider veterinary rehabilitation therapy to help your dog recover from vestibular disease. It can involve techniques such as helping a dog posture appropriately, supporting them with a sling while walking, soft tissue massage, passive stretching exercises, underwater treadmill activities, and other controlled exercises that increase the dog's awareness of its body position to help with balance.

About half of dogs with idiopathic vestibular disease may have a head tilt for the rest of their lives (Orlandi 2020), and some may seem a little unsteady after shaking their head, but everything else returns to normal. The signs may relapse in a few dogs (less than 18%). (Jeandel 2016, Orlandi 2020, Radulescu 2020)

Two contrasting outcomes

Luckily, my sister's dog Kalick's test results were normal and she was better with supportive care within a week. My furry niece had only a mild residual head tilt that no one but myself and my sister noticed.

However, I appreciate how hard it can be to take a dog through the recovery stage of vestibular disease or manage a dog who has long-term signs. I remember another family I helped who had a 15-year-old yellow Labrador retriever named Diesel. They called me and were frantic because they thought Diesel had had a stroke. When I arrived at their house, Diesel was rolling like an alligator and was unable to stand. After I evaluated him, I discussed vestibular disease and its possible causes and treatment options with the family. They didn't want to hospitalize him, and they chose to see how he would do in the next day or two. I prescribed antinausea medication and we set up a safe space for him in the home.

Two days later, Diesel had shown little improvement. His caregiving was intense. Diesel was urinating and defecating on himself. Feces were smeared into his fur, and the room they had restricted him to was badly soiled as well. Diesel's continued rolling was the worst part, plus he had been unable to eat.

The family could not manage Diesel at home, nor could they afford to hospitalize him. Even with hospitalization, I couldn't guarantee his full recovery. Diesel's parents were nervous and hesitated to tell me that they wanted to euthanize him. They were afraid I'd think they were giving up on Diesel. I didn't hesitate in supporting their decision.

When I gave Diesel the initial sedative to prepare for the euthanasia injection, he stopped rolling. Diesel finally looked like himself again, sleeping soundly. This helped remind his family of the Diesel they knew before his illness. And it gave them peace to know they were doing the best thing they could do for him.

 Questions to ask your veterinarian

- Will my dog need supportive therapy such as antinausea or motion sickness medication?
- Will my dog need fluid therapy or sedation?
- Will my dog benefit from specific exercises or rehabilitation therapy?
- When should I expect to see an improvement in my dog's signs?
- If my dog doesn't improve, should we see a veterinary neurologist?

CAREGIVER TIPS AND HOME HACKS

- Keep your dog confined to a safe, padded area if needed to avoid injury.
- Block unsafe areas (such as stairs) with baby gates.
- Place bumper pads on sharp or hard edges or ledges.
- Keep furniture in its usual location.
- Use soft, comfortable bedding and let your dog rest in positions most comfortable to him.
- Use potty pads or diapers to protect bedding.
- Keep your dog clean and dry.
- Keep food and water close by and easily accessible.
- Allow your dog to rest quietly in her preferred position and stay still as much as possible, because movement likely causes dizziness. Help her turn every few hours to prevent pressure sores, but keep in mind that some resting positions may not be tolerable and may make your dog's dizziness or anxiety worse.
- Limit environmental stimulation from other dogs, kids, television, loud noises, and bright lights.
- Avoid car rides when possible.
- Frequently reassure your dog and provide a calming presence.
- Consider using calming pheromone diffusers, sprays, or collars designed specifically for dogs (e.g. Adaptil–Ceva, Comfort Zone–Central Garden & Pet Company).
- To help relieve anxiety, consider giving a supplement such as alpha-casozepine (Zylkene–Vetoquinol) in dogs or a probiotic for dogs such as Purina Pro Plan Veterinary Supplements Calming Care.
- Place a night light where needed.
- Use a sling or harness to help your dog walk or eliminate.
- Place a ramp over stairs if needed and non-slip flooring (yoga mats, non-slip bath mats) where possible.
- Entice your dog's appetite with canned dog foods; warming the food slightly may also help.
- If your dog is not eating or drinking, talk with your veterinarian. Assisted feeding, giving fluids under the skin, or hospitalization may be needed.

 READING AND VIEWING RECOMMENDATIONS

- For information about veterinary rehabilitation and to find a practitioner: American Association of Rehabilitation Veterinarians
https://rehabvets.org/

- American College of Veterinary Sports Medicine and Rehabilitation
  https://vsmr.org/
- One dog parent describes her experience with vestibular disease in her dog: CandidMommy YouTube video: Old Dog Vestibular Disease
  https://www.youtube.com/watch?v=DE4iOsJp_os

CHAPTER 19:

Cognition:
Cross my mind... or not

"How do you run from what is inside your head?"

— UNKNOWN

My Anatolian shepherd, Sam, is 14 years old. She and I have been struggling with her mobility because she has spinal cancer. Plus her appetite has wavered, her joy levels have dropped, and she has bouts of fecal incontinence. Just when I thought I had all of those problems under control, in the wee hours of one night I heard strange, anxious barking. I bolted out of bed and raced into the living room to see if Sam had gotten stuck somewhere and couldn't get up. But there she was, just lying on her bed, barking.

Her bark was different—a bark I hadn't heard before. It wasn't Sam's bark for "I must vanquish the stranger in the driveway!" I can easily recognize each of my dogs' different barks—the subtle differences in the urgency, excitement, pitch, and growly undertones of their "language." Sam has a specific bark for package delivery people (menacing), one for pizza delivery people (ecstatic joy), one for our neighbors and their dogs (cordial), one for familiar wildlife (irritation), one for unfamiliar wildlife (sinister), one for my arrival (ecstatic joy [aka "pizza delivery bark"]), one for family who live elsewhere (jolly), and one for familiar friends (tickled pink). I knew this bark conveyed new meaning.

Sam doesn't bark to ask to go outside, and she didn't seem to want to go out that night. I took her out anyway, and she urinated a little. Afterward she went back to sleep. But Sam's new bark became a much bigger issue. During subsequent nights, she'd wake up two or three times and start the same type of barking. If I laid down with her until she calmed down, she fell back to sleep. So to make things easier, I started sleeping on the couch in the living room near her.

Then, Sam also began this "worry" barking randomly in the middle of the day *and* after dinner. It's a loud, high-pitch, slow, but constant bark. "Woof."

Pause. "Woof." Pause. "Woof." Pause. "Woof..." To get her to stop, I had to lie down next to her on the floor and pet her. This seemed to comfort her. But Sam's new barking behavior made me wonder whether her mental functions were declining. It also strained my emotional budget, and I felt a twinge of caregiver fatigue setting in.

Signs of brain aging and cognitive decline

Many of my patients' families know about the typical age-related changes their dogs may experience, like shifts in body composition (more fat, less muscle), decreased sensory abilities (impaired vision, hearing, and smell), and diminished metabolic processes (sluggish digestion, decreased immune responses, slower healing). But many pet parents are not aware that their dogs can have behavioral changes associated with aging, and that this out-of-character conduct may be caused by changes in their dog's brain.

At any age, changes in a dog's typical behavior or temperament are good indicators of illness or a new behavior problem. But some senior dogs exhibit odd behaviors and signs of mental deterioration that cannot otherwise be attributed to underlying medical or behavioral problems, nor to typical age-related sensory decline.

The behavior changes may be subtle at first, and pet parents tend to attribute them to their dogs "just getting old" or "having senior moments." Affected dogs take longer naps during the day and wake up in the middle of the night and seem anxious. They miss greeting you at the door on some days and seem surprised you are home. They don't bring you toys to toss as frequently. They weirdly bark randomly. They may forget which side of the door opens, so they stand and wait or stare at the hinged side. They ask less often for belly rubs. Some seem confused and wander between rooms. Their thrill of going for walks disappears or they act grumpy when other animal friends want to play. Some dogs become more clingy. Of course dogs who have fatigue, discomfort, or vision or hearing problems related to a variety of ailments can show these signs, too, but in senior dogs, these signs may indicate diminished mental processes.

Senior dogs who exhibit these types of behavior changes may have physical  changes in their brains, such as tissue shrinkage and nerve loss [Borras 1999, Tapp 2004, West 2000, Prpar Mihevc 2019], buildup of protein fragments called beta-amyloid plaques, and twisted fibers of another protein called tau [Smolek 2016, Schmidt 2015, Abey 2020, Fiock 2020]. These behavior changes and structural brain abnormalities are similar to the symptoms and brain changes that people with Alzheimer's disease and senile dementia have. (Vite 2014)

In dogs, these signs of age-related mental decline and brain abnormalities are called *cognitive dysfunction syndrome*, and it tends to progress with age, seriously affecting the dog's and family's daily quality of life. Affected dogs may:

- Not recognize their owners
- Seem disconnected
- Become aggressive toward other dogs or cats
- Have episodes of intense anxiety
- Have an increased fear of noises, lights, or new environments
- Pace incessantly
- Bark or howl randomly
- Get stuck in a closet, in a corner, or under a table
- Be unable to figure out how to get out from under bushes in the yard
- Forget which side of the door opens
- Experience sleep-wake cycle disturbances (sleep more during the day, be restless in the evening, and then awake more throughout the night)
- Urinate or defecate in inappropriate places in the house, sometimes right in front of you (Landsberg 2010, Landsberg 2012, May 2019)

Similar to people who have dementia or Alzheimer's disease, dogs who have cognitive dysfunction may also have perception, posture, and gait problems. One study indicated that dogs with cognitive dysfunction may exhibit tremors, head drooping, swaying, or falling. (Ozawa 2019) The same study pointed out that dogs with cognitive dysfunction often have impaired vision or reduced sense of smell—and that such signs may help veterinarians identify cognitive impairment earlier. (Ozawa 2019) Perhaps what we tend to think of as "normal" age-related vision and sense of smell changes in senior dogs are caused by the same types of brain changes that cause cognitive dysfunction.

Recognizing the signs of cognitive dysfunction earlier in the course of the disease gives dogs and pet parents a better chance to effectively manage their dogs' signs and relish more happy, good-quality-of-life days together. Apparently healthy dogs can show signs of cognitive impairment as early as 6 years of age. (May 2019) Cognitive deficits tend to progress, but the rate of these changes varies—they may progress slowly or quickly. (May 2019) Use the "Cognitive Assessment Checklist for Dogs" at the end of this chapter to monitor middle-age and older dogs, especially during their senior years, and go over it with your veterinarian if you notice changes.

Sam's witching hours

Most of Sam's barking episodes start at around 7 p.m. and last until around 10 p.m. I lovingly call these events her "witching hours." She lies on her bed, stares at me, and then starts to bark. The time I spend sitting with and petting her to calm her and help her stay quiet is also our "love time," but I'll be honest—it's getting a little difficult to do every night.

In people who have dementia, sunset can bring increased confusion, frustration, and agitation, and it is often referred to as *sundowner's syndrome* or *sundowning*. Some dogs with cognitive dysfunction can show similar signs at or shortly after sunset. One theory is that dogs produce less melatonin as they age.

Melatonin is a hormone produced in response to darkness and helps with circadian rhythms (the body's 24-hour internal clock) and the normal sleep-wake cycle. So melatonin supplementation is often recommended for dogs with cognitive dysfunction whose sleep-wake cycle is reversed. I started giving Sam a daily regimen of melatonin, and so far it has helped her (and me!) sleep through the night—she has fewer 2 a.m. barking episodes!

How common is cognitive dysfunction?

It's difficult to say precisely how many senior dogs have cognitive dysfunction because the age at which a dog becomes senior varies with the breed and individual, and because the criteria used to evaluate and measure signs have evolved since cognitive dysfunction was first described in dogs in 1995. (Ruehl 1995) While the percentage of dogs affected varies among different studies, the percentage increases dramatically as dogs age. (Salvin 2010)

Overall, at least 14% of dogs 8 years of age and older have signs of cognitive dysfunction based on surveys of their owners, and this percentage does not differ by breed. (Salvin 2010) Another study using the same survey showed that 18% of dogs 10 years of age and older are affected. [Ozawa 2019] And an earlier study indicated that up to 68% of dogs age 15 to 16 years exhibit signs of cognitive dysfunction. (Neilson 2001)

According to the American Veterinary Medical Association (AVMA), nearly 37 million dogs in the United States (about 48% of all dogs) are 6 years of age or older. (AVMA 2017/2018) The AVMA considers small dogs as senior at 7 years of age and larger breed dogs as senior at 5 or 6 years of age. Taken together, these numbers suggest that at least five million senior dogs may be experiencing signs of cognitive dysfunction.

Is it cognitive dysfunction or another condition?

Because a diagnostic test isn't yet available to pinpoint cognitive dysfunction, veterinarians must make a *diagnosis of exclusion*. This means we look first for another medical or behavioral problem that could be causing the pet's signs. Your veterinarian may ask you to complete a questionnaire or checklist designed to screen senior dogs for signs of cognitive dysfunction (similar to the checklist I mentioned above).

If your dog has signs of cognitive dysfunction, the conditions your veterinarian may concentrate on ruling out first include:

- Impaired hearing, vision, or smell that could be related to aging or other diseases
- Urinary tract infections
- Kidney disease
- Bladder stones or bladder cancer
- Painful mobility problems such as arthritis or spinal column disorders
- Thyroid or adrenal gland disease
- Diabetes
- Liver disease
- High blood pressure
- Seizures
- Brain tumors
- Other types of behavior problems

Your veterinarian rules out these other conditions by taking a good medical and behavioral history, performing a thorough physical examination, and running routine blood and urine tests. Sometimes radiographic or ultrasound exams will also be needed, as well as additional tests to assess heart, liver, kidney, or other organ function. Your veterinarian will also ask about all medications (including supplements or nutraceuticals, herbs, or over-the-counter drugs) your dog is receiving and any previously diagnosed behavior problems.

If another condition is identified, it can be treated or managed first to see whether your dog improves or the signs resolve.

Occasionally, diagnostic testing for other conditions can't be done because of a pet parent's budget limitations or because the dog needs immediate help to mitigate her signs. In that case, veterinarians may suggest starting therapy to alleviate signs of cognitive dysfunction, then assessing the dog's response. If the dog doesn't respond to therapy, additional diagnostic tests will still be needed to identify the cause of the signs.

If your dog's examination and tests don't uncover another cause of your dog's signs and the diagnosis points to cognitive dysfunction, your veterinarian may use a canine dementia rating scale to assess whether your dog's cognitive dysfunction is mild, moderate, or severe. (Madari 2015) Veterinarians can also use the scale to evaluate how well dogs respond to their treatments for cognitive dysfunction.

"Is he just getting old?"

I remember visiting a senior Australian shepherd at home whose family had been managing his severe arthritis well with medications. And the household modifications they'd made for their grandmother—installing a ramp from the deck and placing slip-resistant flooring in the kitchen, dining room, and bathroom—had helped their dog's mobility as well.

The family's primary concerns were that their dog couldn't seem to relax and would wander from room to room most of the night and pace. During the day he slept more and had stopped greeting them at the door. He often acted like he didn't recognize them. They'd frequently find him frantically scrambling under the dining room table, like he didn't know how to get out from under it. They also began finding urine spots and realized he had stopped asking to go outside as often as he had before.

"We took him to the vet, and his test results were normal," they told me. "Is he just getting old?"

I explained that I suspected that the biggest factor affecting their dog's quality of life (and the family's) was severe cognitive dysfunction, caused by abnormal changes in his aging brain.

"You mean, like doggie Alzheimer's?" they asked.

I answered, "Yes, very similar."

We discussed options for additional measures to support their dog. They told me they had reached their emotional limitations, especially because they were managing another family member's serious illness. They elected to have their dog euthanized the following weekend, after a really good week of showering him with lots of love and treats.

What are the risk factors?

Our relationships with and caregiving for dogs have progressed, along with vast improvements in pet nutrition and continual advances in veterinary diagnostics and treatments. It's wonderful that dogs have longer lifespans as a result! And, not surprisingly, because dogs are living longer, their risk of developing cognitive dysfunction increases as they age. (Nielsen 2001, Azkona 2009, Schutt 2015, Salvin 2010, Bejanirut 2018, Katina 2016) In fact, age is the biggest risk factor for developing cognitive dysfunction in dogs.

Other risk factors for cognitive dysfunction include:

- Dogs with epilepsy have a higher risk and may show signs of cognitive dysfunction at a much younger age (4 years). These dogs show more signs of memory problems (similar to people who have epilepsy) rather than signs of altered social interactions. This may be because the brain changes in dogs with epilepsy differ from those typically identified in dogs with age-related cognitive dysfunction. (Packer 2018)
- Lighter-weight dogs may have a higher risk because they live longer than large-breed dogs do. However, large-breed dogs have shorter lifespans because they age at an accelerated pace, (Kraus 2013) which implies that large-breed dogs would develop cognitive dysfunction sooner. This in

turn spurs the thought that the brain aging changes that lead to cognitive dysfunction happen faster in smaller dogs. (Packer 2018) And yet, other studies have found no correlation between size or body weight and cognitive dysfunction. (Fast 2013, Benjanirut 2018) So we don't yet know for certain whether a dog's size or body weight are risk factors!

- Sex and reproductive status have been evaluated as possible risk factors. But it isn't definitively known whether male, female, neutered, or intact dogs have a higher risk of cognitive dysfunction because studies have shown contrasting results. (Hart 2001, Azkona 2009, Fast 2013, Katina 2016, Benjanirut 2018)
- A low-quality diet—one not appropriate for the dog's nutritional needs, life stage, or health status—may increase the risk. (Katina 2016) Nutrient deficiencies can adversely alter brain structure and function and hasten brain aging. (May 2019) In addition to age-related structural and functional changes in the brain, the brain's ability to use energy (the brain's primary energy source is glucose) decreases by as much as 25% in dogs by the time they are 6 years old. Such disruption in energy metabolism contributes further to degenerative processes within the brain and to cognitive decline. (May 2019)
- Dogs with chronic painful problems such as osteoarthritis may need to be assessed and monitored for cognitive impairment. People who have long-term painful conditions show faster cognitive decline than people who don't have similarly painful conditions. (Robertson [3] 2020)

Preventive measures and management

Identifying cognitive abnormalities earlier and providing supportive measures sooner may slow cognitive decline, which helps keep the bond strong between you and your dog while improving your dog's overall well-being and quality of life. (May 2019) And regardless of your dog's age or cognitive ability, cognitive support can be provided!

Hard fact: Cognitive dysfunction can't be cured. The goal of therapy is to lighten the physical and emotional toll on dogs' daily activities and slow disease progression if possible. Caregiving requires patience and flexibility to find what works best for an individual pet as well as all affected family members.

To prevent or delay cognitive decline in dogs, enhancing dogs' diets and promoting behavioral enrichment activities are considered more effective than using only one therapy. (Chapagain 2018) So a multifaceted approach is likely to provide the most benefit. Those many facets include:

- Fine-tuning the home environment
- Giving supplements and possibly transitioning to feeding a different diet
- Administering medications when indicated

- Bolstering social interactions
- Encouraging mental engagement

That's a lot! So it's important to assess the level of emotional and financial investment you are willing to commit.

Below I outline measures to help you mitigate the effects of cognitive dysfunction in your dog. Keep in mind that as with many things, moderation is key! Making extreme changes to try to slow cognitive decline in a dog who is already moderately or severely affected may have the opposite effect. If you bring a new puppy into your lifelong single-dog household in hopes of encouraging your older dog to be more active or if you take your senior dog to the dog park for the first time, you may introduce stress that intensifies your dog's signs of cognitive dysfunction. On the other hand, I have heard happy stories of dogs who "act like puppies again" in response to families making big changes!

In any case, consider your dog as an individual and introduce novel situations gradually and patiently. And remember that if you have to make substantial changes to your dog's environment or routine, such as moving, welcoming a baby, or traveling, do so mindfully and slowly so that your dog has time to acclimate well.

A Nevada state of mind

Nevada was a 14-year-old mixed-breed dog whose family called me because her panting and pacing consumed her day. They could hear her nails clicking on the tile from across the house as she paced incessantly.

When I met Nevada, she seemed happy and looked fairly healthy. But her facial expression told me that something was amiss. Her ears were pulled back, I could see the whites of her eyes, and her face appeared tense overall. And she would not stop panting and pacing! Nevada's family loved her dearly, but this behavior worried them and caused tension between the family members.

After a thorough physical exam, I could not detect signs of pain or indications of heart or lung disease that would cause Nevada's panting. The results of recent diagnostic tests done by her primary care veterinarian showed she had moderate liver disease. I suspected that Nevada had cognitive impairment, either related to her liver disease or to cognitive dysfunction.

Along with continuing to monitor and manage Nevada's liver disease, we tried different medications to help ease her anxiety, along with home modifications to manage her cognitive issues. The family used shower curtain tension rods to block Nevada's access to unsafe areas and placed bath mats on the hardwood floors where she paced so she wouldn't slip. I also trimmed her nails to reduce the tapping sound that added to the family's aggravation. They placed light-sensor night lights in the areas Nevada wandered at night. When the family was out, they played soothing music or ocean wave recordings to muffle outdoor traffic and people noises. They plugged in calming pheromone diffusers in the rooms that Nevada spent most time in.

Nevada responded well. Her pacing and panting diminished enough for her to maintain a good quality of life and preserve the family's sanity. Nevada lived for longer than a year after my initial visit with her!

Nevada's anxious expression.

 Nevada having a good day.

Nutritional support

Dietary changes or supplements that attempt to ward off or correct adverse changes in aging brains are thought to prevent or slow cognitive decline because certain nutrients are crucial in maintaining brain structure and function. [May 2019] For example, the brain uses glucose as its primary energy source, but as the brain ages, its ability to process glucose diminishes. [May 2019] Dogs as young as 6 years of age may already have less ability to metabolize glucose in their brains—before they even show outward signs of cognitive decline! So if less energy is available in the brain, oxidative stress occurs. And oxidative stress— an imbalance between harmful and protective oxygen-containing molecules involved in cell metabolism—is associated with degenerative nervous system diseases and cognitive decline. [May 2019]

Specific vitamins, antioxidants, fatty acids, proteins (including amino acids and enzymes), plant extracts, minerals, and other nutritional support factors may act alone or together to influence brain processes. Such nutrients have numerous cell and tissue effects, including assisting normal nerve function, influencing neurotransmitters (the chemical signals between nerve cells), changing blood vessel diameter, reducing oxidative stress, guiding gene expression, generating ketones (an alternative to glucose as an energy source), and enhancing mitochondria function (the energy-producing mechanism in cells).

Diet

With age, the brain's ability to use glucose as an energy source diminishes, but its ability to use ketones as energy stays steady. *Ketogenic, or keto diets* shift the body's metabolism away from using glucose as energy and toward using ketones. Traditional ketogenic diets for people are extremely high in fat (70%) and low in protein (20%) and carbohydrates (10%). (May 2019) People use keto diets for weight loss or to manage certain neurologic problems, but they have a hard time sticking with them, and the diets can cause nutritional deficiencies. (May 2019)

Traditional ketogenic diets don't work for dogs because dogs don't produce the same high levels of ketones that people do. (May 2019) However, specific types of fat molecules, called medium-chain triglycerides (MCTs), can promote ketone production in dogs without requiring protein or carbohydrate restriction. MCTs have been shown to enhance cognitive function in healthy dogs and in dogs with cognitive dysfunction, (Pan 2010, Pan 2018) and to reduce seizure frequency in dogs who have epilepsy. (Berk 2020) Concentrated formulations of MCTs are included in some dog diets or supplements. (May 2019) MCT-based ketogenic diets are also becoming popular with people because they don't require such a high-fat diet and are easier diets to stick to.

If your dog has cognitive dysfunction, talk with your veterinarian about which diet is best. Veterinary insight is important, especially if your dog has other medical conditions that may influence which diet or supplements your dog can safely receive.

If you need to switch to a new diet, do it gradually to prevent your dog's gastrointestinal tract from going "cold turkey" (which can cause distressing diarrhea and vomiting). And whenever possible, switch to a new diet when your dog is feeling relatively good. If your dog feels crummy when you try out a different diet, your dog may refuse to eat the new food and never venture to taste it again.

It's more than a gut feeling, it's a microbiome!

Did you know that the gut "talks" to the brain and that the brain responds? Recent research has revealed that the gut and the brain "discuss" many more things than whether you're hungry, say, for a pizza, or whether you're full and regret eating the entire pizza.

In some ways, people have known this for a long time. Think about common expressions we use such as having "butterflies in my stomach" before performing, needing to "trust my gut instincts" when making some decisions, and getting a "sinking feeling in the pit of my stomach" in hazardous situations.

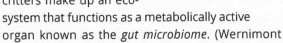

Dogs' digestive tracts— and ours—contain billions (probably trillions) of tiny organisms: bacteria, viruses, fungi, and others. These itty bitty critters make up an eco-

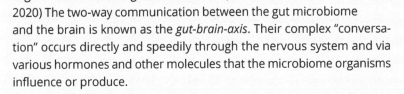

system that functions as a metabolically active organ known as the *gut microbiome*. (Wernimont 2020) The two-way communication between the gut microbiome and the brain is known as the *gut-brain-axis*. Their complex "conversation" occurs directly and speedily through the nervous system and via various hormones and other molecules that the microbiome organisms influence or produce.

The microbiome is shaped and affected by food and other dietary components, drugs such as antibiotics, and beneficial, live organisms known as *probiotics*. The balance between the good and not-so-good organisms that make up the gut microbiome is important for digestive health, but this balance also has a broader influence. The microbiome and brain also communicate about immunity, metabolism, and mood.

Researchers now know that mental processes aren't regulated only by the brain and spinal cord, but that the gut microbiome influences cognition and several brain disorders in people, including depression, anxiety, and Alzheimer's disease. (Zhu 2020) The microbiome may play a role in triggering dysfunction of the immune cells (called *microglia*) in the brain, which contributes to amyloid buildup. Amyloid buildup can be found in the brains of people with Alzheimer's disease and in the brains of dogs with cognitive dysfunction.

People with irritable bowel syndrome (IBS) have a high rate of depression and anxiety compared with people who do not have IBS. For years, doctors thought depression and anxiety contributed to IBS. But evidence suggests that the gastric system nerves in people who suffer from the bloating, pain, and stool abnormalities of IBS send signals to the brain that can spark mood disorders.

Interestingly, the good, or probiotic, gut bacteria called *Bifidobacterium longum* are associated with anxiety relief. In one study of 24 dogs, adding these bacteria to their diets reduced the dogs' anxious behaviors, heart rates, and cortisol (a stress hormone) concentrations. (May 2019, McGowan 2016) Probiotics are available as nutritional supplements for dogs.

The "discussions" between the brain and the gut will continue to be explored in people and in pets. We have much more to learn about the many ways nutrition may be used to influence brain health and well-being.

Supplements and nutraceuticals

In people, limited evidence shows that some supplements may preserve or enhance cognitive function, but, as with drug treatments, an individual's response can be influenced by genes as well as their health and nutritional status, among other factors.

Overall, studies of nutritional interventions in dogs with cognitive dysfunction are also limited, and it can be difficult to conclude which supplements or dietary modifications will benefit affected dogs. Nutrients likely work better in combination than does a single nutrient. (May 2019) In any case, supplements alone likely will not relieve a dog's signs of cognitive dysfunction and may work best when given along with other cognitive support measures.

Your veterinarian can suggest appropriate supplements or nutraceuticals and proper doses for dogs with cognitive dysfunction. Many nutraceuticals are available that include several ingredients such as vitamins, minerals, and antioxidants. It's important to ask your veterinarian for advice because supplements or nutraceuticals that are appropriate for dogs may not be appropriate for cats (or may even be toxic in cats, such as alpha-lipoic acid), and some supplements formulated for people may be dangerous for dogs (e.g. some melatonin supplements contain xylitol, which is toxic to dogs).

In one study, older dogs who received a multi-ingredient nutraceutical showed improvement in many signs of cognitive dysfunction compared with dogs who received a placebo. But after the nutraceutical was stopped, the dogs relapsed. (May 2019) This study highlights how important it is to keep up with supplementation for the long term and as directed by your veterinarian in order for a product's benefits to be seen and sustained.

Examples of supplements that may be useful in dogs with cognitive dysfunction include:

* L-theanine, an amino acid found in green tea leaves. Anxitane (Virbac) is a synthetic version of this amino acid and may help nervous and anxious dogs relax and be calm.

- Gamma-aminobutyric acid (GABA), a naturally occurring amino acid and neurotransmitter that slows nerve impulses in the brain, which may reduce anxiety and stress and promote sleep.
- Gingko, an extract from maidenhair trees, contains antioxidants that may improve cognitive function and enhance blood flow to the brain.
- Melatonin, a naturally occurring hormone produced by the pineal gland in the brain of many animals. Most supplements contain a synthetic version. It may help with sleep disturbances in dogs with cognitive dysfunction. Don't give melatonin supplements that contain xylitol, because xylitol is toxic to dogs.
- Omega-3 fatty acids, which may support cognitive function through their anti-inflammatory and antioxidant effects.
- Resveratrol, a chemical produced by some plants that has antioxidant, anti-inflammatory, and blood vessel-widening effects that may help cognitive function.
- S-adenosyl-L-methionine (SAMe), made in the body from methionine, is an amino acid found in food. It helps regulate hormones and many cell activities. As a supplement, SAMe is a synthetic molecule (Denosin–Nutramax Laboratories Veterinary Sciences) and is used to support liver and brain health in dogs.
- Senilife (Ceva Animal Health), a multi-antioxidant blend (phosphatidylserine, pyridoxine, ginkgo biloba extract, resveratrol, and d-alpha-tocopherol), is used in senior dogs to help reduce behaviors associated with brain aging.
- Alpha-casozepine (Zylkene–Vetoquinol) contains bovine-sourced hydrolyzed milk protein, an ingredient that has calming properties and may be used in dogs to provide support related to anxiety disorders.
- Probiotics such as Purina Pro Plan Veterinary Supplements Calming Care offer support for dogs with anxiety.
- Cannabidiol (CBD) has been promoted by the manufacturers of these products to help reduce dogs' anxiety, but studies of its use for this purpose and in dogs with cognitive dysfunction are lacking. See Chapter 24 "Course of action: Therapeutic options and gaining acceptance from your senior dog" for more information about CBD.

Drugs

Your veterinarian may prescribe selegiline hydrochloride, also called L-deprenyl (Anipryl–Zoetis), for your dog. It is the only FDA-approved drug for dogs with cognitive dysfunction syndrome. It increases the availability of a neurotransmitter called dopamine. It may take 30 days or more to see an improvement in signs of cognitive dysfunction.

Because several other medications—including those commonly used to relieve anxiety in dogs—pose an interaction hazard, your veterinarian needs to know about all other drugs and supplements your dog is receiving. This helps ensure drug interactions won't be a risk if your dog receives treatment with selegiline.

Some dogs with cognitive dysfunction may benefit from an anti-anxiety drug. Many options are available (e.g. fluoxetine, clomipramine, alprazolam, trazodone), so if your dog does not respond to the first drug, your veterinarian may recommend increasing the dose or switching to a different drug (with an appropriate amount of time between stopping the previous medication and starting the new one). It may take two to six weeks to see improvement, so patience and flexibility are key. Some anti-anxiety drugs (and many other types of medications) should not be given to dogs who are receiving selegiline because adverse drug interactions may occur.

Researchers are exploring the possibility of using vaccinations and stem cell therapies to treat Alzheimer's disease in people, and these studies are ongoing. Some of this research has evaluated the effects of these treatments in dogs because their clinical signs and brain changes are similar to those of people who have Alzheimer's disease. These treatments may show promise for dogs in the future.

Acupuncture

Acupuncture may be a helpful adjunct to drug therapy in people who have Alzheimer's disease. (Wang 2020) Acupuncture's effects have shown promise in a small study in mice that naturally exhibit accelerated aging. (Li 2019) However, not much is known about the effects of acupuncture in dogs with cognitive dysfunction.

Activity and sleep

Dogs with cognitive dysfunction commonly experience sleep-wake cycle disturbances. Help your dog be active during the day or in the early evening hours. This exposes them to sunlight, which helps reset their body clock and also tires them out, both of which reduce nighttime restlessness.

Just like for children and for us, your dog benefits from a pre-sleep routine and consistent bedtime. Dim the lights a couple hours before bed to signal the body to produce melatonin, the sleep-promoting hormone. Provide a comfy sleep environment. Talk to your veterinarian to learn whether a melatonin supplement might help your dog.

If your dog wakes up during the night to eliminate or needs a drink, try to avoid turning on bright hall or patio lights. Light signals the body to stop producing melatonin. Use nightlights and flashlights on low instead, which will help you get back to sleep faster, too. Let your dog go out to potty, and bring them right back in and go back to bed. Do not play with them, feed them or give them a treat, because these activities reward them and they'll be more likely to continue waking you up.

Don't punish your dog for waking you up. Punishment increases their anxiety. Keep in mind they may be confused and need reassurance, or they may have thought they had a good reason to alert you to something they heard or smelled.

Environmental and emotional comfort and physical and mental exercise

Dogs with cognitive dysfunction benefit from a familiar, safe environment with furniture in its usual places, their necessities (bowls, bed, potty places) in their ordinary spots, and hazards (stairs, pools, closets) blocked off. Dogs take comfort in a stable daily routine with predictable times for meals, play, outings, and treats. But you and your dog don't need to relive monotonous "groundhog days" either!

Dogs who have cognitive dysfunction can still do—and enjoy!—most of the things they love to do. Going for walks, swimming, fetching or chasing toys, sunbathing, exploring, hunting for treats, and riding in a car, wagon, bike sidecar, or dog stroller are all feasible. Simply engage in activities at a more leisurely pace and with extra care, monitoring, and patience. And add variety to spice up your dog's life. Promoting physical exercise and mental stimulation that your dog enjoys can be therapeutic for both of you!

If your dog is a little unsteady or unable to reliably jump up on or down from usual sleeping spots, consider adding small ramps or steps to help them along. For dogs who are a bit pained by arthritis or other muscle conditions, a certified dog rehabilitation therapist or a certified animal acupressure and massage practitioner may be available in your area.

Dogs who were social bunnies before they started to slow down should still be allowed opportunities to visit or play with people and animal friends they're comfortable with. Gauge their endurance and tolerance levels to avoid over-stimulation and stress.

Studies show that training dogs and engaging them in these activities throughout their lives help dogs retain their attentiveness and problem-solving abilities and protect them from age-related cognitive decline. (Szabo 2018, Packer 2018, Marshall-Pescini 2008, 2009, 2016; Chapagain 2017) It's beneficial to periodically review the commands your dog knows. And consider teaching her new ones! You may also want to teach your dog hand signals that communicate your commands.

Always use training techniques that positively reinforce desired behavior with treat or toy rewards and love, not methods that use confrontation or punishment.

Clicker training works great for dogs. It's a positive reinforcement training technique wherein a distinct clicking sound is used to signal that the dog exhibited a desired behavior. The click must be timed exactly at the moment of the desired behavior and immediately followed by a treat (or a favorite toy or praise).

Keep in mind that you may also need to review housetraining with your senior dog if he seems confused about where to potty:

- Take him outside (or to the appropriate location) frequently to potty in addition to his routine potty schedule (which is important to stick to).
- Reward him immediately (profuse praise or a tiny treat) after he goes potty in the right spot.
- Confine him while you can't watch him—use a kennel or small area of a room where he's less likely to want to eliminate.
- Don't punish him for having accidents.

Food puzzle toys, games of hide and seek, and scent training allow dogs to express their exploratory nature. These activities provide fun distractions and additional time to bond with your dog.

Calming music, dog physical therapy or massage, aromatherapy, and movies or shows that engage your dog can be terrific ways to help your dog relax and stimulate their senses. Dog parents have told me their senior dog loves watching the birds in the movie "Winged Migration" with his younger dog sister, and a 10-year-old Great Dane-mastiff mix I know of gets revved-up like a puppy by watching the werewolves in the "Twilight" movies! And remember that any movie with a loud doorbell may send your dog racing and barking to the door. But movies created specifically for dogs are available, and dog-specific tunes and videos abound on YouTube.

Other measures to consider

- Gentle pressure garments that help reduce anxiety in dogs such as ThunderShirt (Thunderworks) and The Anxiety Wrap (The Company of Animals)
- Pheromone diffusers, sprays, or collars (e.g. Adaptil–Ceva, Comfort Zone–Central Garden & Pet Company)

Research revelation: Do diet and training help? The jury is still out

Veterinary researchers recently studied the effects of diet and training on cognitively healthy pet dogs. They enrolled 119 pet dogs over the age of 6 who represented several different breeds. The dogs had received various levels of training throughout their lives, as reported by their owners. (Chapagain 2020)

The dogs who had received higher levels of lifelong training and were fed a diet enhanced with nutrients to support cognitive function (the antioxidants vitamin C, vitamin E and polyphenols, plus an omega-3 fatty acid [docosahexaenoic acid], a phospholipid [phosphatidylserine] and a greater amount of tryptophan) for one year scored no higher on tests to evaluate their mental abilities than the dogs who had received less training throughout their lives and ate a regular diet for one year. (Chapagain 2020)

All dogs in both groups of the study showed declines in problem-solving, dependency, boldness, and sociability over the one-year period, but their trainability and activity independence remained stable. This means that lifelong training and a nutrient-enriched diet had no effect on behavior or cognitive decline in cognitively healthy older dogs. The researchers concluded that more studies are needed to assess whether and how enriched diets and lifelong training may affect behavior and cognition as dogs age. The researchers also encourage owners to invite their aged dogs to play (within their physical capabilities) to bolster the dog-human bond and to preserve or enhance activity levels to help prevent deterioration in movement abilities. (Chapagain 2020)

In comparing this study to previous studies, we must keep in mind that the diet fed in this study is not identical to the diets previously studied for their cognitive effects in dogs and that most dogs in similar earlier studies were dogs who lived in laboratories, not pet dogs. Also, none of the dogs who participated in this study were categorized as having cognitive dysfunction when the one-year study ended. So the next step is to study the effects of these therapies in pet dogs who have cognitive dysfunction.

Questions to ask your veterinarian

In 2010, veterinarians formally diagnosed cognitive dysfunction in fewer than 2% of affected dogs. (Salvin 2010) While veterinarians' awareness of the disease and the types and reliability of the tools used to identify it have undoubtedly improved since then, many veterinarians may still not routinely screen specifically for signs of cognitive dysfunction in senior dogs.

So if you notice these signs in your senior dog, it's important to alert your veterinarian and ask whether your dog's signs may be attributed to another medical condition, to cognitive dysfunction, or to both. Like people, it is common for senior dogs to have multiple conditions.

Use the "Cognitive Assessment Checklist for Dogs" at the end of this chapter to monitor your dog, and go over it with your veterinarian. Based on your discussion, you may want to know:

- What diagnostic tests will my dog need?
- What supplements, therapeutic diets, or medications might my dog benefit from?
- What physical and mental enrichment activities will help my dog?

CAREGIVER TIPS AND HOME HACKS

- Stick with your dog's usual routines (e.g. meal times, medication timing, walks).
- Adhere to your dog's routine veterinary visits for examinations, diagnostic tests, and wellness care such as vaccinations and parasite preventives.
- Keep your dog's food and water bowls, bed, crate, and potty areas in easily accessible, familiar spots.
- Avoid rearranging the furniture.
- Keep your closet doors closed.
- Block off access to hazardous areas such as stairs and pools (use baby gates or tension rods).
- Use security cameras to check on your dog throughout the day.
- Provide socialization times with other calm dogs and human friends.
- Intermittently explore new areas on walks.
- Review known training commands (e.g. sit, down, stay, come, drop it, heel) and teach hand signals for them.

 Murdog's mom, Debby, installed indoor security cameras to keep a loving eye on her boy.

- If your dog has seemingly forgotten his housetraining, rehousetrain him, or retrain him to potty on an absorbent pad or in a doggy litter box or another acceptable location. Reward him for eliminating outside or in the new location. Don't punish him for having accidents.
- Take 10 to 20 minutes each day to love on your dog—groom her or simply sit and pet her or give belly rubs or gentle massage. This also helps you stay attuned to any new lumps or bumps.
- Keep your dog's nails trimmed.
- Allow opportunities for your dog's favorite activities—chasing or retrieving a toy, going for car rides, swimming, hunting for treats.

- Intermittently offer new toys and puzzle toys or rotate old toys to keep them "new."
- Provide comfy, not too warm, not too cool sleeping spots, and consider providing a heated dog bed (that your dog can move off of if he wants to) during the winter months.
- Launder your dog's bedding or covers once a week. Dogs love "clean sheets" as much as we do!
- Maintain a bedtime routine—go potty, turn down the lights, go to the sleeping spot.
- Minimize stress associated with veterinary visits. Speak to your veterinary team for pointers.
- Monitor your dog during outdoor time to prevent wandering, and keep an ID tag with your contact information on his collar. If your dog does not have one already, consider having a microchip implanted. And remember, you or your veterinarian must register the chip. A microchip is not a GPS tracker and is useless if it isn't registered to you.
- Attach a small signal LED light to your dog's collar to help you keep track of her in the yard at night.
- Use empty Greenies Pill Pockets or other flavor enhancers as frequent treats. Your dog will look forward to them even when they do contain medication he needs.
- If your dog typically receives only dry kibble at mealtimes, consider introducing a "Sunday/Wednesday dinner special" wherein you mix in a small portion of canned food one or two days a week. If possible, use the canned food version of your dog's dry food to help prevent gas or mild stomach upset. Many dogs will enjoy this novelty and start to look forward to it. You may be surprised by their ability to learn the days of the week!
- For especially picky eaters, try cutting or otherwise forming their food into small squares or tidbit-sized chunks, and then serve them spread out on a flat, washable surface (such as a cheap plastic cutting board or plate) rather than in their bowl. The new "serving platter" may make them more eager to snarf down what you're offering as well as provide another novelty at mealtimes to promote their sense of "snuffling" (foraging) for food!
- Use pheromones: Adaptil sprays or diffusers.
- Use a Hatch Baby night light that you can control from your phone.
- Play soothing music or nature sounds. Many sound machines are available. My dog Sam loves the sound of "babbling brook" the best.
- Hang a sign on your front door asking people not to ring or knock.
- Small dogs may be soothed by a baby swing in which they're safely and comfortably strapped in.

 Petunia has bad bouts of cognitive disturbance and difficulty falling asleep. Her pet parents discovered that a baby swing calms her and she falls asleep quickly.

Fun enrichment ideas to help stimulate the brain

- Cut a few small holes that are slightly larger than your dog's treats or kibble along the length of an empty cardboard paper towel roll. Staple one end of the tube together and pour treats or kibble in, then staple the other end together. Your dog will need to roll the tube around for the food to drop out. Supervise your dog whenever he uses it to make sure he doesn't chew up and eat the roll or the staples.
- Drape a hanging shoe organizer over the back of a chair and put treats in each reachable shoe compartment for your dog to find.
- Fill a small nonbreakable dish (a plastic cat bowl works great) with yummy low-sodium soup (like chicken noodle) and freeze it. Give it to your dog as a treat; it keeps them engaged and occupied while they lick it.
- Instead of feeding your dog's meals in their bowl, place the kibble in a trail around the edge of a wall or around the kitchen so they have to track their food. The hiding spots do not need to be elaborate!
- Use a Wooly Snuffle Mat (Paw5)
  https://paw5.com/pages/wooly-snuffle-mat
  or a Lickimat (Best Buddy Dog Products)
  https://www.bestbuddydogproducts.com/products/lickimat-soother
  to feed your dog or to place treats on.

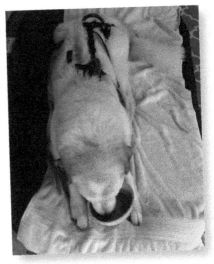

 Sam stays occupied for an hour licking her frozen treats.

- Place a treat in each cup of a muffin tin, then place tennis balls on top of each one, Now it's time to watch your dog hunt! For smaller dogs, place the treats in an empty egg carton and cover each compartment with a ping pong ball.
- Fill a small plastic baby swimming pool with plastic balls and watch curious dogs go nuts!
- Fill a laundry basket with plastic balls and hide a few of your dog's favorite (or new) toys inside so she can hunt for them.
- Place a few treats under a newspaper page or a small towel so your dog has to hunt for them.

 Sam enjoying her snuffle mat.

PRODUCT RECOMMENDATIONS

Brain support diets for dogs:

- Hill's Prescription Diet b/d Brain Aging Care
- Purina Pro Plan BRIGHT MIND
- Purina Pro Plan Veterinary Diets NC NeuroCare

Probiotic for dogs:

- Purina Pro Plan Veterinary Supplements Calming Care

Omega-3 fatty acids (from fish oil):

- Nordic Naturals: **https://www.nordicnaturals.com/petVet**

 READING RECOMMENDATIONS

- Animal acupressure and massage: **https://www.nbcaam.org/**
- Veterinary physical rehabilitation **https://rehabvets.org/training.lasso**, **https://vsmr.org/**

Copy and complete this checklist and share it with your veterinarian during your dog's semi-annual examinations. Schedule a veterinary visit sooner anytime your dog's signs concern you, or if your dog exhibits any of these signs once a week or more. Scan this QR Code to get a blank assessment:

Dog Cognitive Assessment

Cognitive Assessment Checklist for Dogs

Date	Dog's Name	Male/Female	Age	Breed

Current known medical or behavioral conditions

Category	Sign	Does not occur or is not applicable	Occurs once a month	Occurs once a week	Occurs once a day/night	Occurs more than once a day/night
Disorientation	Appears to get lost in the house or yard					
	Paces back and forth excessively or walks in circles					
	Vocalizes without apparent reason (barks or whines, or yowls)					
	Stares into space or stares absently at the floor or walls					
	Stands in corners, or stands at the hinge side of the door to be let out					
	Gets stuck under or behind furniture or other objects					
	Doesn't seem to recognize family members or housemate pets					
	Has trouble finding food or water bowls					

Category	Sign	Does not occur or is not applicable	Occurs once a month	Occurs once a week	Occurs once a day/night	Occurs more than once a day/night
Interactions	Less or no interest in greeting family members					
	Hiding or sleeping in unusual places					
	Less or no interest in being petted/more aloof					
	Irritable or aggressive with family members or housemate pets					
	Increased anxiety when family is away/doesn't like being left alone/more clingy					
Sleep/wake cycle	Sleeps more during the day and is awake more during the night					
	Paces at night, or is restless during sleep hours					
House soiling	Urinates inappropriately in the house					
	Defecates inappropriately in the house					
	Urinates but seems unaware					
	Defecates but seems unaware					
	Doesn't signal a need to go outside					
Activity and learning	Less or no interest in play or toys or in exploring new things					
	Less or no interest in going for walks					
	Seems to have forgotten trained commands or name					
	Exhibits repetitive behaviors (excessive grooming, licking inanimate objects)					

Category	Sign	Does not occur or is not applicable	Occurs once a month	Occurs once a week	Occurs once a day/night	Occurs more than once a day/night
Additional health concerns (from Pet Health Journal)						

CHAPTER 20:

Cancer: Things that go bump in senior dogs

> "Research has beaten polio, research has beaten smallpox, research is beating HIV and one day research will beat cancer. And the more research we do, the sooner that day will come."
>
> —CANCER RESEARCH UK VIDEO

My Doberman pinscher Neo had his first pee-pee accident in the house when he was 9 years old. I knew instantly that something was wrong, because even when he was a puppy, he was a model citizen during housetraining! Also, he'd never chewed up anything he shouldn't have. And he'd never been sick a day in his life, not even with anything minor like throwing up grass. He was pure perfection!

My mind quickly shuffled through a medical decision tree of possible causes for Neo's urine flood in the living room. I wasn't worried that his urine had crept onto a nearby area rug and a gym bag lying on the floor (although the bag wasn't

Neo was a perfect puppy!

Perfect grown-up Neo!

mine—whoops!). I worried about *why* it had happened. My thoughts settled on the top three possible illnesses for a canine boy his age: kidney disease, diabetes, and adrenal gland disease.

Neo didn't show any other signs of sickness. His body condition was perfect—he was sleek and muscular like a small stallion. His appetite was good. He didn't seem to be drinking more water, which any of the three illnesses I was worried about would have caused. His coat was shiny. Apart from his unexpected pee misadventure, he was perfect.

The next day I took Neo to the animal hospital where I practiced in South Florida. His radiographs looked fine, and his urine and blood test results didn't suggest diabetes or kidney disease, but they did indicate possible adrenal gland disease. The two adrenal glands are located in the abdomen near the top of each kidney, and they produce hormones that help regulate many body functions.

I began watching Neo more closely at home, and I realized he *was* making more trips to the water bowl than usual. So I tested his adrenal gland function with a blood test called an adrenocorticotropic hormone (ACTH) stimulation test.

The results confirmed Neo had *hyperadrenocorticism*, which meant one or both of his adrenal glands were overactive and producing too much of a steroid hormone called *cortisol*. Cortisol influences several body functions. One effect of too much cortisol is that it makes a dog drink more water and urinate more, which is why Neo had his first accident.

Hyperadrenocorticism (also known as *Cushing's syndrome*) can be caused by a tumor in the pituitary gland in the brain or in an adrenal gland. Dogs who receive high doses of corticosteroids (medications that produce the same effects as cortisol) can have signs that mimic hyperadrenocorticism, but Neo wasn't receiving any corticosteroids.

I needed to figure out whether Neo had a pituitary or adrenal tumor because their treatments differ. One way to do that is by looking at the adrenal glands with ultrasound. A pituitary tumor that sends too many messages to make cortisol makes *both* adrenal glands get bigger. (It's like sticking with an upper body workout program—both biceps get bigger if you lift weights equally with each arm!) If only one adrenal gland is big, then the tumor is likely in that adrenal gland, and not in the brain.

So one week after his first urinary accident, Neo was lying on his back in a quiet, darkened veterinary exam room having an abdominal ultrasound. He was so good-natured that he didn't even need to be sedated for his "belly-rub." A board-certified veterinary radiologist visited our clinic to do Neo's exam. It turned out that only one of Neo's adrenal glands was enlarged, and it was BIG! I kicked myself for not spotting it on his radiographs, but it's not always easy to see, which is why ultrasound is needed.

The next stop for Neo was surgery. He had a 50:50 chance that his adrenal tumor was benign, or self-limiting—a tumor that doesn't spread to other sites in the body. Of course that also meant that Neo had a 50:50 chance that his adrenal tumor was malignant. Malignant means harmful, uncontrolled growth that is invasive—a tumor that spreads to nearby tissues or elsewhere in the body. Still, I liked those odds! Because by surgically removing a benign adrenal tumor, Neo would be cured and I wouldn't need to treat his overactive adrenal gland medically.

Adrenal surgery is tricky and risky, so I enlisted the skills of Dr. Nick Bacon, a board-certified veterinary surgeon at the University of Florida College of Veterinary Medicine to perform Neo's surgery. He's not only an expert surgeon, he was one of my professors in veterinary school.

And I knew Neo would also be under the best care of the college's board-certified veterinary anesthesiologists and their team who I knew well (thank you Dr. Sheilah Robertson and Dr. Luisito Pablo and all the anesthesia nurses!).

A week later, I dropped Neo off for surgery and went back to my hotel room to wait for the call that he was out of surgery and in the recovery room. I spent the first of six stressful hours trying to answer work emails but had a hard time focusing. So I tried to zone out in front of the TV but couldn't focus on that either. Then finally came the call—Neo's surgery went well! Dr. Bacon told me I could visit Neo and said he wanted to show me Neo's tumor.

 Neo's angry adrenal tumor.

When I got there, I gave Dr. Bacon a big hug of gratitude. Then he placed the container that held Neo's tumor on the exam table and used tongue depressors to lift the tumor out of the preservation solution. Now, not all tumors follow this rule (and cells need to be examined under the microscope to confirm), but if a tumor is smooth, evenly round, and walled off (encapsulated)—not gnarly looking—then it's likely a benign tumor. But the thing he pulled from the container looked like a small, angry alien! It was unevenly bumpy, had semi-organized lobes, and was downright fierce-looking—like it had nowhere to go except everywhere. My heart sank, because I knew the odds now favored that this was a nasty, malignant tumor.

Dr. Bacon told me that he also took biopsy samples of Neo's liver, spleen, and a few of his abdominal lymph nodes to check whether the tumor had spread. We would need to wait for a veterinary pathologist (a veterinarian who specializes in diagnosing disease by looking at cells, tissues, and blood and other bodily fluids with a microscope) to review the samples.

Within a few days after surgery Neo had recovered like a champ and was discharged from the veterinary hospital. We made the five-hour drive home together, and he played with his squeaky toys the moment we arrived. He was in good spirits and acted like nothing was wrong. A couple days after that, I got the news confirming that his adrenal tumor was malignant and had already spread to his liver.

I wanted to know all the next potential treatment options for this cancer, so I made an appointment to consult with Dr. Stephanie Correa, a veterinary oncologist (a veterinarian with advanced specialized training in treating cancer in pets) in South Florida. She greeted me with a big smile and loved up on Neo. Then she turned to me and said, "His cancer is really aggressive and the prognosis is not good."

In a nanosecond, I forgot my educational background and went from knowledgeable veterinarian to scared pet parent. "What does that mean, Dr. Correa?" I asked.

She instantly recognized that she needed to explain everything to me like she would for every other pet parent. Dr. Correa told me the survival statistics for malignant adrenal tumors in dogs. Then she gently said, "You will have seven weeks together without chemotherapy, and seven months together with chemotherapy."

I had a decision to make.

Almost everyone that I tell this story to assumes that I didn't choose chemotherapy for Neo because I wouldn't want to "put him through that." But he'd recovered so well after his surgery, and I knew that if I decided against chemotherapy, I would sorely miss having him in my life for those extra months that the chemo could've given us. I knew that his cancer would kill him, not the chemotherapy. So if this additional treatment would have minimal side effects, then I wanted us to have that extra time.

So we began Neo's trips to the oncologist every few weeks so he could receive chemotherapy (and lots of love from the whole team at the oncology office).

A leading life-threatening disorder

Entire books have been written about cancer in dogs, and I feel I do this disease an injustice by devoting only one chapter to it. But my goal is not to cover every type of cancer and its treatment options. I want to cover the basics, list abnormalities to watch out for, and suggest questions to ask your veterinarian. And if your dog has a cancer diagnosis, I hope to provide some comfort as you navigate that news and your dog's care. Cancer is such a plague for senior dogs, so I want to provide a bit of insight.

At least 4 million dogs develop some form of cancer every year. (Vail 2019) But the exact percentages of dogs who have cancer or who are likely to develop cancer have been a challenge to determine, and these numbers are still not precisely known. (Vail 2019) Other cancer estimates suggest that roughly 6 million new cancer diagnoses are made in dogs and cats each year. (NIH reference) Cancer is the number one cause of death in dogs over 10 years of age—50% of older dogs develop some form of cancer, and about one in four dogs ultimately die from it. (Davis 2014) In a survey conducted by the Morris Animal Foundation in 1998, cancer was said to be the biggest cause of death related to disease in dogs (47%) and cats (32%). (Vail 2019)

I also wonder whether these percentages are a bit low, because over 30% of dogs are not seen by their veterinarian during their geriatric lifestage (M. Gardner, DVM, unpublished data, August 2019) and many undiagnosed cases of pet cancer probably exist.

Rogue cells: the building blocks of destruction

Cells are the basic building blocks of the body and contain thousands of genes. Cells divide all day every day to grow, to repair themselves, or to replace abnormal cells. When a cell divides, it follows a stringent set of "rules," and a copy of its genes is passed along to the new cell. However, sometimes cells go rogue and begin to grow and divide without rules! These rogue cells are referred to as:

- a growth, a mass, or a tumor—tumor means "swelling or protuberance" or "abnormal cell growth"
- a neoplasm, or neoplasia—which means "new growth of abnormal tissue"
- cancer—which refers to a tumor or to neoplasia that is malignant.

Tumors and neoplasia may be benign (self-limiting) or they may be malignant (invasive). By definition, the term cancer always means malignant.

These rogue cells can grow so large and numerous that they crowd out normal cells and an affected organ can no longer function properly. The rogue cells can also invade neighboring spaces, and they can even travel to other parts of the body through the circulatory system and cause havoc far from where they started. In some cases, the rogue cells also continue to function but overproduce the substance they are supposed to make, such as a hormone, which causes illness—Neo's encounter with Cushing's syndrome being the perfect example.

A tumor is usually described by the organ it affects and named after the type of cell it originates from. For example, in Neo's case, he had adrenal adenocarcinoma. The affected organ was his adrenal gland. And adenocarcinoma means that the tumor originates from the epithelial cells (cells that line body surfaces—skin, organs, blood vessels, urinary tract) within a gland.

Many of the tumors and cancers we see in dogs are the same that we see in people. Some tumors grow slowly, and we may not catch them until they have done years of damage. Some tumors grow extremely quickly and seem to appear out of nowhere. Some stay put and some travel. Some can be treated with surgery, while others need chemotherapy or radiation therapy or a combination of all of those things. Cancer is tricky!

Lumps and bumps

Cancer cells often form a cluster that becomes a mass, growth, or tumor. Veterinarians need to take a sample of the tumor to identify the cell origin and evaluate whether the cells are benign and self-limiting or malignant and aggressively invasive. It's important to evaluate every single lump and bump on a dog!

In fact, my good friend and veterinary oncologist Dr. Sue Ettinger started a program for veterinarians and dog owners called "See Something, Do Something: Why Wait? Aspirate!" (Visit her website at **www.drsuecancervet.com/why-wait-aspirate**.) This memorable phrase signifies that if you, your groomer (sometimes they find bumps first!), or your veterinarian *sees something* like a lump or bump on your dog that is the size of a pea or larger and it has been there for a month, then your veterinarian needs to *do something*—evaluate it. Veterinarians can evaluate a lump or bump by removing cells from it with a needle (called a fine-needle aspirate) or by performing a biopsy (surgically cutting a small sample from the mass or removing the mass entirely) and looking at the cells under a microscope.

One of my senior canine patients had about 20 grape-size and larger bumps in various places on his body. His owner told me, "They are nothing. They are just fat bumps, doc!" And for the most part, he was right. Except one of those bumps turned out to be a mast cell tumor. Mast cells are a type of blood cell involved in immunity, especially in the body's response to allergies. Mast cell tumors need to be surgically removed. Some can behave in a benign manner for a long time, or they can be malignant and extremely aggressive from the start. The dog's owner was grateful that we aspirated and evaluated every one of his dog's bumps.

It's important to be proactive and test a lump or bump and not simply "keep an eye on it." And if the test results show that the growth is indeed "nothing" (benign), then that's the best news to receive, and the best news is always well worth the cost—it's priceless peace of mind.

So remember the "see something, do something" rule, and schedule a veterinary visit to evaluate every single lump and bump!

Tumor behavior

Benign tumors stay put and don't invade other tissues, so if the tumor has been confirmed to be benign, they are usually fine to leave alone. But sometimes they can get aggravated or can obstruct surrounding tissues. One of my canine patients had a fatty bump (technically called a *lipoma*–a benign tumor that contains fat cells) on his hind leg that he would not stop licking, so the skin around it kept getting infected. I surgically removed the lipoma, his infection went away, and he stopped licking the area.

Many lipomas stay small and don't cause trouble, but some grow extremely large and get in the way. I once removed a lipoma from a dog's flank that had grown so large that he couldn't move his right front leg properly. After I removed the lipoma and sutured the gaping wound, I put the tumor on the scale. It weighed a whopping 11 pounds! The dog weighed 88 pounds on the way in and 77 pounds on the way out! More importantly, he could walk smoothly from that day forward.

Malignant tumors can be slow or fast-growing. Their cells can invade neighboring tissue or catch a ride in the bloodstream or in the lymphatic system (a network of vessels, tissues, and organs that help fight infection, maintain fluid balance, and remove toxins) and can end up anywhere in the body (called *metastasis*). The treatment options include surgery, chemotherapy, radiation therapy, and others—or a combination of treatments. And you may also decide not to treat it at all.

Overview of lumps and bumps that may affect older dogs

BENIGN BUMPS

- **Adenoma.** Affects the gland cells in many areas of the body including the skin (e.g. sebaceous gland adenoma), thyroid gland, intestine, and mammary gland.

- **Fibroma.** Sometimes referred to as a skin tag, these small skin growths usually occur on the upper legs and lower chest of dogs and may stem from persistent pressure or friction.

- **Hemangioma.** Involves the cells of the blood vessels and can occur in the spleen.

- **Hematoma.** Informally known as "blood blisters." They occur if blood vessels rupture because of an injury, clotting disorder, or after surgery, and the blood collects in a pocket. I mention them here because hematomas typically occur as a swelling under the skin or on the outer ear. They can also occur in the spleen.

- **Lipoma.** Consists of fat cells.

- **Meningioma.** Originates from cells that line the membrane that covers the brain and spinal cord.

- **Papilloma.** A small, round cauliflower-like wart caused by a virus.

- **Sebaceous gland adenoma.** A small, round tumor that stems from the skin's oil-producing glands.

MALIGNANT MASSES

- **Adenocarcinoma.** Start in gland cells that produce fluids or secretions that keep tissues moist. They can affect many areas of the body, including the nose, throat, trachea, lung, stomach, intestine, gallbladder, or salivary, anal/perianal, sweat, and mammary glands.

- **Fibrosarcoma.** Stems from cells called fibroblasts that make up the body's fibrous soft tissue. These tumors can occur in the mouth or be felt as lumps under the skin on a dog's legs or trunk.

- **Glioma.** Originates from one or two types of brain cells.

- **Hemangiosarcoma.** Affects cells that line the blood vessels and is often found in the spleen and sometimes the heart.

- **Lymphoma.** Involves rogue cells in lymphocytes (white blood cells involved in immunity). This cancer can affect lymph nodes throughout the body, including those associated with the gastrointestinal tract and skin.

- **Mammary gland adenocarcinoma or carcinoma.** Stems from breast tissue gland cells. Primarily affects female dogs who are not spayed or who were spayed after 2 years of age. (Benign forms of these tumors can also occur, which are called mammary gland adenomas.)

- **Mast cell tumor.** Involves cells that produce histamine, a chemical released in response to allergy and causes itchiness. Mast cell tumors are most commonly found on the skin, but can affect the spleen, intestines, liver, and bone marrow (a specialized tissue in some bones that produces blood cells).

- **Melanoma.** Stems from the pigment-producing cells of the skin, so can also involve the toenail bed. It can also affect the mouth and eyes. (Some melanomas may be benign.)

- **Osteosarcoma.** Originates from bone cells and most often affects large- and giant-breed dogs.

- **Squamous cell carcinoma.** Stems from skin cells so it may also involve the toenail bed and paw pads; can also occur in the mouth.

- **Transitional cell carcinoma.** Involves urinary tract cells and most often affects the bladder.

How Summer saved her "fat" brother

Summer was a yellow Labrador retriever who had horrible hip dysplasia and arthritis. She was about 12 years old when her family asked me to euthanize her. When I pulled up to their house, two yellow Labradors were in the front yard sniffing the grass, and they both came to the car to greet me. Summer was a sweet girl, and the way she moved conveyed how stiff and uncomfortable she was. Her brother, Luke, was quite a character who wore a smile that stretched ear to ear. Luke was eager to lead me into the house. I noticed right away that he had quite a pot belly—it swayed when he walked!

When Summer, her human family members, and I got comfortable on the living room floor, Luke plopped down nearby, which made his bowling ball belly overly obvious. His mom caught me checking out his paunch and said, "We know. Luke is fat! He has put on a lot of weight in the last three months. We've been taking care of Summer and have been neglecting him. We've been giving him more treats because we feel guilty."

But I knew Luke was not fat. His was not a treat-induced belly. The rest of his body was quite slender, and only his abdomen was swollen. So I answered, "I'm here to help Summer, so I want to concentrate on her of course. But Luke isn't fat. I'm worried he has something more serious. Without examining him and running tests I can't be sure, but one of the things I'm worried about is that he has a mass on his spleen that slowly leaks blood into his abdomen." I went on to explain that these leaky masses are common in older large-breed dogs, and when the belly swells with blood, we call it *hemoabdomen*. And because of the slow internal blood loss, dogs have episodes of weakness and are almost unable to get up some days. Or they have a day where they won't eat and seem very tired, but then the next day, they seem better.

Luke's dad looked at me like I was a psychic and said, "YES! That is exactly how he has been acting!"

I knew that heart failure and a few other problems can also cause abdominal distention, so I encouraged the family to take Luke to their veterinarian for evaluation as soon as possible, and we turned our focus back to Summer.

The next day, Luke's mom called me to say that their veterinarian confirmed that Luke did have a splenic tumor, and they elected to have it and his spleen removed right away. The tumor weighed a whopping 16 pounds! A month later, Luke's family followed up and emailed me the great news from his pathology report that his tumor was benign. They also sent me a picture of Luke on a walk. He looked like a young, healthy, skinny boy again!

> ### Ticking time bomb tumors: Masses involving the spleen
>
> The spleen stores blood, removes old blood cells, and helps fight infections. Splenic masses can be benign (hemangioma, hematoma) or malignant (hemangiosarcoma). Some veterinarians refer to these masses as ticking time bombs. They are dangerous because at any moment the tumor can rupture, and the slow bleed turns to life-threatening hemorrhage. The treatment is removal of the tumor along with the spleen, and dogs can live normally without a spleen. If the tumor is benign, the pet can go on to live its normal lifespan. If the tumor is malignant, the surgery often helps them feel better for a few to several weeks. Dogs with hemangiosarcoma who undergo surgery and chemotherapy may live another five to 12 months and can have a good quality of life.

Tumor staging and grading

In addition to identifying the type of tumor and whether it is benign or malignant, veterinarians often need to identify the grade and stage of a malignant tumor. The grade tells us how aggressive the cancer cells are. The stage tells us whether the cancer has spread, and if it has spread, where it has gone and to what extent. Grading and staging help veterinarians identify the cancer's severity and treatment options as well as give a prognosis—a forecast about a dog's chance of recovery, the course of their disease, and expected survival time.

Grading involves sending a biopsy or tissue sample to a veterinary pathologist who evaluates the tumor cells under a microscope to see how abnormal the cells look compared with normal cells of that type. Cancer cells in low-grade tumors look and organize themselves more like healthy cells. Low-grade cancers have a better prognosis because they are usually less aggressive. The more abnormal and unorganized the cells look, the higher the grade. High-grade cancers are usually more disruptive and have a worse prognosis.

Staging means finding out how much cancer is present in the body and where it's located. It may involve special testing of the blood or cancer cells, imaging exams (radiography, ultrasonography, endoscopy, computed tomography, or magnetic resonance imaging), and biopsy of other tissues.

Follow-up tests may also be needed during and at the end of treatment to see how well the treatment is working. This may be done by repeating some of the initial tests done for staging and comparing the results.

Tumor treatments

Treatment options depend on the type, location, and severity of the cancer, along with treatment availability. Some treatments may need to be provided at other practices or at veterinary specialty hospitals. Another important factor involves carefully considering your caregiving and financial abilities.

Many cancer treatment options are available and more than one type of treatment may be needed. Some treatments can be curative, others can delay the cancer's growth or spread, and some may not work against the cancer at all. Keep in mind that a certain treatment that worked well for a friend's dog may not work for your dog—every patient is different and not all tumors respond in the same way.

In addition to treatment for the cancer, dogs may need supportive treatments such as pain medications, antinausea medications, appetite stimulants, antibiotics, probiotics, nutritional supplements, and subcutaneous or intravenous fluid therapy.

Surgery

If a tumor can be surgically removed, the surgeon attempts to take out the entire tumor along with enough tissue around the tumor to obtain "clean margins." This means that normal cells are present at the edges of the removed tissue and presumes that no tumor cells have been left behind to continue growing.

Veterinarians are fairly good at evaluating where a tumor starts and stops, but we still can't use only our naked eyes or simply feel a tumor to know how far the tumor cells reach. So we also use established surgical guidelines for tumor removal to decide how much tissue around the tumor to remove. Then we send the tumor and tissue to a veterinary pathologist who uses microscopic examination to identify whether the tumor has "fingers" that extend from the tumor and, if so, how far. If the pathology report says "clean margins," that means no tumor fingers extend to the edges and the tumor has been adequately removed! If tumor cells are present at the margins, another surgery or a different type of treatment may be needed.

In patients with tumors too extensive to completely remove or too close to vital structures, the surgeon removes as much of the tumor as possible. This is called *debulking*. It's also sometimes done to alleviate a patient's discomfort or to reduce the number of cancer cells, which can help us better attack the remaining cancer cells with other treatment methods, such as chemotherapy or radiation therapy.

Chemotherapy

A wide variety of chemotherapeutic drugs are available and are used to attack fast-growing cancer cells. Depending on the drug, your dog may need to take pills or injections under the skin (subcutaneous), into the muscle (intramuscular), or into the blood (intravenous). Many of the drugs used to treat cancer in dogs are used to treat cancer in people.

Dogs usually tolerate chemotherapy well. About 80% to 90% of dogs experience no side effects from chemotherapy. Less than 5% of dogs need hospitalization related to chemotherapy side effects. (Chun 2007, MacDonald 2009) Side effects can happen because chemotherapy agents often also attack fast-growing normal cells like those in the gastrointestinal tract, bone marrow (which produces blood cells), and hair.

The side effects that occur in 10% to 15% of dogs are typically milder than those that occur in people. Reduced appetite, nausea, and diarrhea are most common. Often we can provide medications that alleviate some of those side effects, and I suggest giving them regardless of whether those side effects occur. For example, when Neo was receiving chemotherapy, I gave him medication to treat nausea and diarrhea on the morning of his treatment and continued it for three days afterward. It's easier to keep discomfort at bay than try to chase it away! Sam got the same preventative treatment during her chemotherapy.

Many pet parents are surprised to learn that hair loss is not a typical side effect of chemotherapy in dogs as it is in people. The hair growth cycle of dogs differs from ours. However, breeds (or some mixed breeds) who need regular haircuts, such as poodles, Old English sheepdogs, schnauzers, shih tzus, Maltese, and terriers, may indeed lose hair. And any dogs who have shaved areas during chemotherapy (e.g. because of surgery for tumor removal) may regrow the hair in that area quite slowly, and the regrowth may be a different color. Hair loss is not a sign that chemotherapy should be stopped, and the hair that is lost during chemotherapy typically regrows afterward.

Some chemotherapy drugs cause bone marrow suppression, so fewer blood cells are produced. The blood cells most often affected are neutrophils (a type of white blood cell that helps fight infection) and platelets (cells that form blood clots to prevent excessive bleeding). A low number of neutrophils circulating in the blood is called *neutropenia*, and a deficiency of platelets is called *thrombocytopenia*. Veterinarians will monitor these cell counts during chemotherapy and adjust the timing of treatments if needed.

A few of the chemotherapeutic drugs can cause organ-specific side effects like heart or kidney injury, and veterinarians monitor dogs closely for indicators of these problems as well.

Radiation therapy

For some types of cancer, delivering high doses of radiation to the tumor is the best option. Radiation is targeted to the tumor, and usually no other organs are damaged, although surrounding skin or mucous membrane irritation can occur. Radiation therapy requires multiple treatments, and the dog must be anesthetized each time because the dog has to stay still while the radiation is delivered.

 My girl Sam received palliative radiation therapy for cancer in her spinal cord. Here she's anesthetized and ready for treatment.

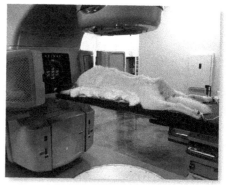

 Sam's radiation therapy took only 10 minutes, once a day for five days.

Immunotherapy

Veterinary-specific treatments that recruit a dog's immune system to fight some types of cancer are available for dogs, including monoclonal antibodies and vaccines. Monoclonal antibodies used in cancer treatment are molecules that act like the body's natural antibodies to recognize cancer cells and tackle them in a variety of ways. Vaccines include inactive components similar to those within cancer cells, and these components teach the body to recognize them so the body can launch an immune response against the cancer cells.

Do (somewhat) nothing

Another option is to not pursue cancer treatment. I hesitate to say "do nothing," because you won't truly be doing nothing—you will still be caring for your dog by treating and managing their symptoms and evaluating their quality of life.

Regardless of the decisions you and your family make about treating your dog's illness, you are making the right decisions for your situation. Every dog, every cancer, every family, every circumstance is different. In order to make the right decision and know that you have done so, it's crucial to first gather all the information, and then make an informed decision.

Seeing a veterinary oncologist

A primary care veterinarian (like myself) can help identify, stage, grade, and even treat many cancers in dogs. However, some cancer treatments require specialized knowledge and skills as well as specialized equipment, such as specially ventilated areas where chemotherapy drugs are prepared, advanced imaging technology like computed tomography or magnetic resonance imaging, or a linear accelerator, which is a machine that delivers radiation therapy. So your primary care veterinarian may recommend that you visit a veterinary oncologist.

Veterinary oncologists are invaluable. They have the latest and greatest cancer knowledge and medications plus access to advanced equipment. They also know the treatment outcome statistics better than anyone. Each of my own dogs who have had cancer have been evaluated by a veterinary oncologist, even if it was only for me to consult with the oncologist about my dog's options and prognosis.

Your veterinarian can recommend the oncologist closest to you. Depending on where you live, they are not always nearby. I know many dog owners who have driven hours to see a veterinary oncologist. Your veterinarian may also

consult with an oncologist using a teleconsulting service like Fidu (**www.FiduVet.com**). Oncologists can work directly with your veterinarian to provide information and treatment options and help guide

Duncan at the veterinary oncologist's hospital, waiting to get his melanoma vaccine.

them during treatment when appropriate. To find an oncologist near you, you can also search the Veterinary Cancer Society website: **www.vetcancersociety.org**.

Neo's response to chemotherapy

Neo tolerated chemotherapy well. He didn't mind the car rides to the oncologist, and he always got extra love during his treatments. I have been so impressed with the level of care all my dogs received at the oncology practice. Oncologists know that we pet parents need extra TLC as well.

During the last six weeks of Neo's life, he started showing signs of decline. He began to have muscle wasting, eating became a struggle, and he got weaker. I knew that his cancer was taking over. And I doubled down on caregiving and love!

I stocked up and got Neo about 20 new squeaky toys to keep him busy, we took tons of pictures and videos of him playing, and I started to home cook for him. He had become a picky eater, so I expanded my "chef skills." I learned that he loved scrambled eggs and that I could hide his medications in them fairly well. I started a daily diary and tracked Neo's joy level, appetite, and medications.

Neo and a few of his play buddies.

Neo loved to attack the sprinkler heads in our yard, so I turned them on a few extra times each day so he could joyfully engage in his water battles.

After he started having accidents in the house every few hours, I created "Neo's Zone" in one of our hallways. I filled it with fluffy towels, bath mats and other things that I could easily wash. I had to barricade his zone with a baby gate, and it broke my heart to

Neo's "accident-approved" zone.

put him in there, even for only a few hours. So I gave him a new toy every day to keep his mind active and happy while he was "in jail."

Thanksgiving that year was extra special—I was especially thankful to have my boy Neo to share it with. I learned so much from Neo—not only about Cushing's syndrome, cancer, and chemotherapy, but also about caregiving and the feeling of hopelessness. I also learned about how important it is to have a great support network and to rely on my colleagues, like Dr. Correa, for advice.

Mutual best buddies, me and Neo.

Neo's diagnosis was made in April of that year and he died in late November, exactly seven months after I first met with Dr. Correa. Many people disagreed with my decision for Neo to receive chemotherapy, but I know my decision gave him a good quality of life and a longer life (at least five extra months, and for a dog of Neo's age, that may equal about 1.5 people years!). And of course it gave me the gift of those extra, awesome months with him. I have no regrets!

See your veterinarian if your dog:

- Has a mass that's the size of a pea or larger that has been there for a month.
- Has a wound that won't heal.
- Has a mass that changes shape, color, or size.
- Constantly licks, rubs, or scratches at a spot.
- Has nose bleeds.
- Frequently paws at his nose or mouth.
- Sneezes excessively.
- Has bad breath or trouble chewing.
- Drools excessively.
- Has pale gums.
- Has a swollen belly.
- Exhibits abdominal pain. Dogs with belly pain sometimes stretch out in a "prayer position" with their front legs extended on the ground in front of them and their hind end in the air, or they stand rigid and hunched up. Dogs with abdominal pain may also cry out or resist being picked up.

- Strains to urinate or has discolored urine.
- Has seizures.
- Exhibits other signs of illness: vomiting, diarrhea, having accidents in the house, behavior changes, coughing, unexplained weight loss, weakness or exercise intolerance, excessive panting or shortness of breath, lameness, rough or thin hair coat or hair loss.

 ## Questions to ask your veterinarian (or veterinary oncologist)

- What diagnostic tests will be needed? What are the costs?
- Does my dog need to be sedated or anesthetized for the diagnostic procedures?
- Why does the aspirate, biopsy, or tissue sample need to be sent to a pathologist?
- What will happen if I choose not to do tests?
- How long will my dog live without treatment?
- How will the disease progress if I choose not to pursue treatment?
- Does my dog need to visit a veterinary oncologist?
- Will the treatment cure my dog? How long will my dog live with treatment? Will the treatment help my dog feel better?
- What treatments will be needed, how will they be given, how often, and for how long?
- What are the side effects of treatment? Will the side effects subside? Can the side effects be treated?
- What signs or problems do I need to watch out for?
- What do I do if problems occur after regular business hours?
- How will we know whether the treatment is working? How long before we know whether it's working?
- What follow-up tests and exams will be needed and how often?
- Does my dog need a special diet or nutritional supplements?
- Will other therapies like acupuncture, herbs, or homeopathy help my dog in addition to standard treatment?
- Will my dog benefit from physical rehabilitation therapy?
- If a standard cancer treatment is not an option, is my dog eligible to participate in a cancer treatment clinical study?
- Will my dog benefit from hospice treatment now or in the near future?

CAREGIVER TIPS AND HOME HACKS

- Provide a cozy, supportive bed and comfy sleeping area.
- Keep food and water easily accessible.
- Provide non-slip walking surfaces and ramps or steps where needed.
- Keep a dog health journal to track your dog's attitude, appetite, and activity.
- Treat your dog's pain, nausea, and diarrhea by staying ahead of their symptoms and giving medications consistently and on schedule.
- Limit your dog's stress and stick to routines.
- Provide calming pheromones. Ask your veterinarian about calming supplements and mild sedatives if needed.
- Take a few minutes every day to engage your dog in an activity she enjoys.
- Feed highly palatable foods appropriate for your dog, and feed canned food or moistened kibble if needed. Talk with your veterinarian about diet options.
- Comb or brush your dog regularly to help him groom and to check for lumps and bumps.
- See Chapter 5 "Nose: The better to smell you with" for tips on managing a dog's bloody nose (for dogs who have nasal tumors).

 READING RECOMMENDATIONS

- Veterinary oncologist Dr. Sue Ettinger's website: **https://drsuecancervet.com/**
- Morris Animal Foundation website: **https://www.morrisanimalfoundation.org/**
- Veterinary Cancer Society website: **http://vetcancersociety.org/**
- Book: "The Dog Cancer Survival Guide" by Dr. Demian Dressler and Dr. Sue Ettinger

CHAPTER 21:

Pain:
If only our dogs could talk
about discomfort, malaise,
anxiety, and suffering

"And even if an animal could talk, would we listen?"

— VIRGINIA MORELL, AMERICAN SCIENCE WRITER

I've always had a soft spot for Doberman pinschers, and my classmates in veterinary school knew that if one was admitted to the teaching hospital at the University of Florida, I would jump on the case! One morning during my small animal medicine rotation, the attending veterinary resident brought the students up to speed on a Doberman named Sasha who had been admitted the night before for treatment of severe, massive burns on her back.

Sasha's injury had occurred about five days earlier while the family was on vacation. Sasha's dog sitter took her to the family's primary care veterinary clinic where she was hospitalized, but her wounds had become infected. Well-intentioned use of a heating pad that had gone awry was suspected to have caused her burns. Sasha needed additional specialized care to heal properly, so the primary care veterinarian referred her to the veterinary school hospital.

The resident started to ask which student would take Sasha's case, but she didn't have a chance to finish her sentence before I playfully snatched the chart from her grasp!

I reviewed Sasha's medical record and hurried off to start her morning treatments. As I approached the intensive care unit doorway, a horrendous odor hit me. Then I saw Sasha, a black and tan Doberman, standing gingerly still in the ward, as if she were afraid to move. Most of her body was bandaged except her head and legs. She looked at me with her sweet, sad eyes, and I fell in love.

I carefully lifted her onto the examination table. The smell of her wounds almost made me gag as I introduced myself. "Hi, Sasha, I'm Mary. You are such a GOOD girl!" I was surprised to see her little tail nub, which was sticking out from behind her bandages, wiggling back and forth. A hint of joy despite her recent suffering.

 Sasha on her way to recovery during my senior year in veterinary school.

I gently unwrapped Sasha's mummy-like bandages, and I was horrified. She had third-degree burns (the top layers of her skin were gone) over the entire top of her back. Her tissues were swollen, oozing, and smelly—clearly infected. It broke my heart. I was grateful to be there to alleviate her pain and help her heal. Sasha stood like a statue while I treated her wounds. She didn't snip at me; she didn't even growl. Other students stopped by and commented, "She's being so quiet; she must not be in any pain." And I could not disagree more. Of course she was in pain! Normally, Sasha should be bouncing around like a happy young dog. Instead, she barely moved. Although she wasn't vocalizing in pain, I knew her pain was something we needed to continue to proactively treat, along with her wounds.

Sasha was one of the most distressingly injured AND most amazing patients I helped treat during veterinary school. She was hospitalized for a month and received intensive wound care, skin graft surgery, and intensive postoperative care that included antibiotics and opioid pain medications. I always gave her extra TLC and treats, made sure her bedding was as comfy as possible, and kept noise in her ward to a minimum as best as I could. Sasha healed well and returned to her happy, bouncy self. She ended up with a massive scar on her back, but she was still a gorgeous girl and had no long-lasting issues from her injury.

Sasha's scar. Still a beautiful, happy girl!

Understanding the pathway that pain travels

When we badly stub a toe, the nerve endings, called *nociceptors*, in our skin, muscle, and bone sense it. They detect mechanical, thermal, and chemical tissue damage. (Nociceptors are also present in our organs.) The pain signals travel as electrical impulses from the nociceptors along nerve fibers to the spinal cord.

In an area of the spinal cord called the dorsal horn, the signal travels between neurons through junctions called *synapses*. In the synapses, chemical messengers called *neurotransmitters* are released. Neurotransmitters send signals back

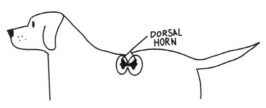

down to your toe as a reflex (and you jerk your foot back!) and, at the same time, send signals up the spinal cord to a part of the brain called the *thalamus*.

From the thalamus, the message is distributed to many different brain compartments for additional processing so you know where the pain came from and how much it hurts; whether to be sad, angry, or afraid (or all of those!); and whether you need to take further action. The brain also begins to process how that particular pain will be remembered.

The part of the brain responsible for physical sensation is called the *somatosensory cortex*. The part of the brain responsible for emotions is called the *limbic system*. And one of many parts of the brain responsible for personality and consciousness is called the *frontal cortex*. All or some of these parts of the brain become involved in the pain pathway and influence how the body responds to pain!

What's the point of all this messaging?

Pain allows us to know that something harmful has happened and that we need to respond to it to make it stop. Processing pain messages helps us avoid, prevent, and remember unpleasant incidents or encounters and protect ourselves from more hurt. In this way, pain messages are beneficial. But if pain lasts a long time and isn't adequately relieved or if it is extremely severe even for a short time, pain messages can become harmful and provide little or no benefit.

A peek at some of the many causes of pain

- Physical trauma such as falling or getting hit, cut, or bitten
- Thermal trauma such as sunburns, frostbite, or heating pad burns
- Chemical trauma such as burns from corrosive substances

- Internal organ problems such as pancreatitis (pancreas inflammation), gastritis (stomach inflammation), urinary tract blockage, or a tumor of the spleen
- Skin, ear, tooth, and eye infections
- Surgery such as stomach or intestinal foreign body removal (e.g. toys, rocks, socks, bones, fishing line or hooks), tumor removal, tooth extractions, or fracture repair
- Degenerative and inflammatory conditions such as arthritis
- Brain or spinal cord problems such as a brain tumor or intervertebral disk disease

Short-term pain vs. long-term pain

When it comes to pain, veterinarians and physicians generally distinguish between two types—acute and chronic. Acute pain is sudden and typically lasts until the insult is removed and the injury has healed. Chronic pain is long-term and accompanies an ongoing condition or continues after an injury has healed.

Another way to describe pain is to use the terms *adaptive pain* and *maladaptive pain*. (Robertson [3] 2020) Adaptive pain is beneficial; it's necessary for survival and results from the "early warning" nociceptors that signal damaging stimuli such as high heat, blunt force, and inflammation associated with tissue damage. Adaptive pain is usually reversible or self-limiting if it's treated correctly. Maladaptive pain isn't beneficial; it results from nerve damage or nociceptive system malfunction, and it contributes to decreased pain threshold and hypersensitivity. (Robertson [3] 2020)

Acute pain

People usually describe acute pain as a sharp pain, and it can last a moment or for a day—or several weeks. Acute pain in pets can result from trauma (e.g. hit by a car, broken leg), surgery (e.g. to repair a knee injury or remove a foreign body or tumor), or disease (e.g. dental infection, bladder inflammation).

Acute pain occurs because of tissue damage, and the nerves in the area send signals to the brain to tell us to avoid the source and help prevent us from using the injured area and doing more damage while we heal. After Sasha's injury healed, we expected that she would no longer be in pain. Still, acute pain must be managed! In fact, pain control is known to help speed healing. Pain control also, of course, improves quality of life.

Dogs usually show outward signs of acute pain that are obvious to us. They may whine, yip, flinch, growl, bite, hide, or limp. But keep in mind that dogs with pain may also still wag their tails, lick you, eat, sit on your lap, be happy to see you, or even try to run on a broken leg. Many clients who brought their limping dogs to me for evaluation would tell me, "Well, he's eating and wagging his tail, so I don't think he's in any pain."

If an animal is limping, the animal has pain. If an animal has inflammation, the animal has pain. If your dog has an injury or condition that would clearly be painful if you or I had the same problem, your dog is in pain. Unless their pain is extreme, dogs who have pain often still have an appetite. And wagging tails are not diagnostic tools that confirm the absence of pain (oh, how I wish they were!).

Chronic pain

Chronic pain persists. The pain signals keep coming long after the injury has healed, and it can last months or years. (In people, chronic pain is often described as pain that lasts longer than six months.) Chronic pain can also stem from long-term health problems that continuously cause damage.

The most common chronically painful condition I see in dogs is arthritis, also called *osteoarthritis* and *degenerative joint disease* (see Chapter 17 "Mobility: The weak, wobbly, and unsteady"). Often, the dog's family doesn't notice the signs. For example, dogs with healthy joints get up from a lying down position by putting weight on their hind legs first and using them to push their body up, followed by their front half. But when dogs have hip, knee, or lower back arthritis, they switch it up. They get up from lying down by putting most of their weight on their front legs first.

Like acute pain, chronic pain must be managed. Pain relief improves quality of life for dogs and prevents or helps reduce the long-term effects of chronic pain, such as worsening of pain, anxiety, and chronic stress. Pain management also helps maintain a healthy, happy, interactive bond between pet parents and dogs. Recognizing and managing chronic pain can be lifesaving because chronic pain that is inadequately identified and poorly managed can lead to premature euthanasia. (Epstein 2015)

The non-helpful effects of chronic pain

Pain stimulates stress responses that involve hormones and other chemical messengers, which are good in the short term because they help an animal decide whether to fight or flee the source of the pain. These chemical messengers also stimulate other cells that are recruited to help with healing. But long-term pain and stress responses can be damaging.

Chronic stress suppresses the immune system so the body can't fight off infection and heal its wounds as well. Stress may even promote cancer spread, as studies in mice have shown. (NIH National Cancer Institute) Stress-related changes you may notice include muscle weakness, hair changes, and weight loss. Hair changes?! People often say, "I'm losing my hair from stress!" Dogs can experience this coat-depleting characteristic as well because of stress-related chemical reactions in the body induced by chronic pain.

Another uncomfortable effect of chronic pain - the central nervous system (brain and spinal cord) can overreact to chronic pain. The nerve fibers that carry pain signals and the nerve fibers that carry touch signals end in different locations in the brain. But with chronic pain, chemical mediators stimulate the growth of some nerve fibers, and the pain and touch fibers become intertwined like a hair knot. This allows the touch nerve fibers to signal pain to the brain in response to normal, nonpainful touch. This is called *hypersensitivity* or *allodynia*. It explains why some dogs snip in response to simply being petted, when previously they would have welcomed a good love session! Even something as benign as a fan blowing on a dog can cause them pain with allodynia.

The pain nerve fibers can also grow in different directions, which increases the size of the painful area. And pain receptors can become more easily stimulated, which lowers the pain threshold and increases the amount of time that the pain lasts. When this happens, what would normally feel like a minor pain feels much more painful.

Anticipating and fearing pain

Dogs with acute or chronic pain or hypersensitivity can have anticipatory pain, which means the dog responds *before* the painful stimulus occurs because they know it will hurt. For example, you reach for your dog and they growl or snip before you touch their painful area. It's their way of saying, "Please don't!"

In addition, results of a 2018 study suggest that noise sensitivity in dogs may be a sign of pain. Dogs with underlying painful muscle or bone conditions who hear a loud noise and tense up experience more pain that they then associate with the noise. So dogs who seem anxious or fearful when they hear or anticipate loud or sudden noises should have a veterinary examination to check for pain-related problems. (Lopes Fagundes 2018)

Did you know? Pain, older age, floor surface, and obesity can make hallways look longer!

A study in people who have chronic lower back or leg pain revealed that they perceived a long hallway to be 30% longer, compared with people who do not have pain. (Witt 2009) By simply looking at the hallway and estimating its distance (and not walking it), people with chronic pain estimated that the hallway was longer than the estimates of people without painful conditions.

Similarly, a separate study showed that older adults estimate distances to be farther compared with younger adults' estimates. Older adults also estimate distance to be farther on surfaces that are more difficult to walk on (carpet covered with a plastic tarp vs. carpet alone) than younger adults do. (Sugovic 2013)

Furthermore, another study found that people who are overweight or obese estimate distances to be farther than normal weight people do. (Sugovic 2016) The researchers stated that these results suggested that because heavier people perceive their environment differently, they may choose to do less demanding tasks that affect their lifestyle choices than normal weight people do.

While we can't ask dogs to estimate distances, the results of these studies make me wonder whether these factors also similarly affect our dogs' willingness to participate in certain activities and walk on slick surfaces.

Assessing pain in dogs

Veterinary medical caregivers use pain scales to decide whether to adjust a patient's pain treatment protocol. For example, Colorado State University's Veterinary Medical Center developed pain scales to assess signs of acute and chronic pain in dogs (CSU Canine Chronic Pain Scale). A dog's facial expressions, body postures, specific behaviors, and responses to touch are evaluated and correlate with a scale of 0 (no pain) to 4 (extreme pain).

To help you recognize some of the subtle to more obvious signs of pain that dogs may be communicating, I've highlighted components of the Colorado State University Canine Chronic Pain Scale. Most of these signs overlap with dogs who have acute pain.

A dog with a pain score of 0
(therapy to relieve pain is not needed)

- Appears happy and energetic, has a confident posture and sits or stands with even weight distribution, has perky ears and a relaxed and alert expression, appears to be comfortable when resting
- Is interactive—interested in and curious about his surroundings, stands and walks with ease, bears weight evenly on all limbs
- Is responsive and appreciates attention, has minimal body tension and does not mind being touched, does not react to gentle handling of limbs or joints

A dog with a pain score of 1

(needs therapy to relieve discomfort)

- Appears quiet, is slightly restless, has an alert and slightly tense facial expression, holds her ears lower than normal and slightly pulled back
- Is subdued in interactions, is still easily distracted by goings-on in the environment, stands normally but may shift weight at times, may walk with mild lameness
- Is responsive but may not initiate engagement, has mild body tension, doesn't mind being touched except in the painful area, reacts mildly and turns to look at the painful area when the area is gently handled

A dog with a pain score of 2

(adjust or add therapy to better relieve pain)

- Appears anxious and uncomfortable even at rest, looks less bright-eyed, holds ears and head low, tucks tail and stands with weight unevenly distributed
- Hesitates to interact, still looks around to watch what is happening, may be uncomfortable at rest
- Is reluctant to come when called, is moderately lame when walking
- Has a mildly or moderately tense body, doesn't mind being touched far away from the painful area, pulls away if the painful area is touched

A dog with a pain score of 3

(further adjust or add therapy to better relieve pain)

- Appears afraid and may be irritable or aggressive, has dull eyes and lowered ears and head, stands in a tense or awkward posture—may have a slightly tucked abdomen and arched back
- Avoids interacting with people or anything happening in the environment, may lick or rub a painful area, won't put weight on a painful leg when walking, shifts body weight and changes position to guard the painful area
- Has moderate body tension; tolerates touch far away from the painful area; may yip, whine, bark, growl, snip, or bite when the painful area is touched

A dog with a pain score of 4
(further adjust or add therapy to better relieve pain)

- Appears depressed, lethargic, and uncomfortable even at rest; may be unresponsive
- Is difficult to distract from pain, is reluctant to get up, refuses to walk more than five steps, won't put weight on a painful limb when walking or standing still
- Has moderate to extreme body tension, dislikes being touched anywhere, reacts aggressively if the painful area is touched

Malaise

Sometimes dogs may not be feeling well and have malaise: discomfort, tiredness, weakness, and uneasiness. Malaise differs from acute or chronic pain but should be addressed. Nausea, dehydration, high blood pressure, diarrhea, acid reflux, congestion, fever, toxins in the bloodstream, and anemia are only a few of the problems that can cause malaise. For example, nausea may not be considered to be painful, but I think it's as serious as the pain that occurs with arthritis, and, in some ways, nausea is worse.

I broke my foot a few years ago and it was painful! It swelled and turned purple, was ugly to see, and I could not walk on it for weeks. I took pain medications and sat on the couch with my leg propped up. I could watch TV, talk on the phone, eat the meals brought to me, and work from my laptop. I could tolerate the foot pain and I knew it would be better in a few weeks.

Two months after my foot healed, I caught a bad case of the flu. I had a fever of 103 F, chills, no appetite, and extreme fatigue. All I could do was lie in bed and moan about getting over the flu! I didn't feel like watching TV or reading, and working was out of the question. I remember being absolutely miserable and thinking that I would rather have *two* broken feet than have the flu. This was malaise, and to me, it was worse than pain. And at times, the malaise was even worse—I was suffering!

Anxiety

Norrin, my pointer-foxhound mix, has separation anxiety and is highly reactive to other animals. He has a hard time being left alone—he paces and whines excessively. Separation anxiety is a behavioral disorder wherein dogs become overly distressed when they're separated from their human family. Norrin also has anxiety around other dogs and cats and acts aggressively toward them. He lunges at them, barks frantically, yawns and licks his lips repeatedly, and rapidly and furiously wags his tail.

It has been a challenge to get Norrin to relax ever since I adopted him. From the moment I saw him at the shelter, I knew that he was not well. His ears were pulled back, he hung his head low, and his eyes were wide—his whole face reflected worry. It has taken a lot of training and patience and even some medication over the years to get him to a calmer emotional state. I had not fully appreciated the suffering that anxiety causes in an animal (and a family's experience in trying to manage it) until I adopted Norrin.

Medical conditions can also cause or contribute to various types of anxiety in dogs. Cognitive dysfunction and diseases that cause respiratory distress are at the top of that list for dogs, just as dementia and breathing trouble can cause anxiety in people. Many geriatric dogs have increased anxiety in a variety of situations, likely because they become less adept at responding to environmental changes or social cues as their body systems age. (Horwitz [1] 2020) In turn, anxiety can exacerbate pain, so take care to alleviate stressful situations that can lead to anxiety, such as aggression between housemate dogs or punishment for undesirable behavior. (Robertson [4] 2020)

Dogs who are stressed and anxious (and dogs who have separation anxiety) may yawn, lick their lips, shake off (like they have a wet coat), pant, pace, howl, whine, lick obsessively, scratch frantically at the door, drool, dig, escape, and destroy furniture. To me—and many of my colleagues agree—anxiety is a form of pain and suffering that dogs may experience and it should be treated to address the underlying cause and manage the dog's responses.

Suffering

Nearly every pet parent tells me, "I just don't want my dog to suffer." And I concur! I do not want any animal to suffer. When veterinarians take the veterinary oath, we swear to prevent and relieve suffering.

But what is suffering? We all have a general idea that suffering is to feel or undergo pain or distress, but the definition of suffering can be varied and highly individual. It can also carry religious and philosophical perspectives.

Suffering may involve a wide variety of extreme unpleasant experiences that stem from physical or psychological stimuli. (ACVAA Website) Physical suffering may include pain, hunger, thirst, illness, and dying. Mental suffering may include grief, anxiety, and loneliness. Unrelieved pain can cause suffering. (ACVAA Website) For me personally, suffering is a state of being where I can't think of or do anything besides concentrate on my pain, whether it's physical pain or emotional pain. When I was ill with the flu, I experienced physical suffering. When I lose a dog, I suffer emotionally. I appreciate how Cicely Saunders (a physician and pioneer in human hospice care) approached the concept of total pain—a mix of physical, emotional, and spiritual discomfort—which we now more commonly call suffering.

An easy way to think about suffering is that it is the opposite of happiness or pleasure. When I broke my foot, I still experienced happiness. But it is really hard to be happy while one is truly suffering.

Can animals be happy? I once was discussing happiness in animals with a group of veterinary students in Oregon, and one of the students asked, "Dr. Mary, aren't you anthropomorphizing when you say that animals can be happy?" I replied, "No, I am not. Animals can feel pleasure. They can be happy, and they can suffer."

As you navigate whether and how to treat your dog's illnesses and make their end-of-life decisions, you may think, "I don't want my dog to suffer," which can be hard for you to define. Instead, consider thinking, "I want my dog to be happy." Whether your dog can regain happiness or pleasure in life may be an easier attribute to strive for and an outcome that is clearer to visualize. (Also see Chapter 31 "Life quality: Doc, when is it time?")

When to see your veterinarian

Pain, malaise, anxiety, and suffering can be alleviated. Recognizing these problems in your dog and seeking treatment for the underlying cause as well as treatment for the pain itself helps preserve the bond you and your dog share. Please see your veterinarian if your dog exhibits any evidence of pain based on the pain scales included above or any of the following signs:

- Pants excessively (beyond what is expected in relation to exercise or warm temperatures)
- Persistently paces
- Is reluctant to sit
- Is slower to stand from a sit
- Is slower to get up or lie down
- Has difficulty getting up or lying down
- Avoids walking on tile or hardwood floors
- Holds head or tail lower than normal
- Preferably sits on one hip or the other with rear legs off to one side
- Shifts weight to one side while standing
- Shakes or trembles
- Is reluctant to be picked up
- Is hesitant to lift head or turn head to one side or the other
- Winces or moves away while being petted
- Is reluctant to be groomed

- Shies away from being touched in certain areas
- No longer gets up on the couch, bed, or favorite spot like before
- Is reluctant to jump into or out of the car
- Shows a new preference to lie on tiled floors (may be seeking cooler surfaces to ease joint or muscle pain)
- Is reluctant to go up or down stairs
- Exhibits personality changes, such as more fatigue, less activity, being quieter or depressed, being more irritable
- Has tense muscles or postures
- Has trouble posturing to eliminate
- Develops sensitivity to loud noises or seems more jumpy in response to sounds that didn't used to bother him
- Limps
- Exhibits a sawhorse stance
- Stands or walks with a tucked abdomen or arched back
- Stretches out in a "prayer position" with front legs extended on the ground in front of him and his hind end in the air—like a bow
- Is less bright-eyed—may have a sleepy, squinting, or vacant look; pupils may be enlarged
- Is lethargic or reluctant to move
- Eats or drinks less
- Hides; rests or sleeps in unusual places
- Prefers to eat or drink lying down
- Exhibits restlessness—repeatedly lies down and gets up again; may occur especially at night
- Has atypical vocalizing—whimpering, whining, growling
- Excessively scratches or licks
- Shakes, paws, rubs at, or scoots on a painful area
- Protects a painful area
- Drools excessively
- Has diarrhea or constipation
- Begins having urine or fecal accidents in the house

Managing pain

Response to pain varies tremendously among individuals and is influenced by many factors, including species, age, health status, sex, and breed. (ACVAA Website) For example, young animals may have a lower acute pain tolerance than mature animals, but may also be less likely to have anticipatory pain. Animals who are ill have a lower pain tolerance than healthy animals, and severely ill animals may experience severe pain but may be unable to exhibit signs of pain and therefore it may go unnoticed and untreated. Working dog breeds may have a higher pain tolerance than toy breed dogs (perhaps a bit like some human athletes who "play through the pain"). An individual dog's response to various forms of pain relief also varies.

The sooner we address pain, the better! Chronic pain is harder to treat, and multiple attempts that involve different therapies may be needed. (ACVAA Website) Whenever possible, taking care to not allow pain to develop in the first place is especially important. For example, veterinarians (and physicians) often provide *preemptive analgesia* by giving pain medications before surgery. This ensures that pain medications are "on board" *before* the pain stimulus occurs. And sticking to an optimal pain medication dose and on-time administration schedule after surgery, injury, or illness (and adjusting it as needed) allows pain medication to be reliably and continuously "on board," giving pain less opportunity to break through and send uncomfortable messages to the brain.

It's crucial to avoid repetitive pain signals because the nerves become more excitable and remain overreactive. This is called pain *wind-up*. When wind-up occurs, pain is more difficult to relieve. It often requires higher drug doses to control, and additional medications may be needed, which can result in added expenses, increased caregiving time, and additional side effects. Pain wind-up can also contribute to unremitting chronic pain.

I always say it's easier to keep pain away than to chase it away. Preventing or alleviating pain can also increase your dog's lifespan, which is invaluable.

Apart from resolving the underlying disease or condition, there is not one best way to address pain or malaise. Your pet's comfort is the goal, and it's important for pet parents to recognize that completely eliminating signs of pain is unusual, particularly in pets with chronic pain. In fact, it's helpful to think about chronic or maladaptive pain as a disease itself that must be managed. (Robertson [3] 2020)

Always work with or ask your veterinarian which medications and other therapies are right for your dog and your dog's ailment, and do not give your dog your own medications or another pet's medications.

I usually attack pain using a multimodal approach that may include one or more medications with or without non-drug treatments: (Also see Chapter 24 "Course of action: Therapeutic options and gaining acceptance from your senior dog.")

 Drugs used to relieve pain or malaise:

- o Gabapentin
- o Amantadine
- o Non-steroidal anti-inflammatory drugs (NSAIDs) (e.g. veterinary-specific drugs such as carprofen or grapiprant, meloxicam, or robenacoxib; also, do not give NSAIDs for people to your pet because they can be extremely harmful, and never give acetaminophen to cats)
- o Opioids (several types are available via prescription from your veterinarian)

- o Corticosteroids
- o Local or topical anesthetics
- o Alpha-2 agonists
- o Sedatives and tranquilizers (some of these drugs provide little to no pain relief, but they decrease anxiety and the emotional component of pain or boost the effectiveness of other pain medications)
- o Anti-nausea medications
- o Fluid therapy
- Nutraceuticals or supplements such as omega-3 fatty acids, glucosamine and chondroitin, and green-lipped mussel extract
- Environmental modifications (see the "Caregiver tips and home hacks" sections in Chapter 17 "Mobility: The weak, wobbly, and unsteady" and in the chapter specific to your dog's condition)
- Nutrition and therapeutic diets
- Physical rehabilitation therapy:
  - o Exercise
  - o Laser therapy
  - o Massage therapy
  - o Cooling or warming packs
- Acupuncture

Future therapies: The monoclonal wars are coming

Pain management is a robust area of research in people and in dogs. Species-specific monoclonal antibodies such as ranevetmab for dogs are being evaluated for their potential in managing the pain associated with osteoarthritis and may be available in the future. (Enomoto 2019, Lascelles 2015) Monoclonal antibodies are molecules that act like the body's natural antibodies (proteins that the body produces to fight harmful intruders or substances). They recognize damaging invaders such as bacteria and viruses, certain abnormal cells (cancer), or destructive cell products (e.g. natural chemical signals that promote inflammation) and tackle them in a variety of ways.

 Questions to ask your veterinarian

- What are the signs of pain associated with my dog's condition?
- Is my pet's noise sensitivity related to an underlying painful condition?
- How will I know whether the treatment to manage my dog's pain is working?

- The pain associated with my dog's chronic condition can flare with stress or overactivity, so can my dog be scheduled on a day when they can have a morning appointment and be discharged soon after? (So they don't have to stay in the clinic all day.)
- Can I bring my dog's favorite toy or blanket to ease stress or anxiety associated with visiting the clinic or being hospitalized?
- Do you use pheromones in the clinic to help calm anxious animals?
- Do you provide special padded bedding for dogs with arthritis?
- If my dog will be anesthetized for a procedure, will you ensure careful positioning and comfort so as not to inadvertently aggravate my dog's painful condition?
- What steps do you take to assess my dog's risk related to sedation or anesthesia (blood tests, radiographs, urinalysis)?
- Do you use topical anesthetic creams before catheter placement?
- Do you use local anesthetics in addition to other analgesics during procedures when possible?
- Do you proactively use pain medications (e.g. before surgery and before my dog shows signs of pain)?
- Do you use sedatives and analgesics to help reduce the amount of general anesthesia needed?
- What steps will you take to reduce my dog's risk related to sedation or anesthesia during my dog's procedure?
- Will my dog receive pain medications after a procedure? How long afterward will my dog receive pain medications?
- How will you monitor my dog for pain after a procedure?
- If my dog needs to stay in the hospital, can I visit?
- Will my dog benefit from physical rehabilitation or other pain management therapies such as acupuncture, nutritional management or supplements, or environmental modifications?

 CAREGIVER TIPS AND HOME HACKS

The household modifications and other environmental comforts you can provide for dogs who have painful conditions often overlap, but they also may differ depending on their underlying disorder. For more guidance, please refer to Chapter 17 "Mobility: The weak, wobbly, and unsteady" as well as the chapter or chapters that address your dog's specific condition.

Even after pain is alleviated, behavior changes that stemmed from a painful condition may be difficult for some pets to unlearn, especially if the behaviors helped the pet change the outcome of a painful situation. (Horwitz [2]

2020) For example, if your pet continues to eliminate in an inappropriate location or is still irritable, this could indicate ongoing pain or a learned behavior. Schedule recheck veterinary exams to assess your pet's response to pain management therapy, and, if needed, talk with your veterinarian about whether behavior modification techniques may also be beneficial.

 READING RECOMMENDATIONS

- A good friend of mine and fellow veterinarian Dr. Mike Petty wrote a book that should be on your bookshelf if you own a dog! It's called *Dr. Petty's Pain Relief for Dogs: The Complete Medical and Integrative Guide to Treating Pain* (Countryman Press, 2016). Dr. Petty is devoted to pain management in companion animals and is a champion in this field. His book thoroughly describes the different types of pain and the signs of pain in dogs, and it explains current pain medications and non-drug treatments and how they can be used together. He also covers home treatment options, what to expect from treatment, and options to consider if care is too costly. It's a great book and I can't wait for him to write one about cats!

- International Veterinary Academy of Pain Management website: **https://ivapm.org/animal-owners/animal-pain-awareness/**

- Colorado State University Veterinary Teaching Hospital Canine Chronic Pain Scale **http://csu-cvmbs.colostate.edu/Documents/anesthesia-pain -management-pain-score-canine.pdf**

Part three:

AGING WELL AND CARING FOR THE GREY MUZZLES

Being prepared for and getting the right help in caring for dogs who have advanced ailments or terminal illnesses can be game changers in improving the lives of dogs and their caregivers. I give insights and tools to help you focus on and enjoy the wonderful moments still to be shared with your grey muzzle friend. You'll learn how to senior-pet-proof and wellness-enhance your home, journal your dog's health, simplify medication administration, and recruit the best support team. I answer questions pet parents frequently ask me about veterinary exams, like:

"Why should my old dog keep up with veterinary visits?"

"Is my dog too old for anesthesia?"

"What do I do if my dog stresses out about going to the vet?"

I also address the most critical question pet parents ask me when they sense the remaining days with their dogs are dwindling: "When will I know it's time?" In most pet parents' lives, there comes a point in caring for your geriatric or ailing dog when you'll question whether your dog is enjoying life and wonder whether it may be time to say goodbye. And these questions often aren't comfortably discussed with family members and friends. People with good intentions may attempt to be reassuring when they tell you, "Don't worry, you'll know when it's time." What I do know, as a veterinarian and as a pet parent, is that you will not always simply "know" when that time has come. And I know that this period is full of heart-wrenching planning and decisions, plus one moment we wish would never come. When treasured days are limited, time seems to pass in overdrive. So in the later chapters of this section, my goals are to help you lighten the load that caregiving may bring and assess what's most important to you as you face the end of your dog's life. I describe the benefits of pet hospice care and give you options for confidently assessing your dog's unique life quality.

CHAPTER 22:

Safety and environmental enrichment: Creating senior-dog-friendly homes

A house is no home unless it contains food and fire for the mind as well as the body.

—Margaret Fuller Ossoli, American journalist

Ah, a dog's life. Meals prepared and served on time every day. Cozy dog beds and cushions to luxuriate on. No laundry to fold, work timelines to meet, or rent to pay. How many of us have dreamed we could have a life like theirs? But stop and consider a moment—we've brought them into our homes, and many dogs are left to their own devices for the day. All dogs—young, middle-aged, and old—need a safe, comfortable, and stimulating environment with caregivers who monitor and attend to their health and interact with them daily. But as seniors, dogs often need extra help to successfully navigate their environment. In addition, being left alone can sometimes be boring, dangerous, unhealthy, and even a bit scary for senior dogs.

In that spirit, we can alter our own homes, routines, and attentiveness to help our senior dogs (and ourselves) live better. This chapter provides a high-level view of creating a senior-dog-friendly dwelling. In the chapters that follow, I'll recommend environmental modifications and caregiver tips related to specific conditions common in senior dogs such as mobility issues, incontinence, cognitive dysfunction, and more.

A dog's-eye view to an aging-friendly abode

Home is familiar, comforting, and safe to your dog. But similar to the home safety and accessibility concerns that arise as people age, the home environment can become more challenging and contain hazard zones for older dogs. For people, the American Association of Retired Persons published a free "HomeFit Guide" to help create an "aging-friendly" current or future home, no matter a person's life stage. (AARP) And companies that specialize in assessing an elderly person's home can be hired to help organize or remodel to reduce accidents and make life easier for "aging in place." In the canine arena, don't worry—you don't have to substantially remodel your space or sell your house and move for your grey muzzle dog! The first step is to visualize the environment from your dog's perspective. Step into his or her paws and take it all in from your home's front door to the back door, including where your dog eats and sleeps, the potty area, where you and other household members sleep, where fur siblings eat and sleep, your car and yard (if applicable), and even the neighborhood.

- What does your dog see?
- Does something look scary?
- Can your dog get to where he needs or loves to be?
- Can she manage daily living comfortably and safely?
- Is he inconveniencing family members?

Once you've had a look about, consider ways to make things more convenient for your aging pup. Keep in mind that your human housemates may find the environmental adjustments troublesome, even though the changes may be OK for you. Keep your own safety in mind, too. For example, if you need to place your dog's bed next to yours, keep it out of your walking path so you don't have to step over it and risk tripping over (or onto!) your dog in the middle of the night. Let's look over some potential improvements.

Safety

Many environmental hazards exist for a dog living with aging ailments. A staircase presents obvious peril, but even a single step can trip up a dog, cause a tumble, and result in serious injury. Dogs of any age can fall into a swimming pool and drown when no one is watching. Slippery tile or wood floors provide little traction for unsteady geriatric dogs—and for dogs of any age. All dogs need

sure-footing and a safe place that is all their own to retreat to and rest. It breaks my heart when I visit clients' homes and see senior dogs anxiously struggling to get up off of slick tiles or tottering tentatively across a wood floor to their water bowl.

All dogs also need to be properly secured in the car, because one quick stop or turn can cause a devastating tumble, and this risk of injury climbs as dogs age and become less steady. Ramps or special harnesses can help weak and wobbly dogs more easily get into and out of the car without discomfort or fright.

Senior dog home safety and comfort checklist

❑ Block access to stairs with baby gates or tension rods if needed or place a wide ramp if possible.

❑ Place non-slip rugs or mats on slippery floors and slip-resistant carpet stair treads on wood stairs (and keep your dog's nails trimmed to optimize traction).

❑ Keep walking paths free of clutter (e.g. toys, shoes, magazines, books, cords).

❑ Train your dog to use ramps or small stairs to access favorite spots that may now be too high to jump up and down from (bed, couch, car). Train dogs to become accustomed to using a ramp or assistance stairs before they have mobility issues.

❑ Place padding on sharp edges that a dog might bump into.

❑ Create a comfy, easy-to-clean area that limits your dog's access to the rest of the house while you are unavailable to supervise her activities.

❑ Adjust where your dog sleeps if the potential to fall off your bed is present. Consider adding baby bumpers or moving the bed against the wall as a barrier.

❑ Place nightlights in hallways and stairwells and near potty areas.

❑ Provide easy access to food and water bowls, dog beds, and potty areas. Add more of each if needed so your dog has even easier access. Dogs with mobility issues may eat and drink less than they should if they have to use stairs to access their bowls, so adjust the bowls' location if needed. Make sure another dog in the household doesn't block access to the senior dog's bowls. Some dogs benefit from slightly elevated feeders (check with your vet!).

❑ Consider an orthopedic dog bed or other extra support to provide more comfort while your dog is resting. Geriatric dogs may appreciate the warmth and comfort of napping with a housemate dog, or if they have a painful condition, they may prefer a bed to themselves. Monitor your dogs' interactions to determine preferences.

❏ Create a safe spot or "den" area for your dog to retreat to when he needs quiet time, or segregate dogs for short rest periods each day (making sure they still have access to potty areas and water).

❏ Offer plenty of interaction and playtime to younger dogs who may be too boisterous to play with their ailing geriatric housemate.

❏ Keep window blind cords out of reach.

❏ If you have glass doors, add stickers/reflectors at eye level so your dog doesn't bump into the glass.

❏ Restrict and always supervise access to swimming pools, ponds, streams, and lakes.

❏ Prohibit access to fireplaces, candles, and outdoor firepits.

❏ Monitor your senior dog's interactions with other human and furry family members and visitors to avoid startling or uncomfortable experiences that may result in conflict or injuries.

❏ Consider dispensing canine calming pheromones (available as room diffusers, sprays, or collars) during stressful periods such as moving, gaining or losing housemates, traveling, hosting visiting dogs, recovering from surgery, or for day to day issues of living with serious chronic health problems. Pheromones are chemical signals unique to each animal species, and they affect the behavior or emotional state of other members of the same species.

❏ Furnish a heated dog bed or fluffy blanket as well as access to a cool surface as relaxation options when needed, making sure your dog can get on or off these spaces of her own accord.

❏ Try to keep a routine feeding, potty, and activity schedule. Potty breaks may need to become more frequent as your dog ages. If you rearrange the furniture or move, take extra time to help your dog adapt and learn the new layout.

Sanitation

Keeping elderly dogs clean can become a big challenge, especially toward the end of their life. Aged dogs may have incontinence or inappropriate elimination, and if they also have mobility issues, they may end up lying in their urine and feces, which creates a much bigger cleaning issue. (See Chapter 14 "Incontinence: Squish squash" and Chapter 17: "Mobility: The weak, wobbly, and unsteady" for additional precautions and tips.) The more accidents they have, the more cleaning they need. Dogs with severe mobility issues who cannot easily move and rotate on their bed can get bed sores that lead to infections.

Sanitation checklist

❑ Provide assistance to go outside to go potty if needed. For example, carry your dog if feasible, use a support harness, or place a ramp if applicable. Consider a stroller to transport smaller dogs living in urban high rises with long hallways and elevators to traverse.

❑ Set up a potty location indoors where it's acceptable for your dog to eliminate if necessary (at least two feet from their food and sleeping areas). Or restrict your dog to this location when you're away. Artificial turf or live-grass pee pads may be an option for high-rise dwellers.

❑ Carefully trim or shave the hair around your dog's hind end, tail, and groin if urine or feces collects there.

❑ Use potty pads and diapers as needed for incontinent dogs, and prevent bed sores and skin infections in dogs with mobility issues and who have difficulty getting up and away from their accidents.

❑ Keep cleaning supplies handy. Good items to have at the ready include dog wipes or unscented, hypoallergenic baby wipes (keep a pack in your car, too) and floor cleaning tools.

Beating boredom and suppressing stress

Hand in hand with a dog's senior lifestyle is often a lack of new things to contemplate (read: boredom), which sometimes morphs into concern: "What was that sound outside?" "What's that scouting about in the backyard?" "Did Mom just get home?" The concern can result in much barking and unease or even, in the case of separation anxiety, destruction of things in the home.

Dogs can experience chronic distress if they're repeatedly exposed to stressful events for a prolonged period or are continuously exposed to a tolerable but stressful situation that never stops. (Horwitz [3] 2020) Conflicts with other furry family members, chronic health problems, frightening sounds, active and noisy children, or being left alone repeatedly for long periods are examples of stressful situations. Add on a cognitive disorder that many geriatric dogs suffer from, and they may experience a full-on panic attack.

Throughout this book I mention that exercise, mental stimulation, and environmental enrichment are important to maintain your dog's health and even extend their lives. Environmental enrichment means providing stimulating activities (as well as opportunities to be alone) that encourage animals' natural behaviors and social interactions. Environmental enrichment stimulates thinking, reduces boredom, and helps animals deal with minor stresses. All too often, I've seen families who assume their dog is "just getting old," so they no longer play with their dog or try to include their dog in family activities. But these interactions are just as important for aging dogs as they are for young dogs. Case in point: many assisted living facilities and nursing homes for people feature game nights, movie nights, arts and crafts, reading rooms, music rooms, resident cats and dogs (sometimes even farm animals!), gardens, gyms, pools, off-site dining events, community field trips, and group vacation getaways.

The key to enrichment for senior dogs is in striking the right balance between the comforts of familiarity and the disturbances of novelty. Senior dogs appreciate predictable routines and may have difficulty coping with change. Inconsistency can induce stress that negatively affects senior dogs' physical and emotional well-being, so introduce new experiences in small doses and make transitions gradually. Provide reassurance, encouragement, and rewards, and stay attuned to and respect your dog's pace of acceptance or reluctance.

Environmental enrichment categories

As we investigate ways to bring enrichment into your home, let's turn to the wild side for a second and consider what zoos do. Zookeepers enhance their animals' environments in a variety of ways to boost the animals' physical and mental health. Mimicking the animals' natural habitat is just one aspect they have embraced. The five general enrichment categories are social, cognitive, physical, sensory, and food (Joseph 2019), and the categories may overlap. Enrichment recommendations that the veterinary field applies to dogs follow the same general principles as those that have been applied in zoos. And when it comes to grey muzzles, most of the same enrichment tips for younger dogs can still be applied.

SOCIAL: Someone to hang out with! Zoo animals may live with fellow animals of their own kind or even other animals found in their natural environments. For dogs, social stimulation may include interacting with other furry housemates or dates with other dog or cat playmates. Most importantly, social stimulation means interacting with you and other human family members or friends, preferably on a routine schedule. Daily petting, sitting on your lap or next to you, grooming, and training all count!

COGNITIVE: New things to stretch the mind! Puzzles to solve and toys to play with bring variety and fun for many zoo animals, and the same applies to pets. Add new toys (dog subscription boxes are one option, such as Barkbox. com), rotate your dog's old toys to keep them interesting, and consider making your own toys. You can also use positive training techniques to teach new commands, tricks, or activities to give dogs a "job" to do and boost their cognitive processes.

PHYSICAL HABITAT: Making home feel like home! Zoo animals benefit from spaces that mimic the animals' natural environments, such as perches, water features, bushes, boulders, and hiding places. Senior dogs, too, appreciate a den of their own to retreat to for rest and quiet. While social interaction is vital, having time to themselves is important for dogs.

SENSORY: New encounters for the five senses! Zookeepers introduce new smells, interactive toys, novel sounds, and more to help keep the animals they care for curious and engaged. Senior dogs may enjoy being combed or brushed or a light massage, munching veggies such as green beans, watching videos designed to hold dogs' attention, listening to music composed for dogs' discerning ears (Robertson 2018), and sniffing out familiar favorite treats around the room or yard or smelling new avenues during walks.

FOOD: A chance to forage! Zoo animals benefit from searching for food in a variety of ways and tasting new flavors. Senior dogs benefit too, such as deciphering food cubes, wobbler toys, ball treat dispensers, complex activity centers, and foraging mats. DIY food puzzle construction ideas abound on the internet, many using recyclables such as empty cardboard rolls and boxes, egg cartons, and plastic yogurt containers.

Going out for a change of scenery

The great outdoors—natural chances for enriching endeavors are simply a step outside, or perhaps just easy breezes bringing faraway scents through a screen door.

THE BACKYARD. Not just the place for all those No. 1s and 2s. Even for those who have a yard, dogs left alone to their own devices in a fenced area day after day become bored and may become stressed. So take time to interact, play, explore, and change things up. Great games of fetch, lounging in the grass, patrolling the perimeter, hunting treats that you disperse around the yard, mini senior-dog-accessible activity courses, or trotting after a flirt pole (a sturdy chase exercise toy for dogs), and more await. The backyard brings bountiful times for bonding moments with you.

WALKS. If your dog is up for it and doesn't have exercise restrictions for medical reasons, you probably already build in regular walks with her, which is a wonderfully enriching activity. Walking about with a trusted human friend brings the chance to spy and smell new things. "Where did that grasshopper go? Was that a squirrel?! Let me sniff out the trail …."

Walks for older dogs may need to be shorter duration, on-leash at the park instead of off-leash (leash walks are always the optimal route unless you have a private place to roam and know your dog won't get lost!), or across smoother terrain than they were during your dog's younger years. Nonetheless, continue to offer regular outings for their exploratory treks with you. Change up your walk routine by allowing a little more freedom in non-congested areas, or you might use an extra-long lead to allow your dog to choose the areas he wants to scout (within reason!) and to stop and sniff at his own pace.

DIFFERENT SPACES. Dog parks. Doggy daycare. Pet stores. Even some retail stores (e.g. Lowe's, Home Depot, Nordstrom, Pottery Barn, Apple Store) let dog owners bring their dogs in on a leash. (Can I bring my dog? Rover.com) Check with your local stores, and if your senior dog is comfortable with these types of new experiences, go galavant!

Staying in and changing scenery

Enriching indoor entertainment opportunities abound, too.

TRAINING. Old dogs and new tricks. There's a world of old-school jokes here, but learning new things remains intriguing for elders of the four-legged variety. Has your dog got things like fetch and stay down pat? Teach new tricks! Spin around, respond with a "woof" to a certain phrase, ring a bell for a treat, high five, walk backward on command, and more.

TREATS. Treats as an enticement are an integral part of training in dogs, but enticing them with a device that requires their manipulation to get to a treat can be enriching, too. Many treat toys dispense bits of yum as a dog rolls the toy about on the floor. Some dog owners give their dogs all of their meals in such food-dispensing devices. Kibble can be tucked into dispensing toys and hidden around the house or placed on a foraging mat. You'll activate their instinct to search for a food reward. It's more active. It takes more futzing around.

Some senior dogs have reduced senses of smell and taste, so feed especially aromatic, delectable treats. Experiment with what most entices your dog. And remember, dogs are smart! They will figure out the quickest wins in the food puzzles, so try several different types of puzzles and switch them out periodically. What's old can be new again—and may get less destroyed!

TOYS. Go into any dog aisle in a supermarket or pet specialty store, and you'll feel like you're walking in the children's toy area. Fuzzy, colorful, fantastical toys in all shapes and sizes entice you to take a look and call you to interact with them. Dogs appreciate toys in different sizes, shapes, and textures and with a variety of movements. Your senior dog may still appreciate playing shorter games of hallway fetch and lighter tug of war. Rotate the toy options to keep dogs interested. Play many dogs' favorite game—rip the stuffing out of that toy beast.

MATINEES AND MOVIE NIGHTS. How do many of us pass the time at the end of a long day? The TV! Your dogs, too, can find entertainment on the tube. Internet streaming services such as YouTube host many channels specifically designed to entertain dogs for hours, which is a great resource when dogs must be left at home on their own. They can draw the eyes of many dogs and keep their minds occupied. You'll find videos of birds flying in and out to snack on birdseed, dogs running along a forest trail or taking a jaunt on the beach, puppies romping, and so much more. Dogs may even key in on a fellow hound or other animal on the screen, perk up their ears and twist their heads when it makes a noise (woof! meow! tweet tweet!), and try to search around the side or back of the TV if it flies or runs off screen. You will be as entertained as your dog by watching your dog being entertained by these moments!

Enrichment queries

- ❏ Does your dog have a variety of engaging activities and experiences to keep him occupied?
- ❏ What activities or experiences do you need to avoid or prevent so your senior dog does not get overly excited, irritated, scared, or repeatedly stressed?
- ❏ What sounds occur throughout the day that you may need to help your dog avoid because they unsettle your dog?
- ❏ If your dog is left alone for long periods or is confined to a restricted access area when you're not home, do you provide enrichment opportunities that she can engage in on her own?
- ❏ Is someone available to spend at least an hour a day with your dog for physical activity and social interactions?

 READING RECOMMENDATIONS

- An excellent book on dog behavior written by veterinary behavior specialists that includes information on environmental enrichment: American College of Veterinary Behaviorists. *Decoding Your Dog.* Mariner Books; 2015.
- Explore Facebook groups for Canine Enrichment to see all the ways pet parents play "mind games" with their dogs: **https://www.facebook.com/groups/canineenrichment**

CHAPTER 23:

Journaling:
Tracking your dog's health

"Write hard and clear about what hurts."

—Source unverified
(the internet attributes this quote to Ernest Hemingway)

A day in the life of your dog. It can change as the whiskers grey. An occasional accident. A stumble during a stroll down the street. A reduced interest in a favorite treat. Some changes can signal something more serious. You know your dog's attitude, activities, and behavior best, so it's crucial to keep track and mention changes or any concerns to your veterinary team. In fact, as your dog ages, your veterinarian will likely be increasingly asking during appointments how well your dog is eating and moving about, whether your dog's interactions with you or other family members have changed, as well as what your dog's sleep and potty habits are like.

During veterinary visits or in times of illness, it can be hard to remember the nuances about changes you've noticed in your dog. It's helpful to keep a senior dog health journal—one that also includes methods to track your dog's symptoms, treatments, and schedule changes.

Create a senior dog health journal

To keep a dog health journal, write your general observations about the types of behaviors, changes, and symptoms I list below and anything else that concerns you, or create your own checklist. Include stories or notes about activities and other things your dog enjoys so you can track whether the level of interest or enthusiasm has changed. Add photos of your dog taken at six- to 12-month intervals, and date each one to help you and your veterinarian monitor changes in your dog.

Health observations:

- **EATING/DRINKING:** What are your dog's favorite foods? Favorite treats? Have his food preferences changed? Has his appetite decreased? Are special enticements or is other assistance needed to get him to eat? Does he drop food while eating or have trouble chewing or swallowing? Does your dog have an increased thirst? Any vomiting?
- **WEIGHT:** Has your dog lost weight without being on a diet or without getting extra exercise? Has your dog been gaining weight?
- **SLEEP:** Where does your dog prefer to sleep? How many hours does your dog sleep during an average day? Does she sleep peacefully? What does your dog do if she gets up during the night? Does she sleep more during the day than she used to and less at night?
- **ACTIVITY LEVEL:** What are your dog's favorite activities, toys, and games? Who are your dog's favorite people? Who are your dog's least favorite beings (squirrels, delivery people, neighbor dogs)? Does your dog have other favorite animal friends or playmates? Has your dog's activity decreased? If so, over what time period—the last few days, weeks, or months, or during the last year?
- **STRENGTH AND VITALITY:** Has your dog's energy decreased in the last year? Does he seem less interested in exercise or favorite activities? Is he weaker during exercise or less tolerant of exercise?
- **MOBILITY:** Does your dog need help on stairs? Getting into or out of the car? Any difficulty jumping on or off the bed or couch? Need help getting up from lying down? Is she dragging her feet or toes? Has her gait changed (slowness or lameness)?
- **URINE, FECES, AND HOUSE TRAINING:** Have you noticed an increase or decrease in urination? Any urinary or fecal accidents indoors? Urine leakage on his bed? A change in fecal appearance? Diarrhea? Fecal incontinence? Constipation?
- **EARS, EYES, NOSE, MOUTH, THROAT, AND BREATHING:** Have you noticed a change in hearing? More reactive to noises? Less reactive to noises? Vision problems in bright light? In dim light? At night? Up close? A runny nose or sneezing? Bad breath? Does her bark sound different? Does she repeatedly clear her throat? Pant more frequently? Breathe faster/heavier? Cough?
- **SKIN:** Does your dog have increased or excessive itching? Lumps or bumps on or under the skin? A bad smell? Licking or chewing his skin or hair? Is his skin flaky, dry, or oily? Have you noticed he has longer toenails?
- **COAT:** Does your dog enjoy baths? Being brushed or combed? Is her coat unkempt? Thinning? Dull? Mats? Are there areas of hair loss?

- **TEMPERATURE AND OVERALL COMFORT:** Does your dog seek out new or unusual areas to rest that are warm, cold, soft, sunny, or hard? Does he shiver easily? Pant excessively?
- **MENTATION:** Is your dog excited to greet you when you get home? Has your dog been less interactive with the family? More clingy or anxious? Does your dog pace during the day? Stare off into space? Seem irritable or act more aggressively? Does she seem disoriented or distant? Become agitated at certain times of the day? Get stuck in odd locations or appear lost? Keep turning in circles? Vocalize inappropriately (bark at night for no apparent reason)? Has she had a seizure?

Symptom tracker

In a later chapter, Life quality: "Doc, when is it time?, I discuss how to annotate symptoms to help pet parents evaluate end-of-life decisions for their dogs. But tracking your dog's symptoms throughout his senior years, starting well before he reaches his final weeks, helps you remember and realistically assess whether he's improved, stayed stable, or declined. This can help your veterinarian construct a veterinary care plan for your dog and remodel it as needed along the way. Tracking symptoms also helps your veterinarian better predict the course of your dog's condition, because how your dog functions in her daily activities provides supportive context for interpreting diagnostic test results and physical examination findings.

Use the health observations questions above to uncover the symptoms your dog may have. Write your dog's symptoms in your dog's health journal or type them into a spreadsheet, as in the example below. First list the symptom, and then its frequency and time of day. Does it happen every day? In the mornings only? Evenings only? How many times a day?

Next note any circumstance that seems to be associated with the symptom, if applicable. For example, does vomiting, diarrhea, or disorientation occur only after your dog eats fatty snacks? Does your dog limp or have difficulty getting up from lying down only after walking up a flight of stairs? Does she have trouble recognizing family members or bump into furniture when the lights are low? Does your dog tire easily or cough only when playing with a furry sibling?

Symptom severity is the next aspect to document. Is it mild and your dog doesn't seem too bothered by it, or does it affect her for the rest of the day? You can also note whether it is a mild, moderate, or severe issue for you as the caregiver.

Finally, note improvements—what helps alleviate the symptom? Does your dog stop limping or wobble less when he finds better traction on the floor? Does your dog sleep through the night when you play soothing music or nature

SYMPTOM TRACKER

Pet's Name

Date	Symptom	Frequency and Time of Day	Association	Severity	Improvements

sounds, or when you sleep in the same room with him? Does he eat more when you soften or warm his food?

Date each entry to help you monitor your dog. You'll see trends starting sooner rather than later and can make adjustments faster.

When tracking your senior dog's symptoms, keep in mind that with the exception of some conditions that may be treatable and resolve, you are not necessarily looking for perfection or a return to normal. You're looking for ways to help slow the progression of your dog's symptoms and help her live well by alleviating as much discomfort as possible—to provide care and love to the best of your abilities. All of these efforts are to help your dog feel better and have a good life quality—and help yourself do so as well.

Treatment tracker

Keeping good notes about your dog's medications, other therapies, and schedule changes is as important as tracking his symptoms. This is a handy reference for treatments you've tried and their effects.

Keep a log of each drug name, dose, frequency (how many times a day it's given) and duration (how long it's to be given), what it's used to treat or manage, and the result (whether it helped or if you noted side effects or new symptoms). If you adjust a dose or frequency of administration, note that as well (note: all prescription medicine adjustments should be made according to your veterinarian's advice).

Remember to include medications, supplements, or nutraceuticals that you purchase over-the-counter. Also note any other therapy such as acupuncture, surgery, massage, chemotherapy, grooming, and any major schedule change such as boarding or daycare. For more information about therapies commonly prescribed or recommended for senior pets and tips for giving them, see Chapter 24 "Course of action: Therapeutic options and gaining acceptance from your senior pet."

Tracking your dog's health, appearance, symptoms, therapies, and schedule changes will help you better evaluate and make decisions about managing the complexities that come along with caring for a geriatric or terminally ill dog.

If you are interested in a complete workbook to journal your pet's health and other aspects of care - scan this code for more information:

Dog Journal Book

TREATMENT TRACKER

Pet's Name

Date	Medication (and other therapy) or Change in schedule	Dose	Frequency and Duration	What it's for	Result

CHAPTER 24:

Course of action: Therapeutic options and gaining acceptance from your senior dog

"We can not only add years to their life but life to their years."

DR. MARTY BECKER

What used to be a simple way of bringing daily joy to my dog Duncan—feeding him and giving him occasional treats—slowly turned into a nightmare for me as he got older. During his early senior years, he had to take medications to relieve his arthritis pain and boost his low thyroid hormone. Duncan had a healthy appetite, so I could easily sneak pills into his food or hide them in tidbits of deli meat. But as Duncan's ailments mounted, his pharmacy grew.

Then came another blow—Duncan was found to have heart disease, so he had to take three more new drugs. And because some pills had to be given on an empty stomach and others had to be given with food, his medication routine became a five-times-a-day process. But I didn't mind. I traded his twice-a-day vitamin container for a huge multi-dose pill box. I set timer alarms to remind me when his doses were due (not counting the refill reminders I had to remember to calculate and follow through on!).

 I made egg bites for my dog Duncan and snuck pills inside!

317

Eventually, like most older, ill dogs, Duncan became a picky eater. I tried several tricks to disguise his medications. It became a huge challenge. Unfortunately, unlike the song "A Spoonful of Sugar," such camouflage doesn't appeal to most fur kids.

Then we reached the day when I realized Duncan's daily joy had become his nightmare, too. He would yawn, lick his nose, turn his head away, or simply walk away from me—all signs of anxiety—whenever I approached him with a "treat." And that broke my heart.

Managing meds in your steadfast senior dog

Obviously our dogs can't help themselves stay healthy in every way that will help them. So all measures that must be taken to give medications, nutraceuticals, supplements, and other forms of therapy usually become activities of daily living, loving, and caring for senior pets. It can sometimes feel like running a senior dog assisted-living home!

In this chapter, I give a basic overview of the therapies I often use or recommend in my geriatric and hospice patients and my own senior dogs—treatments that your veterinarian is also likely to prescribe or suggest. I briefly describe the legalities of prescribing drugs and then cover therapeutic categories and a few of the individual treatments, including some non-drug, non-supplement therapies that aging dogs may need. I don't cover all potential treatments here (that would take at least one more book to write!), but I mention many additional therapies in the chapters that address individual conditions.

The first key to successful treatment: Keep your veterinarian in the know

Always tell your veterinarian about all the medications, vitamins, supplements, nutraceuticals, herbs, and other therapies your dog is receiving. We need this information to make well-informed decisions about your dog's care and to prevent adverse drug interactions and ensure that your dog's therapies support each other. The vital take-home message here—some drugs just don't work well together and can do more harm than good when they're combined.

To successfully treat your dog, your veterinarian also relies on you to carefully follow medication instructions and treatment plans. Always let your veterinarian know if you're having trouble following through.

An important alert: Stop before giving a medication or supplement to your dog on your own without consulting your veterinarian, even if it is one that you know is used in dogs. And hold off on sharing medications among your dogs. One dog's prescription is not necessarily your other dog's remedy! Ask your veterinarian first.

The prescriptions for writing prescriptions

Medications are normally a part of an older dog's care toolbox. They can boost comfort, decrease anxiety, improve mobility, enhance sleep, increase appetite, hasten healing, and provide many other benefits. parents may not realize that veterinarians must follow a few rules to prescribe certain therapies for dogs. Medications that are approved for use in dogs, cats, or other animals by the U.S. Food and Drug Administration (FDA) Center for Veterinary Medicine are legally available only by prescription from a licensed veterinarian. And to legally prescribe a medication in most states, veterinarians must have an existing, valid relationship with the client and the pet (called a VCPR, for short).

A VCPR-what?

A veterinarian-client-patient relationship (VCPR) means that a veterinarian knows a dog well enough to be able to diagnose the dog's problem and oversee his or her treatment, keeps a medical record of the dog's care, and discusses treatment benefits and risks with the dog's owner. A VCPR also means that the pet parent agrees to follow the veterinarian's instructions. Each state's Veterinary Practice Act (which describes regulations for practicing veterinary medicine) may define the VCPR a bit differently.

In most states, knowing a dog well enough to prescribe a medication means that the veterinarian must examine the dog in person to assess the dog's health and his or her need for medication. The vet must also see the dog regularly for healthcare checkups (for example, at least once a year) and be readily available for follow-up if needed.

The VCPR is the reason why if your dog is ill, your veterinarian needs to examine your dog in person before prescribing medication. It's also why if your dog has no medication refills left and hasn't had a veterinary visit for over a year (or has missed follow-up tests needed to check her response to the medication), your dog must be examined before your veterinarian can approve a prescription refill. Because telemedicine services have gained more popularity, regulations related to the VCPR may change in the future.

A prescription that doesn't follow the label: Extra-label or off-label drug use

Fortunately, many drugs have been approved by the FDA for use in dogs with specific diseases or conditions. But not all medications have been studied in more than one species, for more than one disease, at different doses, or in alternative ways to administer them. So some drugs veterinarians prescribe may not be FDA-approved for that particular use.

When an FDA-approved drug is used in a way that is not listed on its label, it's called an *extra-label* or *off-label* drug use. This occurs, for example, when your veterinarian prescribes a drug for your dog that has been FDA-approved for use in cats (or in people) or prescribes a drug at a different dose or for a different disease than the drug label says it is used for. Extra-label and off-label uses are acceptable and legal when certain conditions are met and are a common practice in veterinary (and human) medicine.

This doesn't mean veterinarians (or physicians) prescribe these drugs haphazardly among species or diseases. Off-label or extra-label uses are typically evidence-based and supported by scientific research, patient studies, and clinical experience published in the medical literature.

Changing the form of medications: Compounding

Many forms of medications exist: pills, capsules, liquids, patches, ointments, tablets, chewables, and injectables. Changing a drug's approved formulation to tailor it to the needs of a specific patient—such as making a liquid from pills to make it easier for a dog to take—is called compounding. Compounding is also considered an extra-label drug use, and it is legal when certain conditions are met.

Other examples of compounding include mixing a drug with a flavor enhancer, combining two drugs into one, or formulating a drug into a dose that is not available from the manufacturer. Not all drugs can be compounded, and some compounded formulations may not have the same effectiveness as a drug in its original form.

To obtain compounded medications, veterinarians typically use local veterinary pharmacies or online veterinary pharmacies. Pharmacies for human drugs may offer some types of compounding for pet medications as well.

A close look at some common meds

Let's take a moment to meet some medications that might be coming your way as your dog's muzzle begins to grey.

Pain management options

Most pet parents will encounter a need to administer drugs to manage their senior dog's pain. (We all know, aging can be a pain!) Thankfully, many options are available.

Corticosteroids. Often shortened to "steroids," corticosteroids are chemical messengers called hormones produced in the body to assist in many functions.

Corticosteroid medications such as prednisone or prednisolone are synthetic versions of glucocorticoid hormones produced naturally by the adrenal glands.

These drugs reduce inflammation in dogs with arthritis, inflammatory bowel disease, asthma, or allergies. They also suppress the immune system, so they are used to treat conditions such as immune-mediated anemia in which the immune cells mistakenly attack the body's own red blood cells. Corticosteroids also help slow the progression of some types of cancer (my girl Sam takes a daily dose of steroids for her cancer).

Corticosteroids' side effects tend to be dose-dependent and include increased risk of infection, diminished healing ability, gastric ulcers, weight gain, increased panting, and drinking more water (thus, urinating more often), to name a few. Corticosteroids can also affect a dog's behavior, so it's important for you to know that some dogs who receive corticosteroid therapy may be restless or startle easily, or they might be more anxious, fearful, or irritable. (Levine 2015, Notari 2015)

Corticosteroids are helpful in managing many conditions, and their side effects aren't necessarily dealbreakers. It's just good to be aware of the side effects so you can let your veterinarian know if you have concerns about your dog's response. The side effects should diminish as the dose decreases and should resolve after treatment.

Stopping corticosteroids abruptly can cause other problems, so the dose is gradually reduced. It's vital that you follow your veterinarian's instructions for administering and tapering these medications.

Hanz's "roid rage"

One of my patients, Hanz, a German shepherd, was seriously ill and needed treatment with a high dose of corticosteroids. Hanz's dad called me a week after he started giving the medication. He was furious because Hanz was acting aggressively. He told me that the steroids I prescribed for Hanz caused roid rage (angry or violent outbursts that can occur in people who take anabolic steroids).

Anabolic steroid drugs are not corticosteroids, they are synthetic (man-made) versions of the male sex hormone, testosterone. Anabolic steroids are not often used in veterinary patients, but pet parents sometimes confuse them with corticosteroids.

I told Hanz's dad that I did not give Hanz the type of steroids he was thinking of, but I also explained that corticosteroids can sometimes make dogs more aggressive around food or when disturbed. (Notari 2015) I also asked him whether Hanz had irritable tendencies before he got sick, and he admitted that Hanz *had* been aggressive in the past. So I think the simple truth was that Hanz was finally feeling better, and, well, his personality was also returning to normal. I adjusted Hanz's medications and talked with his dad about identifying and avoiding the situations that made Hanz grumpy—and about rewarding his good behavior!

Nonsteroidal anti-inflammatory drugs. Veterinarians prescribe nonsteroidal anti-inflammatory drugs (NSAIDs) to manage inflammation and pain associated with arthritis, surgery, urinary tract problems, and other conditions. Most NSAIDs work by blocking an enzyme called cyclooxygenase that is needed to make prostaglandins. Prostaglandins are hormone-like lipid (fat) compounds that contribute to pain and inflammation.

Carprofen (brand name Rimadyl, among others) is a common NSAID for dogs that has been available for many years. Other types of NSAIDs, such as grapiprant (brand name Galliprant), are available that work at different points in the inflammatory process. Not all NSAIDs work at the same point in the inflammation pathway and not all dogs respond similarly to NSAIDs. So if your dog doesn't respond to one NSAID, your veterinarian may suggest switching to another type to find one that works best for your dog.

Long-term NSAID use can affect liver or kidney function, so be sure to follow your veterinarian's instructions for follow-up tests and monitor your dog for inappetence, vomiting, diarrhea, and bruising.

NSAID cautions and acetaminophen alert

Dogs are rarely treated with an NSAID and a corticosteroid at the same time because severe side effects can occur. Receiving both medications should be done only when medically required and with close veterinary supervision.

Never give the NSAIDs you may have available in your own medicine cabinet (ibuprofen, aspirin, naproxen, or others) to your dog because NSAID medications for use in people can cause serious or life-threatening side effects in dogs. Aspirin is sometimes used in dogs, but your veterinarian's approval and guidance are needed first..

Acetaminophen (Tylenol), also called paracetamol, is not an NSAID, but I mention it here because it is a pain and fever reducer that most people have at home. Never give acetaminophen to cats because it causes severe illness and can be lethal. Veterinarians sometimes use acetaminophen at low doses to treat pain in dogs.

Polysulfated glycosaminoglycan (PSGAG). Polysulfated glycosaminoglycan (brand name Adequan), an FDA-approved drug to control signs of arthritis in dogs and horses, is an extract made from cow cartilage. It's a shot given in the muscle (at the veterinary clinic) twice a week for four weeks, and possibly continued at a maintenance dose after that. It can also be given off-label under the skin, so your veterinarian may teach you how to do that so you can give it at home.

Gabapentin. Gabapentin's mode of action is not completely understood, but it is thought to inhibit nerve activity. It's used off-label in veterinary medicine to treat pain, anxiety, and seizures. I have prescribed it for my canine patients who have chronic pain or pain related to nerve damage, but studies have recently revealed that gabapentin may not effectively treat pain as well as we initially thought, and the jury is still out. (McKenzie 2021)

The main side effect of gabapentin is sleepiness, which can vary among dogs. I prescribe a low dose to start, given only at night. This helps all family members benefit from their dog's good night's sleep! I usually reassess the dog's response after three weeks to determine whether a dose adjustment is needed.

Amantadine. Amantadine is an antiviral drug approved for use in people that also influences nerve activity. It is used off-label in dogs to relieve pain that can develop after the central nervous system ramps up to respond to pain but then becomes overly sensitive to stimuli. Side effects are uncommon in dogs and may include soft stools or diarrhea.

Opioids. Opioids are natural or man-made derivatives of the poppy plant. They influence receptors throughout the body and have many effects, including effects within the nervous system that help relieve pain. They're often used in human medicine and are usually used to treat short-term pain in dogs, but they can also be given to manage long-term pain.

Because of opioid shortages related to drug abuse in people and because of the potential for abuse in people, veterinarians must often look for alternatives to these drugs to manage pain in dogs.

Bisphosphonates. Bisphosphonates are approved for use in people to prevent or slow the loss of bone density. Veterinarians use them primarily to provide pain relief in dogs who have bone cancer. This medication must be administered intravenously in the veterinary hospital.

Medications to treat nausea

Nausea sometimes causes as much suffering as other painful conditions and negatively affects a dog's quality of life. Medications commonly used to treat nausea in dogs include:

Maropitant (brand name Cerenia) is FDA-approved for use in dogs to treat short-term, or acute, vomiting. It blocks the action of a neurotransmitter in the central nervous

NOT SO FUN FACT

Tramadol is an opioid-like medication that has been used in the past as a pain reliever in dogs. However, it has been proven that dogs do not metabolize Tramadol the way humans can so they do not receive any pain relief benefits. It can make dogs sleepy, so some people confused sleepiness with feeling better and their dog is in less pain. In short – do not use Tramadol for pain in dogs.

system that stimulates the vomiting reflex. It is available as tablets or as an injection.

Meclizine is an oral antihistamine that is often used to prevent or treat nausea associated with motion sickness such as car rides or vestibular disease.

Metoclopramide (brand name Reglan) is an oral medication used more for its effect to boost gastric motility (move food from the stomach to the intestine), and it can also block the sensation of nausea in the central nervous system.

Stomach acid blockers and protectants

Famotidine and omeprazole are oral medications sometimes used off-label in dogs to reduce stomach acid or treat gastric ulcers associated with a variety of medical conditions.

Sucralfate is also used to help treat ulcers. It coats and protects the stomach lining. Sucralfate is given on an empty stomach and not at the same time as certain other medications because it can block their absorption. Follow your veterinarian's dosing instructions closely.

Nutraceuticals or supplements

Nutraceuticals are nutritional supplements formulated from bioactive compounds such as vitamins, minerals, probiotics, dietary fiber, herbal extracts, or other food substances—alone or in combination— that are used to support healthy dogs or dogs who have an ailment.

> **Did you know?** Nutraceuticals don't undergo FDA review for safety and efficacy as drugs do, so a nutraceutical manufacturer cannot claim that their product prevents or treats disease. In fact, the FDA doesn't recognize the term "nutraceutical" and considers these products to be dietary supplements. (FDA Reader 2019)

As I mentioned earlier, it's vital to tell your veterinarian about any supplement or other over-the-counter medication you give your dog. It may contain an active ingredient that counteracts or enhances the effects of other medications, or it may have other unintended effects in the body. Nutraceuticals may provide benefits for some dogs. Let's take a look at some examples:

Glucosamine and chondroitin. These building blocks of cartilage occur naturally in some joints. Glucosamine and chondroitin are used to repair cartilage and inhibit further destruction, and they provide mild anti-inflammatory effects.

These substances can be extracted from animal cartilage or shellfish shells and green-lipped mussels (sciency-wiency name for these New Zealand-exclusive mussels: *Perna canaliculus*), or they can be made synthetically. They are formulated as supplements and nutraceuticals or added to dog foods and marketed to support joint health in dogs.

Veterinarians may recommend glucosamine and chondroitin in addition to other therapies (e.g. NSAIDs, weight loss, physical rehabilitation) for patients with arthritis or after joint surgery. Studies have been done in people, dogs, cats, horses, and other animals and their effects have been hotly debated. The bottom line is that the potential benefits of glucosamine and chondroitin remain questionable. (Bhathal 2017)

Several brands formulated for dogs or cats that contain glucosamine or glucosamine and chondroitin are available: Cosequin, Dasuquin, GlycoFLEX, Phycox, ProMotion, Seraquin, Cani-Flex, Rejensa, and products made by a company called Nutri-Vet—to name a few! Among these products, the active ingredient sources and amounts, other added nutrients, manufacturing processes, and research done to support their effects often differ. Whether your veterinarian recommends glucosamine and chondroitin or which brand they suggest depends on their assessment of these factors.

Melatonin. Melatonin is a hormone produced in the brain, and most melatonin supplements contain a synthetic version. It may help with sleep disturbances in dogs and cats. Do not give melatonin supplements that contain xylitol to your dogs. Xylitol is toxic to dogs and it's best to avoid giving xylitol to cats.

Omega-3 fatty acids. Omega-3 fatty acids (called *eicosapentaenoic acid* [EPA] and *docosahexaenoic acid* [DHA]) from fish oil have multiple beneficial effects for people and for dogs. They're available as supplements, and some dog foods contain added amounts. They play a vital role in cell membrane health to keep cells functioning normally. Only use omega-3 fatty acid supplements made from fish oil, and avoid flaxseed oil and cod liver oil. (Freeman 2010) My favorite brand is Omega-3 Pet by Nordic Naturals. And fair warning: gradually introduce fish oil supplements to your dog over three weeks, because they can cause diarrhea!

Probiotics. Some of the beneficial bacteria that live in your dog's intestines can be given as supplements known as probiotics. They help digestion and boost the immune system, and are used to help treat diarrhea, irritable bowels, and intestinal inflammation.

Probiotics are available as powders, chewables, and capsules. Be sure to obtain a probiotic from a reputable company and one that lists the bacteria on the label.Two brands I often recommend for dogs are FortiFlora by Purina Pro Plan Veterinary Supplements and Proviable by Nutramax Laboratories Veterinary Sciences.

Vitamin B12 (cobalamin). Vitamin B12 is involved in many biological processes. Dogs with gastrointestinal disorders may have a B12 deficiency because they can't absorb it sufficiently from their diet. Weekly injections of B12 may be recommended.

Anti-anxiety medications

Many conditions or situations can make dogs anxious, but in geriatric dogs, anxiety often results from cognitive dysfunction syndrome (see Chapter 19 "Cognition: Cross my mind... or not"). Drugs used to treat anxiety include alprazolam, trazodone, fluoxetine, and clomipramine. Many anti-anxiety medications interact adversely with selegiline, a drug that is sometimes used to treat dogs with cognitive dysfunction. So, again, be sure your veterinarian knows about all the medications your dog is receiving to avoid side effects from drug interactions.

Cannabidiol (CBD): A drug becoming more common

In the past few years, the CBD industry has skyrocketed for people and dogs! But what is it all about?

CBD, terpenes, and tetrahydrocannabinol (THC) occur naturally in cannabis plants. CBD and THC are compounds called *cannabinoids*. *Terpenes* are aromatic compounds that give plants their scents (e.g. lavender, orange and lime peels, and, of course, the unmistakable scent of marijuana!). Terpenes also influence cannabinoids. In short, CBD, THC, and terpenes have a variety of effects in us and in our dogs. These compounds affect us because cannabinoids also occur naturally in our bodies.

We (and our dogs) make our own cannabinoids (called *endocannabinoids*) that work as neurotransmitters (substances that signal nerves), and we have special receptors and enzymes that interact with cannabinoids. Collectively, this is called the *endocannabinoid system*. (Raypole 2019, Richter 2020) Our endocannabinoid system helps regulate mood, appetite, pain, immunity, sleep, and more. When we consume cannabinoids from plants or synthetic sources, they influence our endocannabinoid system.

Marijuana vs. hemp and THC vs. CBD: Effects and uses

Of the hundreds of varieties of cannabis plants, the two broad categories are marijuana and hemp. Marijuana encompasses cannabis plants that contain more than 0.3% THC. Hemp encompasses cannabis plants that contain 0.3%

or less THC. (Remember, both marijuana and hemp also contain CBD and terpenes.)

This distinction between THC content is important because THC produces a "high" (euphoria, intoxication) in people, and CBD does not have these same intense mental effects. Marijuana is illegal according to federal law, but some states permit its sale for medicinal or recreational use in people. THC has been studied and approved for limited therapeutic use in people. Synthetic forms of THC called dronabinol and nabilone are FDA-approved to treat specific types of nausea, vomiting, and inappetence in people.

Marijuana use in dogs is not legal, and because of its higher THC content, it can cause toxicity and serious adverse effects in dogs. If dogs consume synthetic THC, eat their caregivers' weed or edibles, or inhale secondhand pot smoke, they can become woozy and wobbly, lethargic, and hypersensitive to sound or motion. They may dribble urine, drool, vomit, or have slow heart and breathing rates. They can also have seizures or become comatose. No FDA-approved THC medications are available for dogs.

Conversely, hemp is legal according to federal law, but not all states permit it to be grown. Most CBD products are made from hemp, and CBD is federally legal as long as it contains 0.3% or less THC. But CBD is not legal in every state, and in some states its sale or purchase has restrictions.

Although hemp contains very little THC, it contains over a hundred cannabinoids and terpenes that can interact with our (and our pets') endocannabinoid system. Research suggests that CBD and terpenes may be beneficial in helping manage anxiety, pain, inflammation, seizures, and more in people and rodents. (Perucca 2017, Campbell 2020) In fact, one CBD oral solution called Epidiolex is a drug that has been approved by the FDA for treating rare forms of epilepsy in people.

Hemp-based CBD appears to be safe for healthy dogs. (Deabold 2019) Some studies indicate that hemp-derived CBD helps manage arthritis pain in dogs, (Gamble 2018, Verrico 2020, Brioschi 2020), but another study indicates that it does not. (Mejia 2021) One study found that CBD did not reduce dogs' anxiety caused by fireworks noise. (Morris 2020) Another CBD study showed potential beneficial effects against canine cancer cells. (Henry 2020)

Despite the multitude of CBD products marketed for dogs —available as oils, chews, capsules, and treats—none are FDA-approved. (Cannabis Use in Pets/ AVMA) In fact, on a federal level, CBD cannot legally be marketed as a supplement or be added to food because it has already been approved by the FDA as a drug (Epidiolex), and per FDA rules, drugs cannot be used in supplements or foods, *unless* the drug was a supplement *before* it became a drug. (FDA Regulation of Cannabis) (It is confusing!) So the only way veterinarians can legally prescribe CBD for dogs would be to prescribe the human drug Epidiolex off-label. The cost would be about $450/month for a 44-lb (20-kg) dog. (Johnson 2019)

Should senior dogs receive CBD?

The FDA cautions against using CBD in dogs and recommends that dog owners talk with veterinarians about other appropriate treatments. Remember, CBD products cannot legally be marketed to prevent, diagnose, treat, or cure disease.

If you decide to use CBD in your dog, do your research and use only CBD products made for dogs. CBD products made for people are not formulated in pet-specific CBD doses and may contain ingredients harmful for dogs such as chocolate, xylitol, macadamia nuts, or raisins. Check that the CBD product you choose doesn't contain more than 0.3% THC.

Consider CBD products made only by companies involved in clinical studies that investigate the effects of CBD in dogs, that provide a Certificate of Analysis for their products that detail the amount and types of all ingredients, that follow National Animal Supplement Council (NASC) and Current Good Manufacturing Practice (CGMP) guidelines, and that are recognized by your veterinarian.

Why mum's the word for CBD and veterinarians

CBD use in dogs is new. Clinical studies of CBD's effects in dogs are limited. In the vast majority of states, veterinarians are not permitted to prescribe, recommend, or even discuss CBD with their clients. So, unfortunately, veterinarians may not talk with their clients about CBD use in dogs because of legal concerns. In addition, veterinarians may prefer to wait on results from additional clinical studies that support CBD use in dogs before discussing it with their clients. If you ask veterinarians about CBD, they may discuss potential benefits and harms of using it in dogs, but they cannot recommend CBD products. (Rishniw 2019)

Tough pills to swallow?

Getting medications down your dog's gullet can be the biggest problem! Avoid putting medications directly into their regular food, because one displeasing bite may make them reject their food from that point forward.

Ask your veterinarian to teach you how to give medications directly to your dog on the back of their tongue, whether flavored formulations are available, and, if needed, whether you can combine multiple small pills into one larger empty gelatin capsule.

Many helpful YouTube videos demonstrate different tricks that dog parents have tried. But when dogs are nearer to the end of life, they sometimes become even less accepting of pill delivery.

My preference is to first try a variety of tasty disguises to get dogs to "voluntarily" take their pills or capsules. Avoid high-fat or dairy-based treats if your dog is overweight or prone to pancreatitis. Always avoid chocolate, grapes, and raisins, which are toxic in dogs. Use only no- or very low-sodium treats for dogs with heart disease or kidney disease (deli meats and cheeses are high in sodium).

In fact, if your dog has heart disease, food allergies, diabetes, or another chronic condition, always check with your veterinarian on the best ways to conceal your dog's medications.

Given those caveats, here are a few suggestions for disguising your dog's medications:

1. Pill-hiding pet treats such as GREENIES Pill Pockets by Mars Petcare and Pinchers by VetriSCIENCE
2. Deli meat: Try different meats and get thin slices that are easy to roll the pill in. Thick slices tend to make "taco pills" that don't fool dogs as well.
3. Applesauce
4. Whipped cream
5. Plain yogurt (avoid yogurt that contains xylitol)
6. Cream cheese
7. Steak cubes (my dog Sam's favorite!) or chicken cubes
8. Peanut butter (don't use peanut butter that contains xylitol)
9. Processed cheese spread (e.g. Cheez Whiz)
10. Kong Easy Treat (many flavors!)
11. Small (cooked) ground turkey meatballs
12. Hot dog bites
13. Tuna fish
14. Baby food (meat puree)
15. Marshmallows
16. Canned dog food (or meatballs made from canned dog food) that isn't your dog's regular food
17. Liverwurst
18. Honey (stay away from honey that contains xylitol)
19. Banana slices
20. Strawberries—take the top off and make a small hole (like coring an apple) and stick the pill inside

If your dog gets wise to your tricks, prepare their "treats" when they're not nearby. Seeing and hearing you open the medication container puts them on alert and may send them scurrying. Wash your hands after handling their meds to diminish any suspicious scent.

You can also try giving a treat first (without the pill), then give a treat with the pill, then follow up with another treat (without a pill). Or try fooling them by feeding a treat-disguised pill from your own dinner plate. And if your dog is able, ask them to sit or do another trick they've learned, then reward them with the disguised treat. Or toss it to your dog to play catch if they're receptive!

If hiding meds in a 'treat' doesn't work, there are many pilling-assist devices available, and I call them "pill poppers." They're also called pill guns and pill shooters, and they not only help get the pill into your dog's mouth, they reduce the risk of being bitten by an ornery dog.

Medication organization

Giving senior dogs their medications can become so routine and repetitive that it may start to feel like you're Bill Murray waking at 6:00 a.m. each day to Sonny and Cher's song "I Got You, Babe" and reliving "Groundhog Day." You'll have moments when you can't remember whether you gave your dog their medication. You may be certain you did. But wait… maybe that was yesterday? It has happened to me!

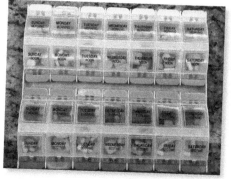

 My dog Sam's weekly four-times-a-day pill organizer.

I love using pill organizers to help track my dog's daily medications. They're available at any drug store. If your dog needs only twice-a-day medications, then a standard "morning/evening" container will do. For additional daily doses, you'll probably need a four-compartment case like the ones I used for my dogs Duncan and Sam. Some multi-dose pill boxes organize up to seven-times-a-day medications!

Also consider creating a "Treatment Tracker" as a handy reference to note various therapies and their effects in your pet. See Chapter 23 "Journaling: Tracking your pet's health."

When I was treating my diabetic dog with insulin (an injectable medication that must be kept refrigerated) there were some days when I would stand in front of the fridge and could not for the life of me remember whether I gave the insulin. And insulin must not be missed or overdosed! Phone apps and fancy medication reminder timers are available, but what

 A simple visual reminder tool helps you track feeding or twice-daily medication administration.

worked for me was a simple magnetic medication tracker—simply move the magnet to the appropriate day and time marker after you give the medication.

Beyond the pillbox: Veterinary rehabilitation therapy

Not all treatments involve medications or supplements. A number of non-pharmacological options categorized under the umbrella of veterinary reha- bilitation therapy (which is similar to physical therapy in people) are available that your veterinarian may suggest for your senior pet.

Veterinary rehabilitation includes various therapeutic exercises that strengthen muscles and improve flexibility and balance as well as passive range-of-motion and stretching exercises. It also includes therapies such as an underwater tread- mill, hydrotherapy, laser therapy, ultrasound therapy, pulsed electromagnetic therapy, acupuncture, and massage.

Special certification is required to provide veterinary rehabilitation services. Ask your veterinarian or search for an expert near you at the American Asso- ciation of Rehabilitation Veterinarians website **https://rehabvets.org/** and the American College of Veterinary Sports Medicine and Rehabilitation website **https://vsmr.site-ym.com/search/custom.asp?id=5595**.

After my dog Serissa had hip surgery, the surgeon suggested that she begin a physical rehabilitation program. I knew from my own experience after knee surgery decades earlier that my physical therapy was instrumental in my recov- ery, so I was all in!

I was amazed by what Serissa's rehabilitation therapists helped her accom- plish. She needed an intense program of weight-bearing exercises to regain muscle tone in her bad leg. But how do you tell a dog to do specific exercises? It's not easy, but those who are trained to do it are like Jedis! I learned so much

from them, and I'm certain Serissa had a stellar recovery because they possess a special "Force"!

As my love for working with older dogs grew, I recognized how helpful rehabilitation therapy could be for so many of them. Although

 Sam doing rehabilitation therapy exercises at home. Treats encourage her to step over the poles.

331

rehabilitation is most often thought of to help injured or postoperative patients return to their original function (like in Serissa's case), it is also used to slow progression of chronic issues. The goal is to help patients, especially those with nervous or musculoskeletal system disorders, attain the best level of function, independence, and quality of life possible. I have even started a training program to become a Certified Canine Rehabilitation Therapist!

In this section, I highlight a few of the therapies used in veterinary rehabilitation: massage, laser, acupuncture, and pulsed electromagnetic field.

Massage therapy

I love a good spa day or massage! I know not everyone likes massage, but studies in people suggest that regular, frequent massage helps prevent stiffness and pain from arthritis, improves blood circulation, increases blood oxygenation, and boosts energy. Massage also decreases muscle spasms, and may "trick" the spinal cord and brain into feeling the good sensations over the pain.

A study published in 2021 of more than 500 dogs treated by practitioners trained in clinical canine massage therapy showed that 95% of the dogs had substantially reduced musculoskeletal pain. (Riley 2021) After three massage therapy sessions over three to four weeks, the dogs had improved posture, gait, daily activities, and behavior, as well as performance (performance was evaluated specifically in the sporting, working, and agility dogs). At the beginning of the study, 40% of the dogs were reported to have a positive quality of life, and this increased to 66% after the first massage therapy session, 83% after the second session, and 92% after the third session.

Sam getting massaged by Tamara, founder of Angel Paws Massage—Sam loves it!

What I love most about animal massage therapy is that pet parents can learn some components of it from veterinary rehabilitation practitioners to use at home. Massage therapy also promotes the human-animal bond. Ask your veterinarian about veterinary massage therapists in your area.

Laser therapy

Laser therapy is also known as photobiomodulation therapy. Light energy in the visible (400–700 nm) and near-infrared (700–1100 nm) electromagnetic spectrum is delivered to target tissue with a laser or light-emitting diode. Research suggests that laser therapy may help decrease inflammation and pain and accelerate healing.

In a nutshell, the light energy reaches cell mitochondria (the cell's "engine") to promote production of adenosine triphosphate—the molecule that facilitates energy transfer within the cell. Free nitric oxide is also produced, which is a powerful vasodilator (widens blood vessels) and an important signal involved in other normal body functions. Vasodilation improves circulation, so this increased blood flow better delivers oxygen, salts, vital sugars, and proteins to and removes wastes from damaged tissue. In addition, reactive oxygen species are produced, and these molecules affect many of the body's important signaling pathways, including the inflammatory response.

Therapeutic lasers may provide benefits in treating a number of conditions in senior dogs, such as arthritis, pain from nerve dysfunction, inflammation, and infections. Laser therapy can only be performed by a veterinarian. A treatment can last a few minutes to about an hour, depending on the size of the treatment area and the intensity of the laser. It's not recommended to use laser therapy in patients who have widespread cancer or to use it directly over a cancerous tumor.

Acupuncture

Acupuncture has been used for thousands of years in people as a component of Traditional Chinese Medicine and is now commonly practiced worldwide. In dogs, acupuncture is also commonly practiced around the world as a component of Traditional Chinese Veterinary Medicine. Very thin needles are inserted at specific points in the body to produce a healing response. Dogs have dozens of acupuncture points and each point has a specific action when stimulated.

 Duncan enjoyed his acupuncture treatments.

Intensive training is required to be certified in veterinary acupuncture, and only a licensed veterinarian can administer acupuncture. Certified veterinary acupuncture practitioners may use acupuncture to help dogs who have arthritis, various types of pain, nerve dysfunction, respiratory problems, gastrointestinal disturbances such as diarrhea, and even anxiety.

Acupuncture usually requires two treatments a week for a few weeks, then once a week, and then every other week. Dogs tolerate acupuncture extremely well and often fall asleep during treatment.

Pulsed electromagnetic field therapy

Pulsed electromagnetic field (PEMF) therapy sends invisible targeted pulses to tissues, which induce electrical changes around and within cells to influence cell behavior. Some evidence suggests it helps decrease pain, inflammation, and anxiety and enhances healing. (Gaynor 2018; Calmer Canine Research)

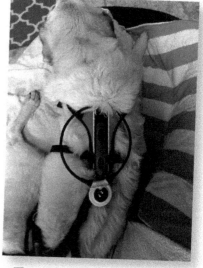

For my dog Sam I use a lightweight, battery-operated targeted PEMF loop called the Assisi Loop that is designed to sit over the treatment area and send pulses for 15 minutes. It can be used four times a day in each area. I simply attach the loop to her harness and turn it on. It is easy to use and most convenient if you purchase one to use at home.

Sam relaxing during targeted PEMF therapy delivered by an Assisi Loop.

The company, Assisi Animal Health, also offers a rechargeable therapy bed called the Assisi Loop Lounge in different sizes. The dog lies on the pad to receive the same targeted PEMF therapy that the Assisi Loop delivers, but it is delivered as a total body treatment. In addition, the company offers a separate loop called Calmer Canine that is specifically designed to send microcurrents of targeted PEMF signals to the brain. It is used to help reduce anxiety in dogs.

So much help for senior dogs

Many treatment options are available to help keep your dog comfortable during their golden years! Some treatments may work better than others for your dog and, more often than not, more than one type of therapy will be needed. Patience and communication are key as you partner with your veterinarian to find the best approach.

CHAPTER 25:

Building your support team: Don't go it alone

A dog's greying muzzle is often accompanied by one or more short- and long-term illnesses, and you may not have control over many aspects of their health outcomes. Having the right team around you is one thing that is controllable. Finding the right team to help you navigate your dog's senior years, whether your dog is starting to require more daily care or approaching the end of life, takes on vital importance. So let's look at who you'll want to team up with!

Your veterinary clinic pro team

Veterinarians. Veterinarians are the pros in primary care veterinary practice! We spend six to eight years total in undergraduate and graduate school, learning most things about dogs, cats, and farm animals—and many things about other furry, feathery, or scaly family members and wildlife. After graduation, our education continues. We keep up with new developments in animal health, diseases, diagnostic tests, surgical procedures, medical treatments, and other ways to make animals' lives better. Veterinarians may work in clinical practice, research, teaching, media, diagnostic laboratories, public health, and more.

Because I developed a keen interest in and love for geriatric pet veterinary care, I have several years' of focused experience with amazing grey muzzle dog patients. I also stay caught up on new findings in human geriatric medicine and end-of-life care and am always on the lookout for opportunities to translate those concepts to help senior dogs live better. This book is one of my labors of learning and desire to share this knowledge with all who share their homes with grey muzzle dogs.

Communicating well with your veterinarian is paramount. Veterinarians want to hear your concerns and questions about your dogs. We have ideas and options that can help. If we get too sciency-wiency as we discuss your dog's health, let us know. I give examples of questions you may want to ask your veterinarian

Dr Davis and staff at Kingsbrook Animal Hospital in Maryland love geriatric dogs. Notice the mat on the table to help this pooch not slip while he gets examined.

throughout this book, so do not be shy about having your question list ready! Your veterinarian should also welcome your wish to seek a second opinion from another primary care veterinarian or to see a veterinary specialist if you'd like. It's our goal to give you options for your dog and access to the level of healthcare support you are comfortable with.

Board-certified veterinary specialists. These veterinarians have completed advanced training in a specific area of veterinary medicine and passed an additional examination to specialize in that area. Veterinarians can become board-certified specialists in anesthesia and analgesia, behavior, cardiology, dentistry, dermatology, emergency medicine and critical care, internal medicine, neurology, nutrition, oncology, ophthalmology, pharmacology, radiology, sports

My dog Duncan's oncology hospital—Veterinary Cancer Group in Tustin, CA— knew how to make us feel special!

medicine and rehabilitation, surgery, zoo medicine, and more. Phew—that's a true A to Z! These specialists typically practice in private veterinary specialty referral centers and university teaching hospitals. Pharmaceutical companies, zoos, and a myriad of other sectors also seek out the super-charged brains of these veterinary healthcare experts.

Primary care veterinarians can also specialize in caring for a specific species such as dogs, cats, birds, exotic mammals, reptiles, or various farm animals. These veterinarians may practice in a species-specific clinic such as a feline hospital, or they may work in a general practice and see other animals as well. And some veterinarians specialize in shelter animal medicine and work exclusively in animal shelters or consult with them.

Your primary care veterinarian may suggest that you seek the advice and care of a specialist. Access to a specialist can be challenging in some areas, so your veterinarian may offer to consult with a specialist by using a telemedicine referral service.

Veterinary technicians/veterinary nurses. Veterinary technicians have two to four years of education after high school and obtain an associate's or bachelor's degree in veterinary technology. They have similar responsibilities to those of nurses and other professionals who work with physicians and to hygienists who work with dentists. These credentialed veterinary team members hold a special place in the heart of a veterinary hospital by monitoring anesthesia and assisting during surgeries, obtaining patients' medical histories and samples for diagnostic tests, providing nursing care, taking radiographs, cleaning and polishing teeth, helping to educate pet owners, and knowing the importance of a personal touch. They are at animals' sides during an outpatient visit or from hospital admission to discharge, helping veterinarians perform medical procedures, administer treatments, and ensure patient comfort.

Veterinary technicians can also specialize by advancing their education, training, and experience in specific disciplines such as anesthesia and analgesia, cardiology, dentistry, emergency and critical care, oncology, zoo medicine, and many more.

Raven, a patient at Kingsbrook Animal Hospital is set up nicely in a treatment area with comfy cushioning and non-slip flooring.... Plus some extra TLC from the veterinary assistant Kayla.

Technicians who successfully complete the specialty academy requirements are awarded the designation of Veterinary Technician Specialist (VTS) in their discipline. Veterinary technician specialists most commonly work in specialty referral centers, university teaching hospitals, and primary care practices.

My dog Sam with Gillian, one of her rehabilitation therapy technicians.

Your away team

Boarding facilities. If you travel for work or vacation or simply need a pet parent break (it's OK to need a rest!), finding the right team with the expertise to provide the best care for your dog is pure gold. With older dogs, it can be a lot of work to manage the numerous medications, special feedings or diet preparations, and frequent trips to the potty—AND to maintain constant vigilance for medical issues.

Look for professional boarding and day care facilities that can handle not only medication administration but also dogs with special medical needs. Do they have non-slip flooring (for dogs who don't walk as confidently as they used to)? Can you bring your dog's orthopedic bed (for dogs who have sore muscles or joints and need just the right comfy spot)? Do they have night lights for dogs who have cognitive dysfunction (throwing a little light on the situation is always helpful for dogs whose minds don't react as quickly as they used to)? Do they use pheromone sprays or diffusers (for those dogs with anxiety issues)? Are licensed veterinary technicians on the team to assess and monitor the dogs?

Many primary care veterinary hospitals have standard boarding facilities that provide routine pet care for daytime and overnight stays. And some of these hospitals offer medical boarding for pets who need special medical care, but they can provide this service only during their regular business hours. So if your dog needs around-the-clock monitoring, a stay at a specialty hospital that offers medical boarding *and* is staffed 24/7 will be needed. Ask your veterinary team for recommendations to find the right boarding facility fit for your dog and the level of care they require.

In-home dog sitters. This is often the best option when you must leave your senior pet, and the one that I prefer. Older dogs appreciate routine and familiarity, and they feel more comfortable and safer in their home environment. Staying home helps them avoid the stress of the unfamiliar noises, smells, and distractions at a boarding facility, and their environment can be better controlled. If you can, have a dog sitter stay with your dog the entire time you are away. This adds cost, but in my

Sam loving a good brush from Jean while I was on vacation.

experience the savings in personal anxiety are well worth it. My personal in-home dog sitter is Jean **https://www.facebook.com/leanonjean/**. (I'm sharing her Facebook page not to sell you on her services but to show you the special care dog sitters all around the country take to keep our furry family members cozy and comfy year round.) I am so fortunate that she has been there for my dogs Duncan and Sam, my cat Bodhi, and a few of my other grey muzzle loves. I could not have travelled for work as much as I did without the reassurance of knowing Jean was caring for my fur kids at home. Thank you, Jean!

Respite care. In caregiving for people, respite care provides temporary relief for someone who is caring for a family member or friend with a serious health condition. It allows the caregiver to take a break, go on a required trip, or even go to work each day. Respite care isn't widely available in the pet services industry, but you may be able to hire a home dog sitter or veterinary technician who will come to your home to provide this care.

When I lived in Southern California with Duncan, Disneyland was 15 minutes from my house. I could see the fireworks at night! When my good friend Christian traveled from the United Kingdom with his stepdaughter Chloe to visit me, they—of course!—wanted to go to Disneyland. This would be an all-day adventure, but Duncan could not be left alone for more than four hours. I wanted to go to Disneyland with my friends! I wanted to have fun! And I needed the break! But, alas, Jean was away on her own vacation. I hired a veterinary technician to stay at my house and care for Duncan on her day off so I could have a day off. Those 12 hours with my friends in the Land of Magic were gold to me. I relaxed, I laughed, I had fun, and I did not have anxiety about Duncan's care. That short break from caregiving gave me the mental energy boost I needed to care for Duncan in the months that followed.

Your dog's glamour team

Groomers. Maintaining a clean, mat-free, tidy hair coat and keeping toenails trimmed isn't all about aesthetics—at least not for your dog. It's about comfort. Overgrown toenails and hair can make mobility and pottying more difficult and uncomfortable. Professional groomers have studied the optimal combing, brushing, and trimming methods for various breeds of dogs. Some groomers even burst into happy songs as they love on dogs and tame their hair!

When senior dogs become less mobile, getting them to the groomer may become a challenge. Look for a mobile groomer who comes to you and understands the special care your fragile one needs. Check out their spa-on-wheels first—does it have non-slip floors and tables? How will your dog be dried? (Hand-drying is safer and less stressful than cage drying.)

Your spirit team

Your friends, family, and coworkers. Here is where the heart is. These people know you. They know your dogs. They know that as your dog grows older, you're keeping a more careful eye to keep her trotting with her tail wagging or to make sure she still enjoys her sunning spot. Your dog's care sometimes takes a lot of effort and makes you a little overworked and over worried. Find family and friends who have special roles in supporting your spirit—those who listen to you, talk with you without trying to control the situation, and are empathetic.

So many thoughts are running around in your brain. Working through all those feelings on your own can make you feel lonely and isolated. Talk with people who will truly hear you and not simply tell you what they would do to try to fix your situation. Good listeners are patient and wait for you to be ready to talk or cry. They also notice what is not being said. They ask open-ended questions, reflect back to you what you've said, and allow you to let out the emotions you may be feeling.

Find people who will talk with you about your difficulties and not simply say things that they think you want to hear. People who will ask for stories, let you share at your own pace, and not rush you to feel better and put a time limit on your pain.

Also seek out family members and friends to support you who have gone through experiences with their dogs similar to yours. Alternatively, this is an area where pet care support groups can help.

340

Your walk-on team

Neighborhood friends. Sheilah is the deli clerk at my grocery store. When I visited her to buy a variety of meats to wrap pills in for my dog Sam, Sheliah handed me a slice to taste. I raised my hand as a 'no thank you' gesture and said, "This is not for me, it's for my dog. She's old and I wrap her pills in tasty treats so she'll take them."

Sheilah's eyes lit up and she answered, "Well, then, you must try the liverwurst! I hid my dog's pills in it and he never knew!" She cut liverwurst slices in a variety of thicknesses and insisted that I come back to tell her how it worked. (I did, and Sheilah was right! Liverwurst was Sam's favorite.)

So now I make it a point to go to the grocery store when Sheilah is working. We chat about Sam and about Sheliah's dog. You can find support in the oddest places! So many dog lovers are out there and most of them are excited to share their tips!

Social media. One advantage of social media is that people from all over can connect and share experiences that have helped them. For example, Facebook has groups dedicated to animal enrichment, older dogs, and many specific dog medical conditions. Of course it's important to always consult with your veterinarian before trying the medical recommendations you find, but mostly you will find people who love their dogs and want to help them through their struggles and share what they have learned. You'll find people who understand what it's like to have a dog with the challenges that you're seeking support for. A few groups that I've joined:

- Laryngeal Paralysis (LP) GOLPP Support Group (Dogs):
  https://www.facebook.com/groups/larpar
- Dogs with Cushing's Support and Information:
  https://www.facebook.com/groups/89435412886
- Canine Cognitive Dysfunction (CCD) Support Group:
  https://www.facebook.com/groups/CanineCognitiveDysfunction
- Canine Enrichment:
  https://www.facebook.com/groups/canineenrichment

Your special teams

We all know too well that all good things must come to an end. And our dogs are nothing but good. You will eventually face their death. It may be sudden and unexpected or a planned euthanasia. It's important to begin to think about the options you prefer for your dog and the outcome that you may be able to control, like choosing the right place and the right time and having the right people around you. This will help you manage the grief you will surely experience. (see

Chapter 34 "Grief wellness: Anticipating and experiencing loss" and Chapter 38 "Euthanasia: The ending is what matters most")

Pet loss support groups. These groups of understanding individuals can help while you navigate anticipatory grief and pet loss. Not every town has a pet loss support group, but online support groups may be a beneficial alternative. Lap of Love has free weekly online meetings as well as one on one sessions. **https://www.lapoflove.com/our-services/pet-loss-support**

Counselors and therapists. Some people find comfort in speaking directly to a professional, and some therapists and counselors specialize in grief counseling. Veterinary teaching hospitals as well as referral or primary care veterinary practices may offer support to their clients provided by a licensed clinical social worker. Some employers also offer employee assistance programs who may offer these services at no charge.

Free, confidential support for people in emotional distress or suicidal crisis is available in the U.S. through the National Suicide Prevention Lifeline at 1-800-273-TALK (8255), 24 hours a day, seven days a week. Other local support is available by calling your doctor's office or 911.

A beautiful fellowship

I hope you find the right team of people who support you—from your veterinary team to those you interact with every day. A team who is there to help when you need them but also gives you space when you need it. Your support team isn't there to take over your life. You are fully capable—even when you feel overwrought or are grieving and hurting. It's OK to feel those things and to ask for support when you need it. Your support team should be able to recognize if you are about to go off the deep end and will guide you back to calm, shallow water with the reassurance of a warm, comfy, oversize beach towel wrapped lovingly around your being.

RESOURCES

- American Veterinary Medical Association Resources for Pet Owners
  https://www.avma.org/resources-tools/pet-owners
- American Veterinary Medical Association List of Veterinary Specialties
  https://www.avma.org/education/veterinary-specialties
- Veterinary Technician Specialties
  https://www.navta.net/page/specialties
- Suicide Prevention Lifeline website: **www.suicidepreventionlifeline.org**
  Phone: 1-800-273-TALK (8255)

CHAPTER 26:

FAQs: Why not let your vet see your senior dog?

"You know my method. It is founded upon the observation of trifles."

— SHERLOCK HOLMES
(FROM "THE BOSCOMBE VALLEY MYSTERY"
BY SIR ARTHUR CONAN DOYLE)

"Does my dog really need to go to the veterinarian?"

"What is the vet going to tell me, other than 'Rusty is old'?"

"Does my dog really need tests and medications—what good will they do?"

"My dog is old and will probably only live a couple more years. Why should I continue with vaccinations, parasite prevention, and regular checkups?"

"Isn't my dog too old for anesthesia?"

"How can I take my dog to the vet without all the stress?"

Well-meaning families who share their lives with a geriatric dog often ask me questions like these. And to start, I will be straight to the point: Yes! Please take your dog to the veterinarian regularly.

Like us as we age, dogs tend to have more health issues and need more medical attention during their last life stage. I know many elderly people who are stable but have long-standing health issues, and they see their family physician for checkups every three or four months. That isn't even counting their checkups with the doctors who specialize in their health problems.

Did you know that when dogs reach their senior years, routine veterinary checkups are needed every six months? And like us, dogs with chronic medical conditions usually need to see a veterinarian even more often than every six months for rechecks. A dog's final years are the most delicate, and your veterinary team can help shore up the precious time you have left with your dog.

Why so many rechecks? Senior and geriatric dogs need more routine checkups and health monitoring to help detect conditions and diseases associated with aging. Looking for and addressing health threats in your furry family members can help them live longer and more comfortably, all while allowing them to stay as active and engaged (and as happy) as possible.

An engaging life, plus good health, or, if good health eludes us, well-managed health conditions, are what we want for our family members, our friends, and ourselves. Welcoming and watching over your dog's later life stages and partnering with your veterinarian in your dog's healthcare can be splendidly life-changing for your dog and for you.

A prescription for the fountain of dog youth

Senior dogs (really dogs of any age) may have subtle signs of issues brewing that you may not easily recognize. So once dog parents notice something's amiss, the ailment may be advanced. Older dogs are more likely to have months and years of their lives stolen by kidney disease, cancer, arthritis, heart disease, and other health thieves. I always say that it's easier to keep the demon away than to chase it away once it's in the house!

Enlisting a veterinarian's expertise to help catch problems as early as possible and before they progress may help your dog act, look, and feel younger than his age. Yet in 2003, the American Animal

My dog Sam is checking in at the veterinary clinic.

Hospital Association reported that only 14% of senior dogs have regular health screenings as recommended by their veterinarians. (AAHA 2003, Senior Care Guidelines Task Force 2005) One of my goals is to help boost this percentage because it will increase the contentment of so many grey muzzle dogs!

How often should your dog see a vet?

I recommend that senior dogs see their veterinarian at least twice a year. Between those visits, monitor your dog's behavior, appetite, thirst, urination and defecation, breathing, energy levels, and attitude. Keeping a dog health journal will help (see Chapter 23 "Journaling: Tracking your dog's health"). Bring this information along to each routine checkup, and visit your veterinarian sooner if you notice changes.

What will your vet see in your dog?

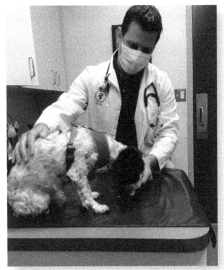

Frequent, routine veterinary visits for your senior dog are similar to our own routine checkups. At my most recent annual checkup, my blood test results and physical examination findings were normal (yay!). And I didn't feel like I'd wasted my time or money because my doctor found nothing wrong. My doctor also asked about my stress levels, workload, and safety in my home environment. My doctor recommended that I take a daily calcium and vitamin D supplement to help prevent osteoporosis, gave me a tetanus booster vaccination, suggested I add two (more!) 30-minute exercise activities each

 This senior dog is getting a checkup by Dr. Jeremy Breitinger at Kingsbrook Animal Hospital in Frederick, Maryland.

week, reminded me to schedule a mammogram, told me I could look forward to a screening colonoscopy within the next decade (eek), and scheduled my checkup appointment for next year.

How does this compare to your dog's visit? A senior dog's routine veterinary examination entails:

- Discussing your dog's medical history and physical or behavioral changes you've noted or other concerns you have (write down your questions ahead of the visit and take your dog's health journal)
- Discussing your dog's diet, appetite, caloric intake, and activity levels
- A physical examination, including assessments of your dog's pulse, breathing rate, temperature, heart and lung sounds, eyes, teeth, skin, coat, toenails, musculoskeletal system, cognition and balance, weight, body condition, and muscle condition
- Blood tests—a complete blood count to evaluate the types and numbers of blood cells, a serum chemistry profile to help evaluate organ function, thyroid hormone measurements to check for an underactive thyroid gland, and a heartworm test (heartworm tests are needed only once a year if you give heartworm preventive once a month and don't miss a dose)
- Urine and fecal tests
- Discussing whether home environment modifications or new enrichment activities would be beneficial

345

- Prescribing medications and scheduling follow-up tests, procedures, or referrals, if needed
- Scheduling the next checkup!

Depending on your dog's medical history and risk factors, other diagnostic tests may be needed routinely as well, such as blood pressure measurement, radiographs, an ECG (electrocardiogram—to assess heart rhythm), or tests for infectious diseases. For example, my Doberman pinscher Duncan had a high risk of heart disease, so he had an echocardiogram (an ultrasound examination of the heart) every year. All of my own geriatric dogs have bloodwork done three times a year and radiographs and ultrasound exams yearly—or anytime there is any whiff or sniff of a problem!

Even if you've noticed no changes and your veterinarian finds no problems at your dog's checkups, your veterinarian can give tips specifically for your senior dog that fit with your lifestyle and your home to keep your dog active and comfortable in the long run.

Vaccine routines—are they needed?

I'm a vaccination advocate. I've seen many horribly sick dog and cat patients and many patients who died because they caught an infectious disease that was preventable, but one that they weren't vaccinated against.

Dogs who visit the dog park or go to doggie day care need to be up-to-date on their vaccinations, not only for their own protection but to protect other dogs. You never know who your dog will be exposed to, and senior dogs tend to have weaker immune systems, so even a mild case of canine influenza could turn fatal.

If your dog lives entirely inside and never goes out and no other dogs visit (meaning your dog basically lives in a bubble!), are some vaccinations really necessary? Possibly not, especially if your dog has immunity confirmed by the results of titer testing. Titers are blood tests that measure whether your dog may be protected against some diseases. The results help determine whether your dog needs certain vaccinations, but the tests are not available for every type of infection that vaccines protect against. Ask your veterinarian whether titer testing is appropriate for your dog.

And remember, if *you* go out, we know that viruses and bacteria can travel on dogs and people, and some of these are readily transmitted. So you could be the source of an infectious bug, even if your dog stays home on the couch!

How many parasite preventives are necessary?

Fleas, ticks, intestinal parasites, and heartworms do not discriminate by age. They love all dogs! If your senior indoor dog truly never puts a footpad outside

346

and other dogs don't live with you or come to visit, then your dog may not need flea and tick preventives. But heartworm preventives are still needed because heartworms are transmitted by mosquitoes. (See Chapter 12 "Heart: Keeping the beat strong.") I live in Florida, and those wily fliers sneak in, even though I have a screen enclosure!

Is my dog too old for anesthesia?

While it's true that geriatric (and pediatric!) age is a risk factor associated with complications after anesthesia, age alone is not a reason to pass up a dog's diagnostic test, medical treatment, surgery, or other procedure that requires anesthesia or sedation.

Additional risk factors to consider before anesthesia include a dog's health status (whether an underlying disease is present and how severe the disease is), her breed, her level of pain and stress, and the type of procedure she needs—because urgent surgeries or long procedures carry more risk. (Grubb 2020, Burns 2020)

Geriatric dogs tend to have underlying age-related diseases and less ability to respond to stress, so they have a higher risk of anesthesia- or sedation-related complications or death. (Hughes 2008) Senior and geriatric dogs simply don't have as much *functional reserve*—the remaining capacity for the body to operate normally—as younger, healthier dogs do. This means they have a harder time responding to or recovering from stress such as the pain associated with their condition or a drop in blood pressure or body temperature during anesthesia. A geriatric dog's kidneys or liver may have a harder time filtering and processing the anesthetics or sedatives, and his aging brain, heart, and lungs may be more sensitive to the effects of these drugs.

The good news is that your veterinary team can reduce anesthetic risks by carefully evaluating your dog beforehand and tailoring the anesthetic plan. The benefits your dog gains by undergoing anesthesia to receive treatments or diagnostic tests often far outweigh the risks of anesthesia. And if your dog has a serious medical condition that increases her risk for anesthetic complications, your veterinarian may recommend that you take her to a referral hospital for the procedure or test, where they have staff who specialize in anesthesia.

Sam's once-a-day anesthesia

I recently had to decide whether my dog Sam should undergo palliative radiation therapy. I knew that it would not cure her cancer, but if it was successful, it would reduce the size of her spinal tumor or at least slow its growth and perhaps help her stay mobile.

The rub was that Sam would need to be anesthetized each day for five consecutive days because she had to stay still during the radiation treatments. Sam is 14 years old, and she not only has spinal lymphoma, she has chronic adrenal gland disease and she's receiving several medications. So she has a higher risk of anesthetic complications,

I talked with her radiation oncologist, and he explained that each anesthetic episode would be tailored to Sam's specific needs (based on her medical history, physical exam findings, and lab test results) and how she was feeling that day. He told me that she would be anesthetized for 10 minutes or less for each daily treatment, that she would be closely monitored before, during, and after each anesthetic episode, and that her positioning and comfort would be carefully attended to. He also told me they would reschedule a radiation treatment if needed based on Sam's physical examination findings and her demeanor each day.

I decided that the potential benefits of radiation therapy outweighed the potential risks associated with anesthetizing my sweet, grey muzzle girl.

How can we reduce anesthetic risks?

Dog parents and the veterinary team all play a role in helping reduce the risks of anesthesia in senior dogs. As well-illustrated in Sam's case, to minimize the risks of anesthesia complications, the veterinary team tailors the anesthesia and monitoring plan to each patient. We consider the patient's age, species, sex, breed, and size. We evaluate the dog's medical history (current diseases and medications, previous responses to anesthesia), perform a physical examination, and assess the results of blood and urine tests, just as your physician would require of you before you undergo anesthesia. Additional tests may be needed depending on your dog's health status. For example, dogs with heart disease may need an echocardiogram.

You can help, too, by asking or allowing your veterinarian to schedule this evaluation a day or two before the procedure whenever possible. This helps the veterinary team identify and address abnormalities before a pet is anesthetized or allows us to more easily reschedule a non-urgent procedure if needed, rather than cancel on the day of the procedure. You can also ask whether your geriatric pet's procedure can be scheduled as early as possible in the morning so your pet may be able to go home the same day and have a shorter hospital stay. (Robertson [1] 2020)

Your role before anesthesia

Pet parents have a role in the anesthesia plan, too, because it begins before the dog leaves home. For example, you will likely need to withhold food as directed by your veterinarian to fast your dog before the procedure. You may need to give pain- and anxiety-relieving medications before the trip to the veterinary hospital to minimize pain, fear, and stress. If your dog tends to get carsick, let your veterinarian know so anti-nausea medication can be prescribed to prevent this. And take one of your dog's familiar toys or blankets along that can stay with him throughout his hospital visit. (Robertson 2018)

The veterinary team's role

At the veterinary hospital, the goal is to keep pets calm from admission to discharge. Minimizing fear, pain, and anxiety helps reduce the amount of anesthetic drugs your dog will need and promotes smoother recovery and faster healing.

The veterinary team performs a preanesthetic patient evaluation (including blood and urine tests if these were not done a day or two earlier). They select the anesthetic, sedative, and analgesic drugs and doses based on these findings and the pet's medical history. Many of the same sedative and anesthetic drugs that are used in human medicine are used in veterinary medicine, as are many of the same types of anesthesia supplies, equipment, and monitors. Administering a sedative before anesthesia helps relieve anxiety and decreases the amount of anesthetic needed. Pets also receive tailored supportive care that includes intravenous fluids (keeps them hydrated), supplemental oxygen (keeps them breathing easy), thermal support (keeps them warm), and comfortable positioning (keeps away physical stress).

Keeping pets warm before, during, and after anesthesia is crucial because hypothermia causes prolonged recovery time and can also delay wound healing and affect mental activity. (Lobprise [3] 2020) Mild hypothermia is common because anesthetic drugs suppress the brain's

normal temperature control mechanisms. Anesthetic drugs also dilate blood vessels, so body heat more easily travels from the body's core to the skin, where heat loss occurs. (Diaz 2010) Pets also lose body heat through their surgical site or from

A patient recovering after anesthesia and being closely monitored and cared for by Registered Veterinary Technician Julie at Kingsbrook Animal Hospital.

349

having their mouth rinsed during dental procedures. On top of all that, a pet's internal thermostat can go a little wonky as they get older (see Chapter 10 "Thermoregulation: Cool canines and hot dogs"), making it harder for them to reset to a normal body temperature. Circulating warm-water blankets, forced warm-air blankets, and warm intravenous fluids are some of the measures veterinary teams use to help pets maintain a normal body temperature during and after anesthesia. (Robertson 2018)

Pets are closely monitored before, during, and after anesthesia or sedation. Their heart and breathing rates, pulses, gum color, hydration status, eye position, jaw tone, overall muscle tone, reflexes, blood pressure, oxygen and carbon dioxide levels, heart rhythm, and temperature are assessed throughout. Like older people, older pets have decreased anesthetic requirements, and this is possibly because the brain shrinks with age. (Robertson [1] 2020) The anesthetic protocol is adjusted as appropriate and additional supportive therapies are given if needed.

Most anesthetic-related deaths in pets occur after a procedure during the first three hours of recovery. (Robertson [1] 2020) Therefore, close patient monitoring continues until your dog is discharged from the hospital. You'll also need to keep a close eye on your dog for several days after she returns home. (Matthews 2017) Speaking of which...

Your role after anesthesia

Although most of the effects of the anesthesia or sedation should have worn off by the time your dog goes home, he may still be groggy and a little unsteady. You continue to play a part in helping him fully recover at home by providing a quiet, warm, and comfortable resting spot, gradually reintroducing meals to your dog as instructed, limiting his activity as directed, giving prescribed postoperative medications, and eventually promoting your dog's return to normal activity per your veterinarian's recommendations.

He may sleep more, have less energy, and be a bit sore for a few days after the procedure. You'll need to continue to monitor your dog for signs of complications according to your veterinary team's instructions, and call your veterinarian right away if you have concerns.

Anesthetic risk statistics in cats and dogs

Anesthetic drugs (and their reversal agents), anesthesia administration protocols and checklists, and patient monitoring techniques have greatly improved, and anesthetic-related deaths have decreased in veterinary patients since the early 1980s. (Matthews 2017) In 1990, one study showed that 1 in 679 (0.14%) healthy dogs and cats and 1 in 31 (3.2%) sick dogs and cats were estimated to have died as a result of anesthesia. (Clarke 1990)

A 2008 study showed that the risk of anesthetic- or sedation-related death was 1 in 1,849 (0.05%) for healthy dogs, 1 in 75 (1.3%) for sick dogs, 1 in 895 (0.11%) for healthy cats and 1 in 71 (1.4%) for sick cats. (Brodbelt 2008) A 2017 study had similar findings, with the risk of death being 0.05% in dogs (1 per 2,000 anesthesia episodes) and 0.11% in cats (1 per 900 anesthesia episodes). (Matthews 2017)

Cognitive decline: An anesthetic complication?

I have heard some pet parents describe their geriatric dogs as "not the same" mentally after anesthesia and say that their dog acted "funny," tired, confused, or anxious. Their geriatric dog's odd behavior usually lasted a week or two before it would improve. I recently experienced this for the first time with my dog!

Sam passed with flying colors during her five daily visits for anesthesia and radiation treatments. Every day she ate afterward, went for walks, and acted like her usual self. Then three days after she completed radiation treatments, she started showing signs of cognitive dysfunction. She would sit and vocalize in a strange, high-pitched bark that I'd never heard from her before. She would do it in the middle of the day, every evening from 7 p.m. to 10 p.m., and even during the middle of the night. She panted more during these episodes, and the only thing that consoled her was for me to sit next to her and pet her. She had never barked like this or been a "needy" dog before.

Sam's new problem was extremely stressful for me and my other household members. By the third week, it was so bad that we even considered euthanasia—not because of our stress, but because Sam acted so odd and anxious that I was concerned about her well-being.

Instead I decided that I could double-down and sleep on the floor next to Sam, pet her throughout those anxious evening hours, and stay home 24/7 for a few more weeks—if it would help her. Finally, during the fourth week she started to improve, and it was like a light switch had flipped—her daytime and late night barking stopped. (THANK YOU, SAM!)

Sam still required extra attention during her 7 p.m. to 10 p.m. "witching hours," but I think that's because she learned (a sign of cognitive improvement!) that if she barked while I ate dinner or watched TV, she got an extra treat to keep her quiet.

Sam's experience made me wonder whether the anesthesia she had undergone to receive her radiation treatments caused this strange temporary behavior. So I looked into this topic further...

Research revelation: Is anesthesia linked to cognitive decline in senior people?

Whether anesthesia alone or anesthesia with surgery can be linked to cognitive decline in dogs has not been studied, but it has been studied for many years in older people. Concern about anesthesia-associated cognitive decline may stem from earlier studies in rodents that suggested that exposure to inhaled anesthetics may be associated with brain changes similar to those that occur in people with Alzheimer's disease.

However, one 2020 study shows that surgery with anesthesia does not lead to changes associated with Alzheimer's disease in people, (Sprung 2020) and a 2021 study indicates that surgery may contribute to memory decline in people who already have brain changes consistent with Alzheimer's disease but have not yet shown symptoms. (Lage 2021) Similarly, the risks of slightly faster cognitive decline in people in the years after surgery may be related to the conditions that necessitated their surgery, or to unmasking of preexisting cognitive impairment.

FUN FACT

Did you know that veterinary technicians/veterinary nurses can become certified in anesthesia? This means they have extra training in anesthetic techniques and monitoring pets undergoing anesthesia.

For now, evidence suggests that people who already have cognitive impairment may have an increased risk of developing postoperative delirium and cognitive dysfunction after anesthesia and surgery. Thus, it is recommended that elderly adults routinely be screened for cognitive impairment before anesthesia to identify their risk. Elderly patients and their families should be properly informed that cognitive dysfunction may be a risk associated with anesthesia, and screening allows the opportunity to discuss other treatment strategies if the patient has a high risk. (Mayo Clinic 2018, Schulte 2018) Based on the studies in people, other pet parents' experiences, and my own, I think it may behoove veterinarians to consider doing the same for our geriatric patients.

But my dog gets stressed by going to the vet!

Oftentimes, taking dogs—especially large dogs with mobility issues—to the veterinarian is easier said than done. (But maybe don't say it out loud, because your dog may try to head for the hills!) Believe me, I understand. I saw and heard about transportation troubles often in general practice, and I was not immune to these difficulties either. I even bought an old minivan to more easily and comfortably transport my mobility-challenged Doberman pinscher Duncan to his veterinary specialist appointments.

Other than scheduling an in-home veterinary visit or a visit from a veterinarian who brings a practice on wheels to your curb, here are tips that may help you more easily get your dog to see their vet.

For large dogs with mobility problems

Use a ramp or a support harness (or both) to help your dog into and out of the vehicle. If your dog is in the back of an SUV, back up to a curb, if possible, to reduce the ramp incline or the distance you have to lift your dog or your dog has to cover when he exits and enters the vehicle.

If you'll need help getting your dog out of and back into your vehicle at the veterinary clinic, let your veterinary team know when you make the appointment and when you arrive. A team member will be happy to come out to assist you.

Booties or "sticky socks" are also helpful once indoors. Consider taking along a clean pair because they can provide bonus warmth to help prevent hypothermia during anesthesia, if your pet happens to be visiting for a procedure (Robertson [1] 2020). It's helpful to train your dog to be comfortable wearing and walking in these. (See Chapter 17 "Mobility: The weak, wobbly, and unsteady").

Veterinary assistant Caitlynn is obtaining a patient's weight at Kingsbrook Animal Hospital. Floor scales with a non-slip mat on top are easy and safe for patients to access.

For dogs with car sickness, anxiety, or fear

If your dog gets car sick or is anxious or fearful about car trips or veterinary visits, plan ahead and ask your veterinarian to prescribe a medication that you can give before you leave to help your dog relax and feel better during the entire experience. Another good tip: spray dog calming pheromone (e.g. Adaptil) on a bandana at least 15 minutes before you place it on your dog, or spray it on your pet's car or carrier blanket ahead of time. (Robertson [1] 2020)

During cold weather, warm up your car before your pet makes a trip, and likewise, during hot weather, cool down the interior before giving your dog a lift. Give your pet a chance to potty before a car ride, too, and place a pee pad under him as a precaution. (Robertson [1] 2020)

Don't fear "bad news": Ignorance isn't bliss

 This old guy is ready for his examination and nail trim!

I dream of all pets having annual veterinary checkups until they reach their senior years, getting twice-a-year checkups during their senior and geriatric years, and receiving routine and supportive veterinary care at least once in the six months before the visit at which euthanasia becomes a consideration.

Some people avoid taking their pet to the veterinarian—and, likewise, sometimes even neglect seeing their own physician—because they want to avoid potential bad news! While I understand that, it's better to catch simmering troubles sooner. And you may receive the pleasant news that your dog is in good or stable health!

Either way, veterinarians can give you information, support, and treatments that will help you and your dog stay bonded and better engaged in the activities you both love during the last chapter of your dog's life.

Questions to ask your veterinarian

- How often do you recommend that my senior dog be seen for routine examinations?
- What tests will my dog need and how often?
- Do you have suggestions that will make it easier for me to bring my dog to see you?
- What accommodations do you provide for my dog with _____ (e.g., mobility, visual, cognitive) special needs?
- If my dog needs to be anesthetized, what will I need to do before the procedure regarding food, water, and medication administration and any other preparations?
- Will my dog benefit from anti-anxiety or anti-nausea medication to be given before we leave home for the visit or procedure?

- Can my pet be scheduled on a day when he can have a morning appointment or procedure and be discharged soon after? (So he doesn't have to stay in the clinic all day.)
- Will you explain the anesthesia process and how my dog will be monitored during and after the procedure?
- Do you have a veterinary anesthesia-certified nurse available to assist during my dog's procedure?
- How will my dog's comfort be addressed with regard to hypothermia, pain management, and positioning before, during, and after the procedure?
- If my dog's health status indicates a high anesthetic risk, should my dog's procedure be done at a veterinary referral center?
- What will I need to do after the procedure to monitor my dog and help in her recovery?
- What will I need to do after the procedure regarding my pet's food and water intake, medication administration, and other post-procedure needs?
- Will my pet benefit from an anti-nausea medication to promote his willingness to eat sooner after anesthesia?

CHAPTER 27:

Bucket lists:
The joys of life

"The bitterest tears shed over graves are for words left unsaid and deeds left undone."

— HARRIET BEECHER STOWE

Early one morning as I was admittedly distracted while walking my geriatric dog Sam, she suddenly veered off course and made a beeline toward the middle of the road. I briefly glanced up from my phone as she pulled me along the empty street, and I noticed a small, smooshed something that she was intent on investigating. She reached it and began joyously sniffing every millimeter of whatever it was, and I got sucked back into reading my emails. Then the sound of Sam's chewing snapped me back to attention!

I immediately pulled her back toward me. She stopped chomping and expectantly looked up at me. A completely flattened, dehydrated lizard was hanging out of her mouth! As gross as this street-jerky was, the glow in her eyes was priceless. And I said to her, "You know what, Sam? That must have been on your bucket list. So you enjoy that!"

And boy, did she. She ate that dried lizard pancake. And she seemed to have a little more pep in her step on the way home.

FUN FACT

In 1999, as Justin Zackham contemplated the things he'd like to do before he kicked the bucket, he made a checklist and called it "Justin's Bucket List." A few years after that, he wrote a screenplay called "The Bucket List." The movie was released in 2007, starring Morgan Freeman and Jack Nicholson. (Zimmer 2015) I wonder whether writing the screenplay was on his bucket list?

Build a grey muzzle bucket list

Maybe you have a bucket list—a lineup of all of the things you want to accomplish, see, or try before you die. A few of my bucket list items: to visit Kathmandu, sit with orangutans, learn to play drums, and—dare I even share—become a contestant on the TV show "Dancing with the Stars." (OK, that last one is a long shot, but I can dream!)

The point is to set fun and relevant goals that you're motivated to accomplish! And if it seems daunting, you can start smaller. The meaning of "bucket list" has expanded to include other wishlists, such as a "summer bucket list"—places you want to go before fall arrives, or a "career bucket list"—the different hats you want to wear before you retire. (Zimmer 2015)

I often suggest that pet parents create a similar list of all the things they want to do for their dog or allow their dog to experience before they say their final goodbye. I have made bucket lists for my own grey muzzle fur kids. When you're thinking about the list, consider: What makes your dog your dog? What brings him pure joy? What brings her ordinary happiness? What 10 things do you want him to experience before you say goodbye?

You can of course add to it or make different plans depending on your dog's health status. I recommend starting to check things off while you can both still relish the activities—whether it's weeks, months, or years before your dog earns angel wings. There may be activities your dog simply cannot do at the end. "Swim in the ocean" may have still been doable three months earlier, but if you wait too long, you may no longer be able to comfortably get your dog in the car, and your dog may struggle to walk across thick sand and dog-paddle against breaking waves.

Bucket list items don't have to be grandiose, either. I think it's safe to say most dogs, especially seniors, savor the comforts of a stable routine and simple surprises. Two of my dog Duncan's bucket list items were visits from all his girlfriends (the human ones, that is), plus a cheeseburger meal from In-N-Out Burger!

Or if you prefer to go all-out, consider making headway on your dog's bucket list with an extra-special celebration. A 2015 Subaru commercial called "Dream Weekend" tells the story of a man celebrating his dog's 14 ¾ birthday with a tear-jerkingly special road trip getaway for the two of them!

A few bucket list ideas floating about the Interwebs include picking up goodies from a dog treat bakery and dishing them out one day at a time for a week, taking your dog on a toy shopping spree, inviting friends over and throwing a "toy shower" for your dog, and letting your dog take a full-length nap on your lap. (TopDog Health)

Specially picked treasures are at the ready as well if you order a surprise toy and treat special delivery from a dog subscription-box service (e.g. BarkBox, VetPetBox, PupJoy Box, or **www.livelikeroo.org**). A leg up on an idea for dogs

FUN FACT

Subaru launched a social media campaign: #MakeADogsDay "to inspire and encourage all dog lovers to do even more for their pets, and to share their ideas with the world." (Subaru US Media Center 2015) The campaign later sparked "National Make a Dog's Day," which is celebrated on October 22 each year (not to be confused with another special occasion, "National Dog Day," celebrated on August 26!). This day highlights adopting "The Underdogs"—pets who are typically last to be adopted from shelters, such as seniors and those with special needs. Their ad "Short End of the Stick" features such dogs. (Subaru of America 2020)

with mobility troubles—take a stroll using a kitty or doggie sling, stroller, or bike pet trailer, and then have a picnic! And be sure to take photos to help hold on to all your memories.

I love bucket lists because when it comes time to say goodbye to your dog, having checked activities and experiences off removes so much regret. It allows you to focus fully on the tender moments with your dog in their final hours, and there's nothing better a loving pet parent can do.

If you're looking for a little inspiration in crafting the perfect list for your dog, check out a few of the lists my patients' parents have shared with me (plus, a peek at my dog Duncan's list).

 Yogi loved the lake. His dad, Greg, put a soft bed in a garden cart and wheeled Yogi there to enjoy the view and smell the air a few days before they said goodbye.

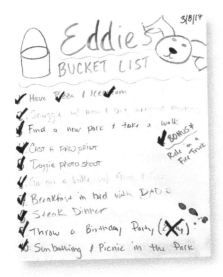

3/8/17

Eddie's
BUCKET LIST

✓ Have Pizza & Ice cream
✓ Snuggle w/ mom & dad
✓ Find a new park + take a walk   *BONUS* Ride in a Fire Truck
✓ Cast a PAW PRINT
✓ Doggie photo shoot
✓ Go on a bike w/ mom & dad
✓ Breakfast in bed with DAD
✓ Steak Dinner
✓ Throw a Birthday Party (Emily)
✓ Sunbathing & Picnic in the Park

Eddie's list included NOT inviting
Emily to his birthday party.

Eddie enjoying breakfast
in bed with dad

Eddie and dad
found a new park

Eddie's ride in a fire truck

Eddie having a
steak dinner

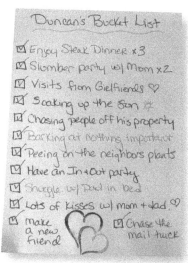

 Buddy loved cuddles best!

 Duncan got to keep guard against strangers, the mail truck, and the neighbor's plants!

Jot down your dog's joys of living

One family created a "Joy of Living" bucket list for their senior dog Buddy (shown above), and I appreciate that twist. What I have recently come to realize with my dog Sam is that I need both lists, for separate reasons.

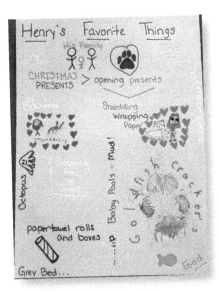

Sam's bucket list contains the things I want her to be able to do before she passes, like eat "road jerky" (accomplished!), take long car rides, eat a pile of French fries, gobble an entire piece of chocolate cake (on her last day of course), and visit her friends at her physical rehabilitation facility. When I wrote Sam's Joy of Living list, I thought of the things that bring her joy all the time: rubbing her face, particularly her closed eyes, sniffing

 Henry's many favorites.

the turtle holes in a field near my house, visiting my neighbor's dog to sniff butts, walking around the neighborhood, sleeping in my office while I work, smelling ground meat cooking. Her Joy of Living list helps me better assess her quality of life—do the things that bring her joy still bring her joy? And when most of them do not, maybe that will help me determine when it's time to say goodbye.

I now encourage pet parents to make both types of lists for their dog. There may be a little overlap between them, but they serve two different purposes.

Henry enjoys lounging in his baby pool, and mud!

Henry loves shredding wrapping paper!

CHAPTER 28:

Veterinary hospice: Living well until the end

"You matter because you are, and you matter to the end of your life. We will do all we can not only to help you die peacefully, but also to live until you die."

—Dame Cicely Saunders

Luis and Luella scheduled a hospice appointment with me for their dog Bogey. Not long before our appointment, his family had discovered large lumps in Bogey's neck. Their primary care veterinarian diagnosed lymphoma. Bogey's disease was already advanced when they identified it, and they knew their time with him was limited. But they wanted to keep him as comfortable as possible during that time.

I rang their doorbell and I heard Bogey's deep, loud bark. I also heard his toenails as he raced to the front door and pranced excitedly, along with his loud panting, all of which expressed, "Hooray! Someone is here!" Bogey's mom opened the door and a handsome golden retriever nearly knocked me over! Bogey had the classic golden personality—brimming with joy and love—even though he wasn't feeling his usual best. After he greeted me, he turned his big body around like a slow-moving cruise ship and gingerly waddled back to his couch. The funniest part was his tail. He wagged it so fervently that he kept throwing off his balance! There was no turning off Bogie's tail—he was excited about everything.

During my visit, I learned about Bogey's medical history, personality, current treatment, and quality of life. I also listened to the owner's concerns, fears, expectations, and hopes. Together we made a plan for his hospice care. At this point, there was no cure for Bogey's lymphoma, but we could still care for him in the best way that he so greatly deserved.

It was mid-December, and the holiday season is always an especially sensitive time for end-of-life decision-making. Luis and Luella asked me if I thought Bogey would make it to Christmas. I could only tell them it would depend on how quickly his disease would progress, which none of us could know. Then Luella asked me a very important question, "Do you think we should put Bogey on our Christmas card?"

Bogey enjoying "his" couch.

For every year of his life, Bogey's photo had graced their family's Christmas card. But now they wondered if it would be wise to do that—what if he didn't make it to Christmas? I did not have to think long to emphatically respond, "Yes! Bogey should be on your Christmas card. Even if he does not make it to Christmas, he will be your Christmas angel. He deserves his honored spot on your card."'

And so Bogey and his family began a hospice journey.

What is hospice?

For humans, hospice is a program of physical, mental, and spiritual care for terminally ill patients. It focuses on palliative care—treating a patient's symptoms without treating the underlying illness to attempt to prolong life—and includes pain control and emotional support. Hospice care can be provided at home, in a skilled nursing or long-term care facility, or in a hospital. The patient's care shifts from treating the disease to treating the patient's quality of life. Hospice can also include support related to household duties such as cleaning and shopping, as well as emotional and spiritual counseling for the patient's immediate family.

A surprising benefit of hospice care

Although hospice patients' care no longer involves an attempt to treat the disease, studies show that hospice patients live longer and have a better quality of life than patients who have similar diseases without hospice care. Hospice patients may live longer and better because their individual needs, preferences, and symptoms are managed better, which helps stabilize their condition. (Temel 2017, Temel 2010, Salins 2016)

A brief history of human hospice care

Although hospice (the word is derived from the Latin word *hospes*, meaning "guest" and "host") was adopted in the Middle Ages by the Roman Catholic tradition as a place of hospitality for the sick and dying, it was not until the mid-twentieth century that the hospice we formally recognize today began. A pioneer in this field was British physician Dr. Cicely Saunders who began work with terminally ill patients in London in 1948. (A Brief History of Hospice reference)

During a lecture she gave in 1963 to an audience of nurses, doctors, medical students, and chaplains, Dr. Saunders introduced the idea of specialized care for the dying that centered around palliation (relieving symptoms) rather than trying to cure the incurable. She showed photos of terminally ill cancer patients before they entered hospice care compared with their photos after they received hospice care. The positive visible difference in the patients' well-being was remarkable. This began the movement of providing hospice care to patients at the end of life in the United States. Since that time, funding for hospice has improved. Legislation was passed and Medicare reimbursement rates increased, so hospice services and professional caregivers increased.

In the United States, Medicare and Medicaid provide hospice benefits for people living with an end-stage, incurable illness. Qualifications differ by state, but usually a physician has determined that the patient has less than six months to live. In 2017, 1.49 million Medicare beneficiaries were enrolled in hospice care for one day or more, a 4.5% increase over the number of patients enrolled in 2016. (NHPCO 2019) Patients spent an average of only 76 days in hospice in 2017. So although patients are eligible for hospice care for at least six months, the median time patients spent in hospice was 24 days—meaning that half of the patients received hospice care for less than 24 days and half received care for more than 24 days. (NHPCO 2019)

More than 18,000 nurses are certified in palliative care, (Seaton 2020) and in June 2020 there were more than 7,000 active hospice and palliative medicine physicians in the United States. (Workforce Data and Reports AAHPM) About 325 new hospice and palliative medicine specialists are trained each year. Experts estimate that this number needs to grow to between 500 and 600 trained each year by 2030 to keep up with the workforce demand for these physicians. (Lupu 2018) This shortage was identified before the tragic COVID-19 pandemic, and the awareness of the demand for and importance of palliative care has since skyrocketed. (Seaton 2020, Parker 2021)

What is the difference between palliative care and hospice?

Palliative care can be provided at any time and for any serious illness or condition, one that may or may not be life-threatening. It focuses on patient comfort and quality of life while curative treatments for the underlying disease are given. If a patient is still receiving curative treatments, the patient can receive palliative care. Palliative care and hospice are both patient-care focused, not disease focused. Palliative care is also a component of hospice, but hospice does not begin until curative treatment for the underlying disease has stopped.

Understanding veterinary hospice

Veterinary hospice is similar to human hospice in that we focus on the dog and the family to manage the signs associated with the disease and the end stage of life. We don't focus on curing the disease and no longer administer treatments that are intended as cures. If you've used hospice services for a human loved one, you know that medical aid and other services to make the end of life as comfortable as possible are deeply appreciated, because we all want to experience the true feeling of being "at peace."

The concept of hospice for dogs is still relatively new and many people don't realize it's an option. In fact, not all of my veterinarian colleagues understand what veterinary hospice is. Another veterinarian once told me that pet hospice was "just prolonging suffering for our own selfishness." I wondered (to myself) whether he would say that to a human hospice physician or nurse. Did he think that because veterinarians can provide euthanasia, hospice is unnecessary? Did he not understand the benefits hospice provides not only for a terminally ill pet, but also for the pet's family?

Hospice isn't prolonging suffering. It's a medically supervised process that involves carefully watching over a failing patient to help the family provide the necessary comfort and support for their pet. Veterinary hospice is for pets who are facing the end of their life, regardless of their age or the condition that led them there. A young adult dog with acute kidney failure, a senior dog with end-stage congestive heart failure, or a geriatric dog with a number of age-related struggles are all candidates for hospice care.

Dogs typically receive hospice care when they have less than three months to live. Unlike human hospice care, government financial support for pet hospice (and other pet healthcare) isn't available. (And similar to human healthcare, private pet health insurance plans differ in the services they cover.)

For dogs receiving hospice care, pet parents still of course have the option to choose euthanasia for their dog when quality of life is poor. With that said, when pet parents choose veterinary hospice, they are not required to choose how their dogs die (euthanasia or natural passing), but rather they are choosing how their dogs live—that is, as comfortably as possible—until they die.

Alleviating a pet's pain and anxiety and helping the family plan for a peaceful exit for their beloved pet are major components of hospice. Veterinarians who provide hospice care work with each family closely to help them understand what their dogs are facing and how they can work together to ensure their dog isn't suffering. Veterinarians know the unknown is scary. Knowing what is coming diminishes dread and fosters calm and courage.

Stopping (or never starting) curative treatment does not mean giving up. Hospice allows you to choose a different care path. Saying no to treating your terminally ill dog's underlying disease while keeping your dog comfortable can allow more time to focus on the time you have left with your dog, and to experience meaningful moments that you may otherwise miss out on.

Five elements of pet hospice

Our terminally ill dogs can't readily tell us how they feel, and even if they could, we still may not know exactly what lies ahead. But it isn't known exactly what each dying person's experience will be, either. As pet parents, we can often reasonably infer from a dog's behavior and actions some of the things he or she might be experiencing. Veterinarians have devoted their lives to identifying clinical signs in animals and interpreting their behavior and actions to help owners ensure that their animals live their best lives. And part of life is the end of life.

My veterinary hospice care program encompasses palliative care, environmental guidance, caregiver support, quality-of-life assessments, and planning for the end of life. During my initial hospice visit with a dog and family, I cover all of these topics with pet parents. Then during subsequent hospice visits or check-ins, I review and reassess these five elements with families and make adjustments throughout their dog's hospice care.

These visits, especially the initial one, involve hard conversations. They are delicate, crucial meetings. In his book *Being Mortal*, Atul Gawande, MD, wrote that Susan Block, a palliative care specialist, told him family meetings that involve end-of-life discussions are procedures, and they require as much skill as performing an operation. (Gawande 2014) I wholeheartedly agree.

Palliative care

Hospice includes palliative care. Palliative care entails assessing the patient's needs and taking measures to prevent or control signs associated with the dog's illness, or associated with the effects related to treating the illness (e.g. surgery, chemotherapy). Components of palliative care include:

- **Managing pain**. Medications and other supportive measures are used to ensure a dog has adequate, continuous pain relief. This includes being able to recognize signs of pain to evaluate whether adjustments are needed.
- **Controlling anxiety**. Anti-anxiety medications and supportive measures are used as needed, for example, to calm a dog who pants or paces at night or has other sleep-wake cycle disturbances. Controlling anxiety can also help reduce pain.
- **Supporting caloric intake**. Nutritional enticements are used to address a dog's hesitancy to eat, where appropriate.
- **Controlling nausea**. Medications are given to reduce nausea, because nausea may cause suffering similar to that of pain.
- **Maintaining hygiene and preventing infection**. Guidance on grooming and physical assistance are provided as needed. Many dogs in hospice care have fecal and urinary incontinence, or they are more likely to have accidents if they can't easily get to where they need to be to eliminate. Sanitary hair trims, brushing or bathing, frequent walks to potty, help to the potty area, frequent repositioning for dogs who are recumbent, and using baby wipes, diapers, and waterproof bedding help ensure a dog stays clean so that painful irritation and infections are less likely to develop.

2 Environmental guidance

Assessing a dog's home and making recommendations to ensure the environment is as safe and comfortable as possible for the dog is paramount during hospice care. Throughout other chapters in this book, I've detailed environmental modifications that relate to several specific ailments that dogs may face.

3 Caregiver support

Caregiver support involves understanding the families' wishes, hopes, and fears, as well as their physical and emotional abilities and their time and financial resources. This understanding helps veterinarians plan and tailor hospice care for each dog. Pet caregivers have the right to be tired, sad, frustrated, and confused. Pet parents should feel assured that they can choose to stop hospice and elect euthanasia for their dog at any time, or continue with hospice care until natural passing occurs, without judgment.

4 Life quality assessments

These evaluations are vital to hospice care! I discuss and assess life quality in detail with the pet parent and other family members, and we create an individualized evaluation method for each dog and family. (see Chapter 31 "Life Quality: "Doc, when is it time?"")

5 Planning for the end

This challenging conversation entails helping families think through and prepare for their dog's last day, so that the family's wishes are met and that they have the dignified goodbye they hope for.

Would you like sprinkles on top?

One year I returned to my alma mater, the University of Florida College of Veterinary Medicine, to give a lecture on end-of-life pet care to the senior veterinary students. As I walked down the hallways reminiscing, I heard a booming voice behind me. "MARY GARDNER!" I instantly knew who it was. I turned and saw Dr. Gary Ellison, the chief veterinary surgeon at the college, standing there in his white coat and scrubs, a wide smile stretched under his surgery goggles! He was a legend.

As I walked back to greet him, he said, "I am so proud of you!"

(I thought, 'ME?! You're proud of me? You're a rockstar surgeon who saves countless lives!') I gave him a big hug and asked him why.

Dr. Ellison explained, "Well, my father had pancreatic cancer. He was in the hospital for weeks battling it. The cancer also brought on diabetes. So a few times every day the nurses came in to take blood samples to check his glucose level. He hated it! Toward the end, we moved my father to hospice. On the first day of hospice, the nurse came in and he immediately asked, like a curmudgeon, 'What do you want?! More blood from me to check my glucose?' And the nurse answered, 'No, Mr. Ellison. I'm here to find out what your favorite flavor of ice cream is!' And my dad's face lit up! That is what hospice is about, and you are bringing that same comfort to veterinary patients and their families, and that's amazing!"

I was honored that he shared this story with me and happy to know how much hospice had helped his father. Dr. Ellison's admiration of my work in veterinary hospice care meant so much to me.

Finding veterinary hospice care

One of the most difficult parts of practice for veterinarians and their teams is saying goodbye to pets at the end of life and beholding the family's grief. In many cases, veterinarians have been caring for the dog and talking with the pet parent since the dog first joined the family.

Veterinarians understand how cherished dogs are in people's lives and want to make sure dogs are as comfortable and happy as they can be as they approach and meet the end of life. So in that respect, helping families say goodbye to their dogs can also be one of the most rewarding parts of practice.

Veterinarians in primary care practice may provide hospice services that include one or more types of consultations and assessments: in-clinic, telemedicine, or in-home. Not all veterinary hospitals offer hospice care, so if yours does not or cannot otherwise work with you on a hospice care plan for your dog, ask for referral suggestions.

You can also explore the doctor locator at Lap of Love **https://www.lapoflove.com/** and the provider directory at the International Association of Animal Hospice and Palliative Care **https://iaahpc.org/**. Keep in mind these are not complete lists of all veterinary hospice care providers.

Most veterinarians who focus on hospice practice schedule appointments to visit your home at regular intervals during your dog's hospice care. That way all the care, love, and concern can be tended to in the comfort of the dog's own home.

 Questions to ask your veterinarian

- Do you provide hospice care and, if so, what does it entail? What are the costs? If not, can you make a recommendation?
- If hospice care is not available in this area, can we work together to create a hospice care plan for my dog?
- Are respite care services or brief periods of hospitalization for respite care available for my dog if needed during hospice care?
- What support do you provide in case of an emergency?

Start hospice sooner than later

My Uncle Ed had been receiving prostate cancer treatment for two years; but the cancer had spread to his bones. In the spring of 2021, he was hospitalized because of breathing issues and pain. My sister and my aunt visited him daily, but the hospital had limited visitation because of COVID-19 restrictions, so I had to rely on second-hand information about his condition. When I was finally able to visit him, I was shocked. He was thin, pale, frail, and struggling to get comfortable. Maybe it was because of my work with terminally ill pets, but I sensed right away that he was not going to get through this and get back home.

Uncle Ed talked with me about his radiation treatment and physical therapy, and about going home. I noticed that he had horrible ulcers in his mouth, but he and my family thought they were caused by the oxygen mask. I knew the ulcers were related to his cancer and his treatments.

The saddest part was that for 90% of the time during my visits with him, he just stared at the poster on the wall that had his name at the top, and a 'faces of pain' scoring system from 0 (no pain) to 10 (worst possible pain) at the bottom. He kept telling me his pain was a 7 or 8. I asked him if he wanted to watch TV, and he told me that he couldn't watch TV or read a magazine. It was obvious that he couldn't get comfortable, and all he wanted to do was stare at the poster. I said, "Ed, you are unable to think of or do anything else besides focus on your pain. You are suffering." This broke my heart.

We asked Uncle Ed's doctor if it was time for hospice, and he simply said, "No." I wonder if he felt that hospice meant we had given up or failed, or if he simply didn't want to destroy our and his patient's hope. My family and Uncle Ed's healthcare team kept talking about getting him out of the hospital. I wanted to get him into hospice. It took another week for Uncle Ed's doctors to finally even say the word "hospice."

Uncle Ed was disappointed about hospice, but he hated the hospital. It took a few days to find a hospice care facility that had space for him. He had spent nearly three weeks in a hospital where he was miserable.

Uncle Ed moved into the hospice facility on a Sunday morning, and he was so happy. His chemotherapy drugs were stopped, and his pain management was increased. His room was lovely, with patio doors that opened to a nearby fountain. Everyone focused on his comfort care from the minute he arrived. And he finally got the mouthwash he needed for his oral ulcers. I was happy he was finally being cared for in a place that would focus on helping him live well.

Uncle Ed passed away the next evening. I feel as though he didn't get enough time to benefit more from hospice. If we

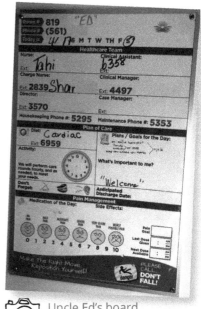

Uncle Ed's board at the hospital.

had gotten him admitted to hospice sooner, he may have lived much better and happier at the end.

I share this story to implore every family not to think of hospice as a failure, but as a way to ensure their pet is well cared for at the end of life. Start hospice sooner rather than later. I wish I had been able to do that for my Uncle Ed.

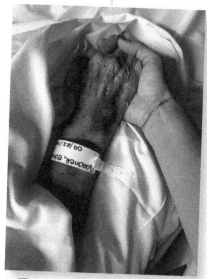

Bogey's auld lang syne

For Bogey's hospice care, I modified his medications to better relieve his pain and anxiety. His family placed yoga mats on the tile floor to help him stay steady when he was up and about. I asked them to add pumpkin to his diet to firm up his stool. To assess Bogey's

Me holding Uncle Ed's hand. Not sure if he knew it, but I did.

daily quality of life, they posted giant sticky notes on the wall where everyone in the family could write how they felt Bogey was doing, how much medication he needed to feel good that day, how well he slept, how his appetite was, whether he pranced at the door when visitors arrived, and more. The family focused on the joys of living that Bogey still enjoyed, like going to the beach.

Bogey did really well with hospice care for a couple weeks. He got to check a wonderful item off his bucket list—he celebrated Christmas with his beloved

Bogey celebrating Christmas with his family.

Bogey and his parents at Christmas.

family! Then by New Year's Eve, Bogey was ready for his eternal sleep, and his family was ready to provide that for their loyal friend.

That morning, the family took Bogey to his favorite beach, so he could feel the wet sand on his paws and sniff the ocean air one last time. Then they called me for his final visit. With his family surrounding him on his favorite spot on the couch and his dear friend, a cockatiel named Buster, perched next to him, Bogey became his family's New Year angel.

 Bogey and Buster.

 Honoring Bogey's final beach walk.

CHAPTER 29:

Goals of care: What matters most in the end

"Fear helps point to the things that you care about, the things you love, the things you're afraid to lose…. And then that becomes a nice compass for our way forward, how we're going to live until we die."

— DR. BJ MILLER, AMERICAN PHYSICIAN, AUTHOR, AND SPEAKER

My good friend and human hospice and palliative medicine physician BJ Miller co-wrote the book *A Beginner's Guide to the End: Practical Advice for Living Life and Facing Death*. It's a valuable reference for anyone facing a friend's, family member's, or their own end of life. I've refined a few tools I've been using over the years in my veterinary hospice practice based on some wonderful concepts from BJ's book, including evaluating your "goals of care," which I respectfully share here.

Thinking about goals of care for your dog encourages you to collect and record your thoughts about the things that will influence your dog's and your experiences near the end of his or her life. It helps you

 Dr. Miller and his super-senior Maysie

examine the situation you are facing with regard to your dog's ailments, which activities are most important for your dog and you, which activities you are willing to give up, and how much treatment you are willing to pursue. It also helps you consider whether your goals for your dog realistically align with your abilities to reach them.

I understand that this can be a tough thought process, and you might be thinking, where do I even start? Asking yourself care-oriented questions can help you identify priorities as your pet experiences the limitations and illnesses that aging brings. Based on the care goals exercise that BJ Miller outlines in his book, I advise pet parents to create a "Goals of Care" journal entry like this:

GOALS OF CARE

Pet's Name .... Date: ....

Circumstances	
Goals	
Compromises	
Road Map	

- **Circumstances:** Write what you know about your dog's diagnosis or condition, and list the resources available to you. Do you need family members and friends to help? Are they available and willing to help? Can you talk with your veterinarian regularly about your dog's care? As your dog's caregiver, what are your financial, physical, emotional, and time limitations?
- **Goals:** Write what you want to do for your dog and for yourself as her caregiver. Do you want your dog to receive all possible curative treatments? Or would you rather focus solely on relieving symptoms? Would you like to supplement your care with veterinary hospice care? Do you have a bucket list you'd like to fulfill for your dog? Do you want to plan for your dog to die at home rather than at the veterinary hospital? Do you want a veterinarian to end your dog's dying process before active suffering occurs? How would you like to memorialize your dog?
- **Compromises:** Truthfully draw your line in the sand. What trade-offs are you willing to make and not make? Will you delay travel for months

because your dog needs extensive care? Will you allow others to care for your dog if you need to be away? Is it acceptable to you that your dog may urinate on pee pads in his bed every night? Does it work with your schedule and finances to take your dog to physical rehabilitation or cancer therapy weekly? Are you OK with not trying or not providing certain therapies that may give you more time with your dog? Are you OK with not starting or with stopping certain therapies that are unlikely to help your dog?

- **Road Map:** List your next action items for providing care and meeting your goals within the guardrails of your compromises and limitations. Do you need to put up baby gates or place bath mats across a slippery floor? Investigate veterinary physical rehabilitation therapy options? Arrange a trip to the beach to fulfill a bucket list item? Schedule a veterinary examination to provide comfort care or discuss hospice? Explore options for aftercare of your dog's body?

You may need to reexamine your goals of care every month as your dog's condition and your situation change. You may find yourself easily caring for your dog one month, but the next month you may feel like you are drowning in managing her symptoms. I also suggest discussing your care goals with your veterinarian—this allows them to understand your wishes and direct your dog's care appropriately.

As hard as we may try, we can't control all things in the end, but we can take steps to help manage the challenges ahead. Writing down the goals of care for your older dog will help guide you when you're in the thick of things, managing multiple symptoms, emotionally and physically exhausted, and on the verge of being consumed with caregiving. The goals of care can help you reset and get back to a comfortable state—and forgive yourself if you reach a breaking point.

Scan this code if you are interested in a complete workbook to journal your pet's health and other aspects of care:

Dog Journal

CHAPTER 30:

Caregiver stress, burden and burnout: When loving hurts

"Love and compassion are necessities, not luxuries. Without them humanity cannot survive."

— The 14th Dalai Lama

Some dogs at some point in their lives—perhaps even as puppies—will face an illness that requires intensive care. And, like aging humans, as dogs age they're more likely to develop a condition that necessitates a more watchful eye or treatment that requires additional daily care—even if they've been otherwise healthy. Their care may entail multiple medications, a special diet, changes in the home, or more frequent visits to the veterinarian.

Even something seemingly as simple as giving pills, especially to a sick dog, can be taxing. And sometimes a dog's medications can produce annoying side effects, such as begging obsessively for food, drinking more water, needing to go outside to eliminate more often, or panting excessively.

In the last decade, I have taken on the role of intense caregiver for many of my dogs. I think I have done a good job. Some of my family members and friends may have thought I went a bit overboard for my senior dogs as they see some of the steps I've taken for my dog's care:

- Pursuing chemotherapy, acupuncture, surgery, rehabilitation therapy, and massage
- Modifying my house and cars to make them dog-friendly
- Canceling vacations
- Hiring in-home dog sitters and mobile groomers
- Purchasing nearly every product designed to assist with my dogs' special needs
- Rearranging my work schedule

- Experimenting with home-cooked dog foods
- Sleeping on the hard living room floor for weeks
- Splurging on nonessentials simply to make my dogs' lives more enjoyable

Have I been an enthusiastic, proud, joyful, and content caregiver? Yes! Have I been a tired, frustrated, mad, and stressed caregiver? Yes! Would I do anything for my dogs for as long as they need me to? Yes! And dare I even admit it—have I been relieved when the intense caregiving was over? Yes, but relieved only to have the weight of the work lifted. The weight of losing my dogs is far heavier and longer to bear. So I gladly carry the heft of caring for them for any amount of time they need.

I'm fortunate to have a background that has probably allowed me to accept and manage my dogs' illnesses a bit easier than many caregivers can. My biggest struggles have been learning to accommodate the viewpoints of others in my home and the need to sometimes place my dogs' intense care in their hands. For example, in a week, I have to leave for four days and my dog Sam's abilities to accomplish her routine daily activities have been declining. She has trouble getting around—she is the epitome of weak and wobbly. Her appetite has waned, so mealtimes aren't as simple as dishing out a cup of kibble. (Fortunately, she gobbles her pills wrapped in bologna like they are going out of style!) She has fecal incontinence, so occasionally she leaves a poop ball on her bed in the morning. All these things I can manage quite easily and happily for her on my own. But leaving Sam with someone who is not as eager to help weighs heavy on my heart. I wish I could cancel my trip.

Not until I dealt with the struggles of caring for my own geriatric dogs did I fully appreciate what caregiver burden meant. I empathize so much with other caregivers. It can be so frustrating and tiring. I get it! Caregiving—it's a hard job, even when you love to do it.

Caregiver stress

I'll be the first to admit that I've been stressed by caring for my old dogs. It's important that you and all caregivers don't feel guilty when you're stressed. You aren't alone.

You may feel stress when the demands of your situation outweigh your resources of money, time, physical ability, and emotional capacity—or anything else that you need to care for your dog and to also take care of yourself. I hope that by sharing some of the experiences of my patients' families and my own throughout this book, you can recognize sooner when those resources are diminishing and take away ideas for replenishing your resources when possible or managing them differently. Caregiver tools and support can lighten the stress of caring for your geriatric dog, and you'll better focus on the good moments that remain for you both to enjoy.

Unpacking the burden

Caregiver burden was first described in human medicine and is defined as the cumulative strain of providing care for chronically ill, elderly, or disabled family members. The challenges of caring for a seriously ill loved one can adversely affect the caregiver's emotional, mental, and physical well-being; financial situation; ability to work; and relations with friends and family members.

Caregiver burden has also been described in veterinary medicine and can occur in people caring for sick pets, especially pets who have chronic or terminal illnesses. The first study that examined the toll of caregiving on pet owners used measures of mental health that have been studied in human caregiving relationships. (Spitznagel 2017) The results showed that compared with caregivers of healthy pets, caregivers of terminally or chronically ill pets had:

- More perceived stress
- More caregiver burden and stress
- More symptoms of anxiety and depression
- Reduced psychosocial function (psychosocial function means the ability to maintain work and relationships and pursue one's full potential [Knight 2017])
- Poorer quality of life

Similarly, another study evaluated pet owners whose pets had cancer or suspected cancer. The results showed that pet owners with greater caregiver burden had higher stress levels, more symptoms of depression, and reduced quality of life. (Shaevitz 2020) Sometimes caring for a pet can make you feel like you're running on empty. Intense caregiving for a loved one—pet or human—can lead to stress, depression, and anxiety.

In people caring for ill human loved ones, the burden of caregiving can lead to *caregiver burnout*, which means that the caregiver's burden has progressed to the point where the situation is no longer doable or healthy for the caregiver or for the person being cared for. (Kasuya 2000) Caregiver burnout is also referred to as *caregiver fatigue*.

Based on the signs of caregiver burnout in people who care for ill human loved ones, (Caregiver Burnout 2019) the signs of caregiver burnout you might notice in yourself or another family member who is caring for an ill pet include:

- Feeling cranky and glum
- No interest in activities formerly enjoyed

- Withdrawal from family, friends, and other loved ones
- Feeling hopeless and powerless
- Changes in sleep patterns
- Changes in appetite, weight, or both
- More frequent illness
- Physical and emotional exhaustion
- Feeling a desire to injure yourself or the pet who requires care

One reason caregivers experience burnout is that they take on unreasonable demands, in part because they view caregiving as their sole responsibility. Another factor that leads to burnout is that caregivers are unable to recognize burnout in themselves and ultimately cannot function effectively. Burned-out caregivers may themselves become sick. (Caregiver Burnout 2019)

You love your dog, and you will do what you need to do, but it takes a physical and emotional toll. It is no small thing to face your dog's debilitating or terminal disease. In addition to spending a lot of time and money to keep your dog as healthy, happy, and comfortable as possible, the emotional toll in knowing that soon your dog may not be with you is one of the toughest and most sorrowful things to face. Although you dig in and devote all of your resources, you need to remember to care for yourself. Your quality of life matters, too.

Easing the stress and burden

Your well-being is a vital part of the equation that adds up to doing the best you and your family can do for your dog. I suggest five coping strategies that have helped me ease the strains of caregiving.

1. Become an expert. The unknown is often scary. "What's going on with my dog?" "What will happen next?" "Is my dog in pain?" "How will I know if the medications or supportive care are working?" Learn about your dog's disease, its expected effects on your dog and the signs you will see, and how you can treat or manage and monitor those effects. One of my goals in my veterinary career (whether it is this book, my blog, or the videos I make) is to help dog parents with precisely those things. Also talk with your veterinary team. Add to your arsenal against the cloudy unknown you may face and read up on your dog's ailments from other reliable veterinary healthcare sources. Your veterinary team can help direct you to additional credible resources specific to your dog's condition.

2. Seek support. Turn to support groups, counselors, or veterinary social workers. One possible outlet—many Facebook groups are centered around specific dog diseases and are full of people who understand your situation. Also seek support from those who will listen and not try to take over your situation and resolve all your concerns. New friends are out there who have a beloved dog facing the same disease your dog has. The internet makes connecting with others who are experiencing the same burden so much easier. For example, one of the wonderful Facebook groups I joined is the Laryngeal Paralysis (LP) GOLPP Support Group (Dogs) (**www.facebook.com/groups/larpar**). I have often seen dog owners struggle with decisions about their dogs' care, surgery options, quality of life, and euthanasia, and this group's support enables them to make better decisions or to at least not feel alone in the challenges they face.

3. Accept help from or call on family members and friends who will help. If someone offers to help, graciously accept! You would likely do the same for them if you could. And don't be shy about asking for help when you truly need help. For example, The CareCorrals (**https://prizedpals.com/canobie**) offers a private online community where dog owners can invite friends and family to join their dog's circle of support.

4. Take a break. Board your dog for a day or half day in the veterinary hospital as needed—the veterinary technicians will administer medications and see to your dog's comfort. Technicians might also be available to provide home care, to sit with your dog overnight for respite care, and more.

One colleague told me about a client at their primary care practice who had a senior Pomeranian with severe mobility issues and a chronic endocrine disease. The dog was otherwise healthy, happy, enthusiastic, and sweet-natured. The client boarded her dog at the veterinary hospital each weekday while she was at work—she dropped her off every morning and picked her up every evening—for three years! The client wanted to ensure her dog would receive her medications on time, get outside to potty when she needed to, and, above all, not be lonely. The dog stayed in her own special "executive suite" set up near the hospital's treatment area, and the veterinary technicians and doctors would see to her daily medical needs and pet, play with, and exercise her throughout each day to keep her physically strong and mentally fit. The dog seemed enthusiastic about her "workday" routine at the hospital and appeared to thrive with the attention from her many "coworkers" who loved her. She lived to be 17.5 years old!

5. Set SMART goals. This tool helps you focus on the specific things you would like to achieve and measure your progress. A SMART goal is:

S = **Specific**
M = **Measurable**
A = **Attainable**
R = **Relevant**
T = **Time-bound**

For example, I know my dog Sam will never return to her normal, healthy self. Her walks are shorter and she eats less. Instead of saying, "I want Sam to walk and eat more," my SMART goals for her are:

MOBILITY:

S = Sam needs to increase her walks to a quarter of a mile twice a day.

M = Sam currently walks an eighth of a mile twice a day. I will use my smartphone to measure and track the distance of each walk and to count the number of times she scuffs her feet (a secondary measure of whether she is making progress).

A = Sam can achieve this goal by gradually increasing the distance of each walk.

R = Sam needs to walk more to maintain her strength and quality of life.

T = Sam will increase her walks to a quarter of a mile twice a day within 60 days.

APPETITE:

S = Sam needs to maintain her weight of 65 pounds.

M = Sam needs to eat at least 600 kilocalories twice a day; I will track her amounts in a diary, note which foods she favors, and record her body weight every Monday.

A = Sam can achieve this goal with occasional appetite stimulants.

R = Sam's caloric intake needs to meet her energy requirements and maintain her weight.

T = Sam will need to consistently consume this number of calories daily.

By setting realistic, measurable goals and tracking them, I feel organized and in better control of the situation. Keeping a diary reminds me to evaluate my SMART goals every week and determine whether adjustments are needed. These goals will also help me evaluate Sam's quality of life and ease the decision to say goodbye when it comes time.

The number one reason why pet parents elect euthanasia for their dog is their decreased quality of life. The number two reason is caregiver burden. My intentions in writing this book are to help you enhance your dog's quality of life and lessen the burden of caregiving—by providing an overview of diseases and ailments and their treatments, to give you a wide variety of tips to better manage the struggles, and give you ideas for enjoying those last months, weeks, and days with your beloved dog.

Caregiver assessment chart

I've created this chart to help you identify and reflect on some of the challenges and stressful feelings you may experience as you care for your ailing dog. Remember, you aren't alone in having these feelings. It's helpful to recognize these challenges and feelings and share them with your support team to identify where additional support may be available.

Caregiver
assessment chart

 # Questions to ask your veterinarian

- What resources do you suggest to help me learn more about my dog's condition?
- What is each medication my dog is receiving used for, and how do I know whether it is working?
- How often and for how long does my dog need to receive each medication?
- Are there medications that my dog has been receiving that can be paused or discontinued?
- Can we work together to better fit my dog's medication and treatment schedules into my daily routine?
- Do you have recommendations for caregiver support groups or a veterinary social worker I can connect with?
- Do you offer medical boarding/daycare or respite care for dogs who need extensive care?

 READING RECOMMENDATION

- This website is dedicated to the scientific understanding of pet caregiver burden, how this stress affects caring for a geriatric or terminally ill pet, and what can be done to reduce it: **https://www.petcaregiverburden.com/**.

CHAPTER 31:

Life quality: "Doc, when is it time?"

"What you love is nothing of your own: it has been given to you for the present, not that it should not be taken from you, nor has it been given to you for all time, but as a fig is given to you or a bunch of grapes at the appointed season of the year."

— Epictetus

When we think of our dogs, what else can we do but smile and rejoice that we've found such exceptional soul mates to share our lives with? We've welcomed them into our families, and they've been through it all with us—putting an ecstatic exclamation point on the good times, bringing a comfort snuggle during the bad times ... wagging up a bit of the whimsical in those dull moments.

Then, seemingly suddenly, the time we have left with our dogs is only a sliver and the end of the joy they bring us looms. If I had the proverbial dollar for every time a pet parent asked me, "How will I know when it's time to say goodbye?" – I could easily afford the grey muzzle pet rescue facility I dream of owning one day.

The answer is complex, and evaluating a dog's quality of life—also called *life quality*, and the term I prefer—is the most important step. The signs of death's approach can be subtle and overlooked when you're consumed with the daily care of your ailing dog.

Please know that I empathize more than you might imagine when you enter this stage of evaluation and are trying to decide when it may be time to give your dog a peaceful goodbye. The emotions can become incredibly painful, so I hope this chapter helps you through this time and gives you the caring confidence you need in making this agonizing decision. I have helped countless pet parents evaluate their beloved pet's life quality and supported them in their end-of-life decisions. Throughout this chapter I share three life quality assessment experiences close to me personally. While we can applaud a dog's lifespan, we must attend to a dog's quality of life and consider it even more worthy of celebration.

My boy Duncan, the warrior

I adopted Duncan, my incredibly handsome 110-lb red Doberman pinscher, when he was 6 years old. He instantly fit into our family a few months after Neo passed. What made Duncan "Duncan"? He loved to hunt moles, eat salmon-flavored treats, keep watch from his orthopedic beds, take long walks, and hug people. He looked strong and fierce, especially because his ears were cropped (a procedure I don't condone and that had been done before I adopted him)—they stood upright and made him look like a soldier at attention—but he was a pure lovebug!

As a senior, Duncan had geriatric-onset laryngeal paralysis polyneuropathy (GOLPP), which was managed well after surgery, but as the disease progressed he developed mobility problems. Then a couple years later, I learned he also had heart disease. When his heart disease progressed to heart failure, I had to start evaluating his life quality and struggle with the difficult decision all of my patients' families are faced with. And so began my daily anxiety of watching Duncan through a different lens.

My sister's dog Kalick

My sister Sharon adored her yellow Labrador retriever, Kalick. Kalick had recovered from an episode of vestibular disease as a senior, but she had struggled with hip and elbow dysplasia. Otherwise, she had a dream life—a yard, a doggie door, a pool of her own, a doting mother, and the best food and toys. But by age 13, her creaky, arthritic hips and elbows severely limited her mobility.

Kalick began living mostly in the living room, on the couch. She was a typical Labrador—she had a great appetite and was always happy. She had occasional fecal incontinence, but her stool was firm and easy to clean up, so she had no hygiene issues. But her mobility progressively worsened.

Sharon struggled with knowing when it would be time to say goodbye because Kalick was HAPPY! She was eating, she wore her Labrador smile every day, she didn't outwardly show signs of pain or anxiety, and she slept through the night. But my sister began having a harder time getting Kalick up to go outside and could not get her in the car anymore. My sister hoped, like many people hope for their dogs, that Kalick would peacefully die in her sleep. But would that happen for Kalick?

My neighbor's dog Sandy

My caller ID signaled "Jill–Neighbor" while I was on a work conference call. I immediately knew she was calling about Sandy, their 14-year-old poodle. A few minutes later, I listened to Jill's tearful voicemail. She said they needed help with Sandy because they thought "maybe it is time."

When I moved into my neighborhood two years previously, Sandy was the first neighbor to greet me. She waddled over with a smile on her face and a wiggle in her tail and weaved her way around my feet. After that I frequently saw her taking a stroll in the neighborhood, which I was thrilled to see because Sandy was overweight. Finally, about six months later, I mustered the courage to tell my neighbors that Sandy was overweight. It's a hard topic to discuss with pet owners because many feel offended. But Jill and Tom took it well and asked for my advice on her snack intake. Carrots became her new treat!

Sandy also had many wart-like tumors scattered over her round body. One on her shoulder bled at times and looked inflamed. Over a few months, it kept growing and getting more irritated and angry-looking.

About 16 months after that I noticed that Sandy was not taking her routine walks around the neighborhood. I still saw her tooling about in her yard, but she didn't venture farther. Then a week before I received Jill's voice-mail, I saw Jill, Tom, and Sandy driving through the neighborhood in their golf cart, with Sandy's ears blowing in the wind and a smile on everyone's face. I anticipated then that they would soon call me for help with saying goodbye to Sandy.

 Sandy couldn't manage her neighborhood walks under her own power any longer, but she still enjoyed her rounds with dad.

After I listened to Jill's message, I walked next door. When Jill opened the door it was clear she'd been crying. Tom got up to greet me and Sandy bounded around the couch to say hi. Jill told me they'd given Sandy a bath and were concerned about the tumor on her shoulder, which to me now looked like an angry alien. But I knew they had always kept the area clean, with her fur clipped around it, and nicely bandaged. It was clear that they cared for her dearly.

We all sat down, and Sandy cuddled up next to Tom (she had always been a daddy's girl). Tom had also been crying. He told me that Sandy slept most of the day, didn't rouse like she used to—not even when he came home—and seemed "out of it" most of the time. She had also started to cough—at first only when she got excited, but now it happened when she jumped on or off the couch and sometimes while she was just resting. Tom had been willingly cleaning up after Sandy (she had fecal incontinence), managing her oozing shoulder tumor, and home cooking her meals. He was worried that Sandy was suffering and he didn't want to hold on to her longer than he should. He was facing the same questions and thoughts that many dog owners have as the end of their dog's life draws near.

And so we began the "How will I know when it's time?" talk—one that I have often with pet parents. This life quality conversation is unique to every family, every dog, every disease, and every situation.

The life quality conversation: How well is the dog, and how well is the family?

During my conversation with pet parents, we discuss life quality considerations in four major categories: the pet's ailment(s), the pet's personality, the pet parent's personal beliefs, and the pet parent's four essential pet care budgets—financial, time, physical, and emotional.

1. The pet's ailments

We may not always have a specific diagnosis, but learning about the pet's ailments guides me in understanding the expected course of a dog's decline in functioning. Is it a mobility issue? Is it a heart condition? Is another organ failing? Is it a cognitive disorder? Does the dog have incontinence? Is the dog completely blind? Does the dog not sleep through the night? Does the dog have a number of those things? Based on what we do know about the dog's ailments, I can figure out whether more can be done to manage the ailments, whether the ailments are causing or will cause discomfort or suffering, and whether the ailments are likely to progress quickly or slowly. This information also helps me determine whether the pet's road to the end will be flat and slightly bumpy, winding through hills and valleys, or heading straight to a sheer cliff drop off.

Duncan's ailments. His mobility was a concern as his nerve damage from GOLPP worsened, and his appetite had started to decline, presumably related to his heart disease. The biggest concern for me was that his breathing had become slightly more labored, and I wanted to ensure he would not struggle to breathe. And because of his heart condition, I knew that could happen fairly quickly. I was doing all I could to manage his ailments, so I was primarily concerned about a sudden decline in his health status, one in which Duncan would be struggling to breathe and I wouldn't be able to give him a perfect goodbye.

Kalick's ailments. Her primary ailment was severely impaired mobility, which would continue to be a slow decline. My sister had already made environmental adjustments to help Kalick get around, and I knew we could manage her pain with medications. But it was likely that one day Kalick would not be able to get up at all and my sister may not be able to help her without causing intense discomfort. I knew that Kalick's road would not suddenly end in her sleep as my sister had hoped—her road would be long and flat with lots of bumps.

Sandy's ailments. Her oozing tumor did not seem to be immediately life-threatening. She'd been living with it with supportive care for over a year. But Sandy's coughing and lethargy concerned me. I wouldn't get the benefit of doing diagnostics such as x-rays and blood tests to learn more about what she was facing. With my stethoscope I could hear that Sandy had a mild heart murmur and her lungs sounded slightly congested. I suspected that she also had heart disease, or cancer that had spread to her lungs, or both. Regardless, if her breathing was affected, then she would likely experience a sudden decline.

2. The dog's personality

Learning about the dog's temperament and individuality helps me help the family assess how their dog is handling the ailments. How well does the dog take his medications? Are there troubling or annoying side effects from the medications? How well does the dog handle being left at home on her own while the family is at work or school? What are the dog's interactions like with other pets in the home? (Does he struggle to get outside when the younger dog crashes through the doorway and pushes him out of the way?) Is the dog stoic and the owner doesn't realize the dog is in pain? How well does the dog handle veterinary visits for treatment? Duncan, Kalick, and Sandy seemed to be handling their ailments fairly well.

Duncan's personality. He was a stoic, loving boy who didn't complain. He tolerated his harness well—the one he needed to wear so I could help him get around easier. He had occasional accidents in his bed, but he didn't seem distressed. He was getting good rest. His appetite started to waiver, so getting him to take pills was challenging. He figured out that his "treats" were disguised pills, so treats made him anxious and he refused them. I had to carefully stick the pills down his gullet, which I hated, but he tolerated that better than the "treat" method.

Kalick's personality. She was the poster child for Labradors! "Nothing gonna get her down!" She loved life, even when she struggled to get around.

Sandy's personality. She didn't like her tumor to be touched and would flip over on her back when I tried to peek at it, so it was clearly uncomfortable for her if it was disturbed. She was friendly and outgoing when she was awake.

She had episodes of being "out of it," but she didn't seem to be anxious during these episodes.

3. The family's personal beliefs

Not everyone in the family may agree when it's time to say goodbye to their pet. Cultural and religious differences and personal preferences may factor into the decision. Sometimes the pet's function in the family comes into play, for example, an indoor dog who travels everywhere with the family in an RV vs. a farm dog who lives outside to patrol the property. When opinions differ, it is important for family members not to judge one another. (See Chapter 33 "A home divided: Conflicts between family members.") Duncan's, Kalick's, and Sandy's families were on the same page about end-of-life decisions, or at least in the same chapter in the book of their dog's care.

Duncan's family. I would do anything for him—every diagnostic test to leave no stone unturned, and every treatment or other support to resolve or alleviate his ailments. Duncan's dad was probably not as gung-ho to try everything. He didn't stop me, but I was definitely the leader of "The Duncan Project!"

Kalick's family. Sharon would do anything for her girl. But there wasn't much else that could be done. Kalick was receiving good chronic pain management, she had the best orthopedic beds, and Sharon helped her move about. Sharon's husband agreed that the decisions regarding Kalick were primarily Sharon's.

Sandy's family. Tom was Sandy's primary caregiver. I got the sense from our conversation that Jill was ready to let Sandy go sooner than Tom was, but that Tom would be the one to decide when it was time. They both LOVED Sandy. But they opted not to seek diagnostics or treatment for Sandy's tumor or worsening cough and wanted to focus on hospice care.

4. The essential pet care budgets

Each of the four pet care budgets—financial, time, physical, and emotional—are critical in ensuring and assessing a dog's care. They consider not only the dog's life quality, but the family's quality of life.

Financial budget. To be factored in: Medications, dog sitters, dog walkers, physical rehabilitation therapy, additional veterinary visits, diagnostic tests, cancer treatments, and more. The additional cost of an ailing dog's care may range from $200 for a few yoga mats and a high-quality harness to support a large dog's mobility, to thousands of dollars for surgery or radiation treatment for a dog's cancer. Many other costs, such as medication, therapeutic diet, and medical boarding fees will differ greatly between a 110-lb Doberman and a 10-lb pomeranian. A family may struggle to afford a dog's care as age and ailments add up. It's important for a family not to feel unnecessary guilt if they cannot afford treatment. Sort out what is most important to provide and do your best. If you are unable to provide care to keep your elderly dog comfortable, clean, and safe, then euthanasia may be an option to consider.

Time budget. Time is precious, and we may not have enough of it to take care of ourselves and a geriatric or terminally ill dog. Are there enough hours in the day for you to care for your dog? If you're awake half the night every other night trying to calm a dog who has cognitive dysfunction, your work or personal time and your health will suffer. Are you available if your dog needs medications many times a day or needs help to get around or go out to potty during the day to avoid accidents in the house? Not everyone has a job that allows them to come and go every few hours for these things. And if you have to travel for work or would like to travel with your family, can you find someone who will take care of your loved furry one?

Physical budget. Consider how well you can physically handle your dog and the effects of her ailments. Large dogs with mobility problems often present the most challenges, but even a small dog is not always easy to manage, and giving dogs their medications can be a workout. Getting your dog into the car for frequent veterinary visits or prescribed treatments may be impossible. Or maybe your dog is easy to handle, but keeping him or your house clean is difficult. For example, my mother has severe physical limitations and cannot bend down or kneel, so when her dog became fecal and urine incontinent, it was impossible for her to keep her home clean.

Emotional budget. Take stock of your emotional bank, in light of everything that is going on. How well are you handling seeing your dog not be his or her normal self, or thinking about when to say goodbye? Are you tired of being a caregiver? Are you fighting with family members about the challenges? Is your dog the last living link to someone you lost? Are you worried or do you have guilt because you think you let another pet go too early, or you hung on too long? The emotional budget is one we tend to discount, but it often weighs more heavily on us than we realize.

For my patients, I support the family's decision to say goodbye to their dog when any one of these budgets is depleted. If they financially can't manage the treatment that may help their dog, that's OK, and I'll help them say goodbye. If they don't have enough time to properly care for their dog, that's OK, and I'll help them say goodbye. If they physically can't manage their dog, that's OK, and I'll help them say goodbye. And if they're emotionally ready, I'll help them say goodbye. I make no judgments, and I don't compare a family's abilities or beliefs to what I would do. It's vital that you don't take on guilt if you've depleted one or more of these budgets. I've seen too many pet owners beat themselves up over not being able to afford their dog's treatment or having to work 12 hours a day so they can't be there for their dog.

A loving rehome

If various circumstances prohibit you from continuing to care for your aging dog, but your senior dog is healthy or your geriatric dog has a readily treatable condition, consider rehoming before euthanasia. Many pets can adapt well to a new home—some do quickly, and some require a longer adjustment period. So if your dog could still lead a comfortable, good quality of life, other family members or friends may be willing to welcome your grey muzzle companion. Seeking help from foster, sanctuary, or shelter services are other options. Many people, like me, love adopting senior pets.

Duncan's family's budgets. All of his big-dog medications were costly, but I had savings, and pet insurance helped reduce the costs. If Duncan wasn't let outside every four hours, he would pee in the house. And that was hard on my family. But I worked from home, so I worked his care into my schedule. He weighed 110 lb and had mobility issues, so although I could physically handle assisting and cleaning up after him, it was often difficult. I was sad, but not burned out. Duncan's dad was ready to say goodbye sooner than I was—he didn't like that Duncan needed so much coaxing to eat and take his pills.

Kalick's family's budgets. She did not require expensive medications, so finances were not a concern. Sharon worked many hours and sometimes had trouble lifting Kalick, so her time and physical budgets were draining. Sharon was sad, but still OK.

Sandy's family's budgets. Tom and Jill didn't plan to seek more treatment or diagnostics for Sandy, so finances weren't an issue. They had sufficient time to care for Sandy, and physically she was easy to care for except for her fecal incontinence, which was difficult to clean up. Dad struggled emotionally because he didn't want to say goodbye too soon or wait too long. Mom was ready to say goodbye.

The quality of death conversation: How well will the dog pass?

It's a common wish for pet parents that their ailing or geriatric dog will die in their sleep so they don't have to face the difficult decision to euthanize. I was once one of those pet parents. But that is rarely what happens, and if it does, it's usually unexpected or does not happen as peacefully as people imagine. So I prepare pet parents for how their dogs may pass if they don't choose euthanasia (see Chapter 37 "Natural passing: What to expect"). I also prepare pet parents who choose euthanasia for how their dogs' ailments may affect the time they have with them at the end. The goal for any death is that it be a peaceful passing—one in which the least amount of pain, anxiety, or suffering (for the dog and family members) occurs. I've found it helps for pet parents to understand the different paths their pets' illnesses are likely to take as their pets near the end of life.

Trajectories of decline

Hospice and geriatric care physicians use the phrase *trajectories of decline* to describe the patterns that illnesses take toward the end of a person's life. (Lunney 2003, Murray 2005, Cohen-Mansfield 2018) Other than the trajectory of sudden death (advancing from normal function to death with minimal forewarning), the three primary trajectories of decline described in people are terminal illness, organ failure, and frailty. I believe pets experience these trajectories, too, although I refer to them differently.

Terminal illness. During the initial stages of illness (which is typically cancer) patients are physically stable, and then experience a rapid decline in the last few months or weeks of life. Hospice was originally developed for people in the final stage of this decline. (Ballantine 2018)

For pets, I call this trajectory "The Dive " or "The Cliff." As in people, dogs maintain a relatively well-functioning, steady state until a threshold is reached and the disease accelerates and the body declines quickly. Diseases such as cancer that follow this trajectory typically allow pet parents ample time for pre-planning to ensure a dog's peaceful passing.

Organ failure. People with long-term and worsening lung, heart, kidney, liver, and some neurologic diseases experience a slow and gradual decline marked by periods of sudden health crises. The sudden crises are triggered by the underlying disease or by a new problem such as an infection. Each crisis may end in death, or the person may recover with supportive treatment or hospitalization but have reduced function, and so on, with each subsequent crisis.

I call this trajectory "The Winding Road" for ailing pets. Like people, these dogs typically experience a gradual decline that involves sudden downturns followed by recoveries. Frequent trips to the veterinarian for "treatment tune-ups" are usually needed. Eventually the disease takes hold and a time comes when no recovery occurs. Kidney or liver failure, diabetes, and Cushing's syndrome or diseases that can cause difficulty breathing such as congestive heart failure and lung or laryngeal issues may follow this trajectory.

Pre-planning is vital to ensure a pet's peaceful passing, because during any sudden downturn, death may occur. Unfortunately, when a pet progresses to the point of respiratory distress, decline goes south fast and pet parents may not be afforded the luxury of planning a good death.

This is why I like to have a preparatory conversation with pet parents so that they can plan as best as possible, which includes me making sure they know which emergency veterinary clinic is closest to their home in case their dog has a crisis at 2 a.m. and is suffering.

Frailty. In people, this decline is extremely slow and the disease may have progressed substantially before a diagnosis, such as dementia, is declared. Or the diagnosis may simply be "advanced age."

In pets, I refer to this trajectory as "The Fade." Chronic and slowly progressive diseases such as arthritis or cognitive dysfunction take a long time for the body to decline. Diseases that progress relatively slowly often afford us time to make the decision about when to euthanize and ensure that the pet's quality of death is good. Pet parents can have a goodbye party and make sure their dogs are comfortable and surrounded by love when they pass. But these decisions can also be difficult because the pet's decline is gradual, and pet parents may not recognize how sick their dog has become during an extended period. Although the underlying disease may not directly cause the pet's death, it often causes challenges that deplete the caregiver's physical, time, and emotional budgets.

Duncan's trajectory. His disease put him on "The Winding Road." Respiratory distress would cause his demise if I did not intervene, and I didn't want him to suffer from struggling to breathe.

Kalick's trajectory. She was experiencing "The Fade." Her arthritis was a slowly progressive disease and she would not pass from that on her own.

Sandy's trajectory. Initially she seemed to be experiencing "The Fade," but her recent downturn and new signs of illness—cough and lethargy—also suggested either "The Cliff" or "The Winding Road" trajectory and a potential sudden "crash" that she likely wouldn't recover from.

"The Roller Coaster"

Almost all dog lovers can agree when a dog's quality of life is good and their signs of joy are evident. Most dog lovers can also agree when a dog has intractable suffering and it would be kindest to relieve their suffering and elect euthanasia. But a huge "grey area" chasm lies between those two points where this decision is not straightforward. Making it across that chasm usually entails boarding what I call "The Roller Coaster." And it is like riding a rickety wooden roller coaster where it seems the cars will fly off the rails and you will plunge into a heap of splinters! I have ridden on this coaster plenty of times—right up front, screaming!

On this roller coaster you have good days and bad days as the weeks and months pass. Some Sunday nights you may think, "we had a really bad weekend, and it's time to say goodbye." But then Monday comes and your dog seems much better, so you don't schedule the euthanasia appointment. This roller coaster is no joy ride, and you will struggle. At what point do you decide it's time for the roller coaster to return to the platform so you can exit? If you had a really bad weekend, and on Monday your dog is doing better but you don't want another bad weekend, it's OK to get off the roller coaster and say goodbye.

Duncan's, Kalick's, and Sandy's families all saw their dog's joys of living diminishing, and all were all on the Roller Coaster. Some were at the beginning of the ride and some were nearing the end. But at any time they chose to say goodbye, it would be my honor to help them.

Sam's "Plane Ride"

As I currently manage my 14-year-old dog Sam's decline associated with her cancer, I'm thinking and rethinking about and revisiting everything I've written in this book. I'm struggling with deciding when it is time to say goodbye to Sam. She isn't well, but she isn't suffering. So far, I have decided four different times, "Yup, this is it. On Sunday I will say my final goodbye." Then I go through a day or two of anticipatory grief and dread about our upcoming "appointment." But when the day comes, for various reasons I decide, "No, not today!"

It's like being on "The Roller Coaster," but I now lovingly refer to this pattern as Sam "Approaching the Airport in Heaven." It's turbulent, and I think we need to land immediately, so some moments I pray for it to be over as we start to make our descent. Then the extreme bumpiness passes, so I pull back and lift our "plane" back out of descent mode. And we just continue in our circling pattern above the airport.

"The Flicker"

Many times I have seen ailing dogs spend days or weeks on a steady downward trajectory, then out of the blue they have a day or two of greatness. They eat better, move around more, run again, sleep through the night, and even play again. You may think a miracle has happened. I call this "The Flicker." However, like a thief in the night, that bounty is stolen and afterward the dogs seem even worse than before they perked up. It's helpful for pet parents to know that some dogs experience a flicker before their flame goes out.

"You'll know" and "The look"

Many people may tell you, "Don't worry. You'll know when it's time." I don't like this advice because you don't always know! Especially when you're evaluating your own dog. It's hard to understand and recognize all the signs of pain, progressing disease, malaise, or anxiety. We simply don't want to say goodbye, and sometimes it's difficult to assess our dog's physical and emotional quality of life.

Other people may tell you, "Don't worry, your dog will give you 'The Look' when it's time." My advice is, please do not wait for this "look." I say this because I'm sure your answer to the question, "Do you want your dog to suffer?" is "NO!" In my experience, if we wait for a certain "look" from our pet, we're waiting for our pet's suffering to be so bad that we can see it plainly. My advice is to try to say goodbye before you would see such a look.

My cat Herbie (the Love Bug!) had a lung tumor that affected his breathing. His disease progressed pretty fast and in about a month he had massively declined. He had always been the epitome of a loving, orange tabby tomcat! He once had a big, round face and seductive eyes. But his lung tumor stole his beautiful look. As his pet mom, I had a really hard time thinking of life without Herbie. But one day, his breathing became so difficult, and he sat on my chest and I realized, "OMG! Herbie has 'The Look.'" I knew he was suffering. I felt such sorrow that I had let my little one suffer. That day I knew I needed to give him his angel wings. We said goodbye outside, on the lawn, in the sunlight, and surrounded by daisies.

 My boy Herbie a week before he died (left) and on the day he died (right).

Knowing when it's time to say goodbye relies heavily on evaluating a pet's quality of life, which can be a challenge. Differences in how to define quality of life, differences between dogs and cats, differences between diseases, differences between caregiver observations (veterinarians, pet parents, other family members, friends), and factoring in the caregivers' potential biases all make evaluating life quality in pets highly complex.

Research revelation: Does science know when it's time?

Many quality of life assessment tools have been published in the scientific litera-ture, and the vast majority are for use in dogs. One 2015 review examined these tools, and their validity and usefulness were difficult to compare because their assessment criteria differ. The researchers identified published, peer-reviewed quality of life assessment tools for dogs and appraised the reliability, validity, and quality of each tool. They outlined parameters that others can use to evalu-ate quality of life assessment tools. (Belshaw 2015) The review underscored the fact that a universally applicable, scientifically validated quality of life assess-ment tool doesn't yet exist for dogs. So where does this leave us in knowing when it's time?

Methods for evaluating your dog's life quality

A wide variety of pet quality of life evaluation tools—surveys with scoring sys-tems, questionnaires with rating scales, and quizzes—are available on the inter-net. All of them have benefits in considering different aspects of pets' lives, and they attempt to provide pet parents with clearer insight on the subjective quality of life observations that differ for every pet.

I've created a Life Quality Assessment tool for dogs which is available on my website: **drmarygardner.com/resources/lifequality**.

Life Quality Tool

Here I'll also cover a few of the other popular assessment methods that you may learn about on the internet, through social media, or from your veterinary team. You may want to use one or a combination of methods to consider your dog's physical, mental, and emotional well-being.

Top Five

One classic quality of life assessment method for pet parents is to list the top five things your pet loves to do and evaluate whether he still loves doing them. Go for a walk, get out in the yard to patrol, sit with you while you watch TV, eat, greet and hang out with friends who visit, watch squirrels from the window, play fetch, get a brand new toy, sunbathe, ride in the car, nap on the couch with his head on a pillow—whatever activities make your dog your dog. Then—presuming that your dog's pain, underlying disease, or health condition has been treated or managed to the best of your abilities or cannot be further treated or managed—when your dog is not doing three of his five favorite things consistently, it may be time to say goodbye.

A caveat with this method is that with some diseases, your dog may be doing her five favorite things, yet she's struggling throughout the day or night. I see this a lot in dogs with cognitive dysfunction. The dog has a great appetite, enjoys going for a walk, interacting with visitors, getting popcorn treats during movie nights, and riding in the car, but she spends half of the day standing still and staring into a corner and becomes overly anxious at night and doesn't sleep well.

One twist to this method is to evaluate four of the dog's favorite activities and one thing that the dog hates. For example, my dog Neo hated the Goodyear Blimp and was passionate about protecting his family from it. The Goodyear Blimp flew over our house at 10 a.m. and 4 p.m. every day. The second Neo heard that motor, he got all worked up and barked and barked at that flying invader until he chased it out of his air space. I knew that if the time came when Neo stopped being upset about the Goodyear Blimp, that would mean he was probably too weak to expend the energy to care, and that he was no longer himself.

I was right, because during the last week of Neo's life, he didn't protect me from the Goodyear Blimp.

The Five Freedoms

As you're evaluating your dog's health status, response to medical treatments, and quality of life, keep these measures of animal welfare top of mind. The "Five Freedoms" were developed in the United Kingdom beginning in 1965 to address farm animal welfare. (Farm Animal Welfare Council 2009) And they have since been applied to address the physical and mental needs of companion animals living in shelters. These five freedoms also readily apply to the care we provide for the dogs we share our lives with:

1. Freedom from hunger and thirst, by ready access to water and a diet to maintain health and vigor.
2. Freedom from discomfort, by providing an appropriate environment.
3. Freedom from pain, injury, and disease, by prevention or rapid diagnosis and treatment.
4. Freedom to express normal behavior, by providing sufficient space, proper facilities, and appropriate company of the animal's own kind.
5. Freedom from fear and distress, by ensuring conditions and treatment that avoid mental suffering.

More good days than bad

One of the most common things I hear from pet parents is "When my dog has had more bad days than good days, then I will know it's time to say goodbye." In this case, it's important to objectively measure what you're monitoring, because otherwise it's very difficult to determine, "Is my dog having more good days than bad days?"

Defining good days and bad days

What constitutes a good day for your dog? This is a subjective determination, and the definition is specific to your dog and to you. Does a good day mean that three things went right? Or one thing? Does it mean that your dog slept through the night? Or does it mean that your dog slept at least four hours straight during the night? Does it mean that your dog ate all of his normal amount of food, or at least half that? Does it mean that she was able to get up on her own without your assistance? That he had cognitive issues for three hours or less a day vs. more than three hours? That she had only two accidents in the house that day? Or is it a good day only when things are almost perfect?

You also need to consider how well your good day definition matches up with that of other family members. My definition of a good day for my dog differs a lot from that of my partner. To me, a good day for my ailing dog is one that may still require me to provide intense caregiving to ensure my dog is still enjoying life and, of course, does not suffer. To my partner, a good day means our ailing dog has no accidents in the house and does not need help getting up. Yet my partner can understand my definition, because I provide the majority of our ailing pets' caregiving and I'll never allow them to suffer.

Write down what makes a good day and a bad day for your dog and you. Everyone in the household should agree on the definition of each. Then monitor your dog each day using those criteria to decide whether he's had a good day or a bad day.

Measuring good days and bad days

You also need to decide what percentage of bad days vs. good days means that it may be time to say goodbye. Is 51% good days to 49% bad days OK? Or do you need your dog to have good days 80% of the time? Or maybe having good days 25% of the time is acceptable to you.

Also consider for what period of time you'll monitor your dog, and whether you'll allow leeway for setbacks that your dog may recover from with additional treatment or supportive care. (Remember the ups and downs of "The Winding Road" trajectory I described earlier in this chapter.) For example, let's say you've decided that you won't consider saying goodbye as long as your dog has at least 60% good days and no more than 40% bad days. But then your dog has one bad week where three of seven days (42%) are bad because she has a disease setback or a new problem such as gastritis. Yet with additional treatment the problem is managed, and the week after that, she has five good days and two bad days (29%), bringing the two-week percentage (five bad days out of 14) to 36%.

Calendar

Visualizing good days and bad days

Write your assessments in a diary or on a wall calendar, or post them on the fridge or wherever it's convenient and all family members can see them. Use a big red X to indicate the bad days. This documentation helps you and your family agree on when it may be an appropriate time to say goodbye.

QUALITY OF LIFE CALENDAR

MONTH

M	T	W	T	F	S	S

YOUR PET'S QUALITY OF LIFE SCORE =

GOOD DAYS
_____
BAD DAYS

NOTES
_____
_____
_____

2	Good quality of life
1.1-2	More good days than bad days but monitor quality of life
1	Good days = bad days
.5-.9	Bad days outnumber good days
.1-.4	Quality of life is not well. Discuss with a veterinarian.
0	No good days at all. Palliative sedation or euthanasia are warranted.

Dr Mary www.drmarygardner.com

This calendar example shows that the bad day to good day ratio is 50/50.

So maybe it would be OK to say goodbye if that ratio is your decision point. But you can also see other trends, not simply declines. In this example, the garbage truck came every Friday morning and the family had not realized how much emotional stress this caused their ailing dog. The rest of the day was horrible for the dog and the family. The calendar allowed the family to see this pattern clearly, and they made sure that someone was home to keep him calm when the truck came. After that, Fridays got better for everyone! Scan here to download a blank version of a calendar.

Discuss good days and bad days with your children, too. One suggestion is to place one jar labeled "Good" and one jar labeled "Bad" on the counter. Put a

QUALITY OF LIFE CALENDAR

MONTH August

M	T	W	T	F	S	S
		1	2	3	4	5
6	7	8	9	10	11	12
13	14	15	16	17	18	19
20	21	22	23	24	25	26
27	28	29	30	31		

YOUR PET'S QUALITY OF LIFE SCORE = $\dfrac{\text{GOOD DAYS } 18}{\text{BAD DAYS } 13}$ = 1.4

NOTES

FRidays he is always anxious when I get home

2	Good quality of life
1.1-2	More good days than bad days but monitor quality of life
1	Good days = bad days
.5-.9	Bad days outnumber good days
1-.4	Quality of life is not well. Discuss with a veterinarian.
0	No good days at all. Palliative sedation or euthanasia are warranted.

Dr Mary www.drmarygardner.com

penny in the appropriate jar for that day. At the end of your predetermined time period, the jar that contains the most pennies will help you consider your decision. It's a simple visual for children to measure how their dog is doing over time and may help you talk with them when the time to say goodbye is appropriate.

SUN	MON	TUE	WED	THU	FRI	SAT
X		X	X		X	X

The "Good Day vs. Bad Day" quality of life assessment works well for me and has worked well for hundreds of pet parents who I've helped throughout my career in veterinary end-of-life care. Afterward, you'll look back on your daily diary and see the upward, steady, and downward trends, and be reassured that you made the best decision.

Other quality of life surveys, scales, and quizzes

A variety of other quality of life evaluation tools are available on the internet and from other resources, and all of them have benefits.

Dr Faith Bank's QOL Scale

My friend Dr. Faith Banks is a hospice veterinarian in Canada. In her quality of life evaluations she includes an assessment of the dog's interactions with their family in terms of whether the dog gave love or took love. Is the dog seeking love and attention, and is the dog also providing love? **mmvhs.ca/quality-of-life-scale/**

Photographic timeline

It's helpful to reminisce with photographs and videos of your dog taken a few months or years earlier. This exercise helps you remember what "good" looks like for your dog. We all change as we grow older, so you need to allow for typical aging changes. If I looked at photos of me when I was 18 years old right now, I would wonder where 30 extra pounds and a road map of wrinkles came from! But often, the pictures and videos can illustrate dramatic changes related to our dogs' ailments and help us remove the denial googles we sometimes wear.

Just the other day, I found a video of my dog Sam playing with my dog Norrin. It reminded me of how much better Sam was only one year ago. It makes me sad, but it is also giving me courage to let her go.

"Denial Island"

Darby was one of my grey muzzle canine patients years ago, and her mom taught me about a mindset called "Denial Island." Darby's health was declining because of liver cancer. And although Darby's mom used quality of life scales, she scored Darby as nothing but "Excellent" or answered "Everything is fine!" Yet she knew Darby was not doing that well. She told me she was on "Denial Island" and could not evaluate the situation properly. So she asked me to complete a quality of life scale for Darby.

My assessment of Darby's quality of life gave "poor" and "everything is NOT okay" results. We discussed my assess-ment and I suggested that it would be an OK time to say goodbye to Darby if she was ready. Darby's mom was not ready that day. So I adjusted Darby's medications and she had a wonderful next day. Darby's mom realized that she did not want Darby to experience bad days again. So two days later, Darby's mom asked me to help Darby earn her angel wings.

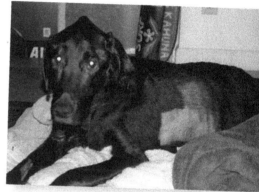

I've been to Denial Island with my own pets. Saying goodbye is heart-breaking and may bring on feelings of guilt about letting go, and denial feels better. I'm pretty sure I've been the

 Darby after her last swim, which she loved so much.

Mayor of Denial Island, so if you are there, too, it isn't unexpected. It's the place I go when my head and heart engage in a war, and my heart takes over because I can't bear the thought of not having my dog in my life. So my brain twists circumstances around to protect me from a truth I'm not ready to face. Denial is a helpful coping mechanism, but it can get in the way when you're facing a difficult decision. It's hard to see the reality when you're by yourself. If you find yourself on Denial Island, lean on friends and family, or, as Darby's mom did, ask your dog's veterinarian to help.

If you find a friend or family member stuck on Denial Island, Dr. BJ Miller, a human hospice physician, says that swooping in to try to extract them could seriously backfire. Instead, he suggests asking questions that may soften their denial and see the circumstances more objectively. (Miller 2019) So I suggest asking questions similar to those he uses to help his patients reflect. For example, when a family member or friend tells me that their ailing dog is OK, I ask, "What is happening with your dog that tells you that?" And, "Do you think there may be something we are missing?" Or, "Is that way of seeing things serving you and your dog well during this time?" Context and tone are vital, because I don't want to sound like I'm coming from "Judgment Island."

Getting to goodbye

Some ailing dogs have only a series of good moments sprinkled throughout bad days. Or some ailing dogs have only a series of a few good days surrounded by bad days. For pet parents struggling with the decision of when to say goodbye, I suggest thoughtfully considering the activities and experiences that bring joy to your dog. What makes your dog... your dog?

I adore Bucket Lists (a list of experiences you'd like your dog to have before they pass) and Joys of Living Lists (a list of activities or things that bring your dog joy all the time). See Chapter 27: "Buckets lists: The joys of life" for more about these lists. These lists can help you assess whether your dog is enjoying life. Write them down. Evaluate them often. Be honest. Look at pictures and videos. Be kind to yourself and prepare yourself. My hope is that when it comes time to get off your roller coaster or land your plane, you won't have regrets. You'll know that not only did you give your dog a great quality of life, but that you also gave them a good quality of death.

Duncan's time. His ability to breathe started to decline despite receiving all the medications and environmental support he needed, and he was struggling. I knew I needed to get off the roller coaster so he did not progress from struggling to suffering. And I was able to prevent that, and give him two good last days.

Kalick's time. As hard as Sharon had and would continue to try, nothing was going to improve Kalick's mobility. Sharon had to say goodbye sooner than she wanted to. Kalick experienced something I hope for all my patients—a really good last day.

Sandy's time. Even with all of Tom's caregiving and extra support, he realized Sandy was not enjoying life the way he wanted her to. Right before Christmas, Tom and Jill decided that it was time. I brought a cupcake for Sandy to enjoy while her sedative

 Sandy enjoying her cupcake with doting dad, Tom.

took effect. Her dad loved watching her lick the icing as she slowly started to get sleepy.

Waffles—Daddy's girl

My friend Larry wrote this beautiful memorial for his girl Waffles.

She's just a dog

They said, "She has no quality of life." They said, "She's just a dog, it's time, it's the humane thing to do." I thought so, too. But deep down I wondered, "Have I convinced myself it's time because I can't bear to see her deteriorating?" Not to mention the seemingly endless extra care she required. Caressing her during seizures, lifting her hind quarters so she could stand, listening to her grunting and crying without knowing why. Did she need to be repositioned, was she thirsty (again), was she hungry, did she want to be cuddled, did she need more pain medication? What?

I could no longer ignore those 14-year-old puppy dog eyes looking up at me saying, "Dad, what's wrong with me?" Those eyes that would look up at me so I could tell her when it was safe to cross the street. Those eyes that had shown her trust in me her whole life.

Eventually I came to the realization that it wasn't selfishness, it was indeed time. We had to put my 14-year-old baby girl to sleep, or put her down, or whatever the softer words are for ending her life. After all, "She's just a dog," they tell me.

My heart was broken. No, the pump is fine. I am broken. But something was still gnawing at me. There was a paradox that I needed to untangle. It slowly crept into my consciousness. Why is it humane to put my beloved pet down, yet my human relatives pass away slowly, and not until their bodies completely fail? Was it true, was

my baby "just a dog" and didn't deserve human tenets? And then it hit me, they got it backward. Our pets are the blessed ones. The dogma and laws that prevent us from ending human life humanely didn't apply to my dog. Our pets can pass on more benevolently and with more dignity than our own parents can.

And so, my Waffles, when you are at the entrance to heaven and they tell you, "You're just a dog," you look them right in the eye and say, "No, I am not just a dog, I'm my Daddy's baby girl." And I guarantee they'll let you in.

CHAPTER 32:

That look: Lucky Smudge

My friend and fellow hospice veterinarian Dr. Faith Banks practices in Toronto, Canada. She wrote the foreword to this book, and this chapter.* She was a pet mom to her cherished Smudge, and she knows firsthand the joys and struggles of caring for an aging dog, the challenges of evaluating her furry family member's quality of life, and the difficulty of deciding when it was time to say goodbye.

Proud new pet mom
Dr. Faith with Smudge.

*This chapter has been updated from Banks F. Chapter 26: The Look. In: Gardner M, McVety D, eds. *Treatment and Care of the Geriatric Veterinary Patient.* John Wiley & Sons; 2017: 317-320.

When friends and family visited our home, they often gave me "that look." They'd watch our dog Smudge struggle to get up, they'd wait patiently as she made her slow, stiff-legged trek to greet them, they'd give her a timid pat 'hello' as she wagged her tail, and they'd invariably say, "Awww, poor thing," then glance up at me with pity.

My visitors' looks seemed to imply it was time to free Smudge of her ailing body and say goodbye. I didn't agree. Was I wearing denial goggles? I hoped I wasn't.

I never looked at Smudge that way. "Poor thing?" Heck, no! Sure, she no longer looked like the glowing, bouncy Bernese mountain dog she had been, even as a senior at 7 years of age. But by age 14, Smudge had lived nearly twice as long as Berners are expected to! And yes, she'd lost the equivalent of a beagle in weight, mostly from muscle loss related to sarcopenia—that sneaky side effect of aging. Geriatrics aren't always pretty. Old dogs can be thin, lumpy-bumpy, grey, hazy, shaky, leaky, spacey, and slow. Smudge was most of those. Senior dogs sometimes potty in the house. Smudge did that, too.

Smudge loved making snow angels.

Pet parents often waver in a murky zone of not wanting to say goodbye to their pet too soon and not wanting to wait until it's too late. When I visit my clients, we discuss and complete a quality of life scale for their pet. Sometimes pet parents think it's harsh to categorize and score their beloved pet's quality of life based on a numeric scale—from 0 (very poor) to 5 (normal). But once we finish the questionnaire, their hesitancy gives way to a clearer perspective.

Of course I scored Smudge's quality of life: appetite...5, potty accidents...2, breathing...5, mobility...2, gives us love and accepts our love...5, and so on. Most pet parents get through all the questions with dry eyes until I ask, "Is your dog happy?" Tears immediately flow as they tell me how their dog used to playfully roll over to beg for belly rubs, jump from their boat to swim in summer, chase balls in the park, and romp in the snow. Dogs who stop doing their favorite things may lack joy in their lives. Smudge's overall quality of life score remained high, despite her "poor thing" appearance in the eyes of others. And she was happy.

Smudge's good score didn't come without effort. I spread a criss-crossing runway of yoga mats along our entire main floor to ensure her steady footing. She received six different medications to treat her low thyroid hormone, cognitive dysfunction, and pain. She had acupuncture and chiropractic treatments. I gave her a massage every night. I raised her food and water bowls to ease her neck strain. She wore a special harness because she needed our help to traverse the two steps into our house. And after a lifetime of having no accidents in the house, Smudge developed fecal incontinence. That odor became a familiar one in our home.

When I surprised my husband with this sweet furball puppy—who had a black spot on her white muzzle that looked like ink smeared from the top of her nose—Smudge became our first baby. We knew our fur kid would help prepare us for the commitment of having our own children one day. She did. And she proved to be a saintly, gentle giant playmate for our kids and their friends. Smudge was always our beloved family member.

Smudge had a wonderful life and she made our lives wonderful. She was loved and she loved us. She deserved a beautiful death. When the time came for me to help her leave her failing body, Smudge was at home, surrounded by her family. We showered her with gentle hugs, loving words, and soft kisses. My 9-year-old son wanted to bring snow inside for her to lie on—one of Smudge's favorite things. Smudge felt only comfort in her final moments—no stress, no anxiety. Euthanasia, by my hand, ensured that she peacefully and painlessly trekked on to her snowy Swiss mountains in the sky. She was never "poor Smudge," in any way. She was always "lucky Smudge."

 The looks of love. Dr. Faith Banks and Smudge.

Part four:

ENDURING THE UNENDURABLE — PREPARING FOR AND SAYING GOODBYE

These may be the heart-heaviest chapters to read. I hope to help you manage the complexities of anticipating the loss of your dog and the grief you and your family members will experience after your dog has passed. Consider how you may wish to say goodbye to your dog, be prepared for what to expect when you do say goodbye, and honor your dog's memory. Based on my experience with my patients as an oncologist, if I were to lose my current dogs, my own dog parent, this final section may give any dog parent some unexpectedly insightful

CHAPTER 33

A home divided: Conflicts between family members about end-of-life care

"Remember, we all stumble, every one of us. That's why it's a comfort to go hand in hand."

— EMILY KIMBROUGH, AUTHOR AND BROADCASTER

"When you get home, we need to talk about Sam." That was the greeting I got when I called home during a flight layover on a work trip. I had dreaded that trip because it meant I had to rely on my partner to care for my dog Sam. Sam's care was a challenge even for me, and when I was away her routine was disrupted, so her caregiving became more demanding. In my absence, she peed and pooped on the carpet twice and only ate about a third of her meals. Thankfully, she still took her pills well. She slept most of the time but needed assistance getting up to go outside.

My partner said he couldn't imagine doing this every day for months to come, and he thought this wasn't a good existence for Sam. I was on another page altogether. To be clear, I'm not a fan of accidents in the house, and I knew the time to say goodbye to Sam was nearing. But I also didn't feel her time would come in the next month, nor did I think it warranted a conversation right then, and not on the phone… in an airport.

My situation isn't uncommon. Oftentimes a disconnect or malalignment of beliefs occurs between family members about their dog's treatment and care-giving, and the end-of-life decision. The division may be between partners or between parents and children—or it may even be a battle you have with yourself every other day. And sometimes this disconnect can get heated.

Jackson's house divided

Jackson was a yellow Labrador retriever who had lymphoma, and his family asked for my help with his life quality evaluation. I love quality-of-life conversations with pet parents because I feel I can make the most difference in my patients' and families' lives during a difficult time, regardless of the path the family chooses to move forward on.

Jackson's mom and dad were devoted to his care and well-being. His mom led most of the conversation. She recounted a long list of enticements she had tried to encourage Jackson to eat. She showed me how she'd made environmental adjustments to make the house more comfortable for him. She gave me a stack of medical records to show me all that she had done to try to treat his cancer. She told me she was not ready to stop trying. At least not yet.

I knew Jackson's dad was upset, but he was silent. I couldn't quite put my finger on the pulse of his feelings.

I evaluated Jackson, and he wasn't doing well. However, he wasn't in a state of intractable suffering. It was clear that his mom wanted to try a few more things to help Jackson. I gently explained my findings from Jackson's evaluation and added, "I support your decision at any time to say goodbye, from this moment forward. Jackson is tired, and it would be OK if we decided to say goodbye. I can tell that you want to be sure in your heart that it's time to say goodbye even if your mind is sure the time is right. So it's OK for Jackson to remain in hospice for a few more days because we can continue to keep him comfortable."

Jackson's mom gave a sigh of relief and tears welled up in her eyes. However, to my surprise, Jackson's dad stood up and shouted, "NO!!!!" Jackson's mom and I both flinched and stared at him, astonished. And he started to cry. Hard.

I stayed quiet, and I let him cry for a long while. He needed to release these emotions. Finally, he angrily sputtered, "This is NOT right! He is dying! He has been dying for weeks! He is not happy; he is not Jackson! He is not eating, he is not sleeping well, and he is just miserable. And I AM MISERABLE! I CANNOT DO THIS A MOMENT LONGER!" Tears continued pouring. He was beside himself with grief and anger.

Because of his initial silence, I had thought Jackson's dad was on the same page with mom. Clearly I had not picked up the signals. I needed to switch gears.

I asked Jackson's dad to sit down, and I gave him tissues. After he collected himself, I said, "Thank you, Paul, for letting me know how you feel. That helps me better guide the two of you. I can tell you both love Jackson more than anything. Do you agree?" And they both nodded their heads.

This is where healing begins. Finding that thread of common ground. And, usually, both people love the dog. So it's a pretty easy place to start.

Walking on common ground

The first step in coming together is agreeing that everyone loves the dog. Then I ask, "Do you agree that you don't want your dog to suffer?" That's always my next question, because no one ever says, 'No, I'd like my dog to suffer." So now the family has taken two steps in common: love, and avoiding suffering.

Then I ask them to write what suffering means to them, whether their dog has signs of suffering, and, if so, what the signs are. I want the family to take time to reflect on their answers and not be swayed by others. Then they each read out loud what they wrote. Typically, their responses are very similar.

I write down the signs of suffering that they each agreed on. And then we talk about the signs that differed. If they then come to agreement on any of those signs, I add those to the list.

Then I ask them to do a similar reflection: "Write down the things that make your dog happy. List the things your dog hates feverishly. Write down the things that make your dog himself or herself. Write down your dog's signs of joy." This usually gets dog parents in a better frame of mind and infuses happiness back into the conversation. And then they again openly share what they wrote. I ask to see pictures of their dog throughout their life and ask them to share their favorite stories.

My no-judgment rule

My biggest ground rule for the family during these conversations and one that I ask them to uphold during their own follow-up discussions is "no judgment." We discuss that tossing unkind comments back and forth and judging the other person's decisions are roadblocks that divert the family from the path of common ground. I encourage them to always circle back to the fact that everyone loves the dog, so what specific things can they do to better support each other?

Drawing a line in the sand

After we have our definitions of joy and suffering, we discuss setting parameters and drawing a line in the sand. I ask questions such as: How many days can pass without your dog eating before you think it's time to say goodbye? Are each

of you willing to put the harness on your dog and to help your dog go outside to potty? How many hours of undisturbed sleep must your dog have every night? I write their responses on a big piece of paper and ask everyone to evaluate these things every day—separately and as a team.

Children—include everyone in the discussion

I've found that older children, particularly teenagers, struggle with decisions about an ailing pet's care, especially when the adult believes it's time to euthanize the pet. Children may feel as though the family could do more for their dog, spend more money, and be more patient with the dog's condition. And they may not fully grasp the entire picture about their dogs' ailments, prognosis, and caregiving needs. I go through the same steps with children and ask them the same questions so they can take part in these quality-of-life conversations and share their stories. It's best to include children at any age, as appropriate, in the caretaking and decision-making so they can share in the common ground.

Consider hospice care

If you're establishing common ground among all family members on your own and you haven't yet considered whether hospice services are an option for your dog, consider talking with your veterinarian about pet hospice. Once a dog has started receiving hospice care, it can be helpful to create their bucket list and make time to complete and check off the activities, and it's essential to do daily life quality assessments. These endeavors empower family members to participate in the dog's care and encourage everyone to stay on the same road and make decisions as a team. See the chapters "Veterinary hospice: Living well until the end," "Bucket lists: The joys of life," and "Life quality: 'Doc, when is it time?'" for more on those topics.

Narrowing the gap

As the "obvious" end of life draws nearer for a pet, disparities that remain between family members about their pet's care narrow. The worst conflict usually occurs during the initial stages of making decisions about end-of-life care. Once a pet's quality of life becomes seriously diminished, decisions about next steps become more apparent to all—which brings us back to Jackson's family.

Jackson's house stands together

Jackson's "joy list" was long! He was a quintessential sweet Labrador who had never had a bad day… until recently. And his mom's and dad's "signs of suffering" lists agreed 100%. We wrote those signs on a new piece of paper and added measurable parameters that they agreed on for each one, such as "How many days will Jackson show no interest in his ball before it's time?" And "How many items on this list need to be happening at the same time for us to say goodbye?"

Next came the hardest part. "Now let's check our list and evaluate how Jackson is doing today."

Their responses on Jackson's lists showed just how far he had crossed the line in the sand that indicated it would be time to say goodbye. His mom broke down, sobbing, covering her face with her hands. After about 10 minutes, her tears slowed, and she lifted her flushed face and said, "Thank you. I can see now that as hard as this is, it is time." She spoke with a sense of calm and relief. She wasn't angry with her husband, or with me.

I offered, "Sometimes we have to suffer, so they do not."

Jackson passed beautifully that afternoon, with tons of kisses on his soft head. Exactly how it should be.

Caregiver tips

Ask these questions of yourself, or use these questions to start a discussion with family or other household members to help get everyone on the same page about your dog's end of life care.

The Big Questions list:

- Do you love your dog?
- Do you want to prevent your dog from suffering?
- What do you think suffering means for your dog?
- What makes your dog himself or herself?
- What brings your dog joy?
- What does your dog detest? (The intent of this question is to identify whether things that typically passionately bother your dog—such as delivery people, the neighbor's dogs, getting toenails trimmed, or squirrels—no longer do.)

After you each define your dog's joys and signs of suffering by answering the Big Questions, set parameters that everyone agrees on so you can stay on common ground about your dog's end-of-life care. Then consider how your dog is doing now, and look at the line in the sand you've drawn, and determine:

- Does your dog have any form of suffering? If so, to what degree?
- Is your dog getting enough moments to be who he or she is?
- Is your dog still getting moments of joy?
- Is your dog tolerating things he or she detests because it's easier not to fight?
- Could pet hospice care help?

CHAPTER 34:

Grief wellness: Anticipating and experiencing loss

> "To retain the memory of love's sweetness without letting the pain of parting and loss embitter it is perhaps the greatest challenge for the bereaved heart, and its greatest achievement."
>
> — MARIA POPOVA

Profound and pensive flashback to a few years ago: The lump in my throat expands and my heart clenches as I watch Serissa totter shakily to her water bowl for an after-dinner sip. Lately her meals include a grand buffet of her favorite "I can't believe you're letting me have this!" treats. Too soon, this light in my life of 14 years will fade to dark, and my eyes cloud with tears at the thought.

My voice cracks when I ask, "You want to go outside, baby girl?" Serissa's expression brightens as she looks up at me. Her Samoyed smile melts my heart. She answers with a soft, raspy, "Roo roo!"

The thick, lustrous white coat of her younger years, when she was a therapy dog who visited nursing homes with me, is now thin and scruffy. She's become a frail geriatric sweetheart herself. Still, she happily parades like a supermodel down the runway of bath mats placed along the slippery tile to keep her sure-footed.

We're *almost* to the door when she suddenly squats and urinates on the mat. And it doesn't faze me for a second! In years past, Serissa never would've done such a

 Scruffy old Serissa.

421

thing, but lately she struggles to hold it. I stand ready to help steady her because her legs tremble and she nearly topples over as she finishes. But she regains her balance and eases up, and then trots a few more steps. Joy fills my heart as she smiles back at me again, wags her scrappy tail, and eagerly waits for me to open the door for our evening outing.

I know my time with Serissa is not long. Maybe just a few weeks. And the anxiety of knowing she will soon be gone is crushing. I almost can't enjoy the time I have with her because I'm worried about the time to come without her. The anticipation is agonizing.

Grief before losing your pet

The death of a pet is, for many, the worst personal loss they have ever experienced. Considering the possibility of euthanasia and the emotions surrounding this decision can be overwhelming for many pet parents. Many people experience what is referred to as *anticipatory grief*. This is what I was experiencing with Serissa and have experienced with every one of my pets since then, when I knew our remaining time together would be short. Anticipatory grief can sometimes drown out the pleasures in the moments we have left with our dogs.

With anticipatory grief, you may experience a variety of emotions before the impending loss of your dog. These emotions may include sorrow, despair, fear, frustration, loneliness, anxiety, guilt, or anger. After learning of your dog's terminal illness or watching the long-term decline of your geriatric dog, grief can begin to manifest. We not only grieve the forthcoming loss of our dogs but also the imminent loss of the relationship, the security, and the role we have as caregivers.

Anticipatory grief may be similar to grief that occurs after the actual death of our dogs, or it may differ. Not everyone experiences anticipatory grief. Each affected family member may express or handle anticipatory grief differently. In addition to the effects of anticipatory grief on one's mental and emotional states, it can result in physical illness. Some people benefit from additional support from a grief counselor or mental health professional and shouldn't hesitate to seek support.

Anger is a common component of anticipatory grief expressed in reaction to the news of a dog's terminal illness. I focus on this emotion here because it can also be a destructive force in client-veterinarian relationships and in family relationships. This anger may be displaced and inappropriately directed in one or more ways:

Toward the veterinarian. Veterinarians deliver the news about a pet's condition or diagnosis, so they're sometimes irrationally blamed for the pet's terminal illness, or for not identifying the problem sooner. In the classic sense of being "shot" as "the messenger," we veterinarians understand that this anger is associated with a pet owner's sudden grief and is usually temporary. Sometimes the cause of a pet's decline and symptoms remain unknown, which can be frustrating for everyone. At times like these, it can be difficult for pet parents to remember that their entire veterinary team loves animals and loves caring for them. The veterinarians and team members also often experience grief after learning the news of an illness in one of their beloved patients.

Toward the dog. A pet parent or other family members may blame their pet for imminent desertion. They may reject the dog and refuse to pet or play with the dog again. The dog won't understand the reason for such a change in behavior or routine. The dog needs their family's love and care even more at this time, especially when they're probably not feeling well. Ailing dogs benefit from additional reassurance and comfort. Offering this kindness and support can help family members begin to heal and avoid regret.

Toward other family members. Children or family members who feel others aren't doing enough for their pet may blame those family members. A child may not understand why parents sometimes cannot afford treatment or that treatment won't change the outcome. So the child may blame the parents for "killing my dog."

For this reason, it may be best that the parents alone hear the dog's care options and that veterinarians not present treatment choices when small children are present. Pet parents need the option to consider euthanasia when it's an acceptable alternative to treatment, and to have time to talk with children about their decisions, without the added stress and guilt that young family members' responses may invoke in the moment.

Toward God or the universe. Whether or not a pet parent has religious beliefs, some blame a higher power for an animal's illness or death. A pet parent may say, "Why did this have to happen to me? Such awful things don't happen to other people who don't even care for their dogs!" It's helpful to seek advice and insights from your religious or spiritual leader.

Toward oneself. This blame often manifests as guilt. "If only I had brought my dog to see the veterinarian sooner." Or "We never should have had this surgery done in the first place." Such thoughts may go through a pet parent's mind when a dog's terminal condition has been diagnosed or when a dog dies suddenly. Pet parents sometimes look for ways in which they or family members contributed to the dog's condition. This guilt and blame are unjustified because it's highly unlikely that anyone intended willful harm. A pet parent may also feel guilty if they don't have the financial resources to care for the dog without forgoing other family necessities. It's important to not take on guilt that isn't yours. Life brings challenges, disease, and loss that we have no control over. We only have control over how we respond to those things.

Coping before loss

Because grief related to pet loss tends to be less socially accepted than grief associated with a person who has passed, feelings of isolation may be magnified in people experiencing anticipatory grief before losing a dog. Pet parents sometimes tell me that they feel like no one understands them or they feel "silly" that they are emotional over "just an animal." But most pet parents do understand, and it's important that this period of grief is recognized. It's beneficial to share feelings with others who understand what it's like to lose a pet and provide support. Veterinary professionals are often able to assist clients in finding support groups or resources during this difficult time.

Anticipatory grief doesn't usually replace or prevent the grief that occurs after a pet has passed. However, the anticipatory grief period can also allow the pet's family time to share activities with their dogs that they may have put off in the past. For some, this helps prompt a conscious closure—reflecting on the gratitude one feels for sharing the dog's life and preparing for what is to come—before the loss. Focus on the pleasures you still have, and consider documenting them to help hold your memories and honor your dog.

Dr. Elisabeth Kübler-Ross, a psychiatrist famous for her work in human hospice care and her 1969 book *On Death and Dying*, said that a person who loses someone will experience more grief if they never said "I love you" to that person. This anticipatory period of time allows you to say "I love you" to your dog every day. It has certainly helped me cope with the loss of my own dogs.

Anticipatory grief can also give you time to prepare for your dog's death and make arrangements that you may not have otherwise considered, such as choosing the day, where you'd like your dog to be, and who will be present.

Neither you nor those around you must forget that the death of a beloved dog changes your life forever. And those changes may start before your dog leaves you.

Dreading a pet's death

If you've planned a day and time to euthanize your dog, you may experience a different sort of stress or anxiety on the scheduled day, during the hours and minutes that lead up to the moment your dog will pass. I believe this differs from anticipatory grief, which relates to anticipating the loss you'll experience after your dog passes. This anxiety that centers on the moment the loss happens seems different.

Even as a veterinarian who has helped thousands of families say goodbye to their dogs, when the time comes to euthanize my own dog, the scheduled day is a day that fills me with much anxiety. My emotions are heightened and every treasured second lingers on that day. I register each of my dog's actions as "the last." The last morning kiss I give them, the last time they totter outside, the last breakfast or treat they eat, the last drink of water after dinner, the last time I need to help them up. I watch the clock and count down until the appointment: six more hours, four hours, two hours, one hour, 30 minutes, 15 minutes ….

I personally suffer from anticipatory grief and post-loss grief. But the day of my dog's euthanasia is a different type of torture to my heart. It's hard for me to concentrate on anything else other than the death that's coming. I share this with you to let those of you who feel the same know you're not alone. I do my best to put this torment aside and focus on making the best of the remaining time I have with my dog. I encourage you to do the same. Time is a treasure you cannot restore.

A planned euthanasia can happen at a veterinary hospital, at home, or in another meaningful location. I believe that whenever possible, saying goodbye at home or in a special location other than the veterinary hospital may be best for everyone. I'd like to avoid that "last drive" to the hospital, and the heartbreaking drive home. If everyone can stay home and focus on comfort and love, the process may be slightly easier.

Grief after losing a pet

Regardless of whether your dog is old or young when they pass, or whether your dog's death is sudden or expected, grief is a normal and natural reaction. At times you may be so submerged in grief it seems impossible to surface for air and the grief is so powerful it drowns out the pleasant memories of the lifetime of love you shared.

Dr. Kübler-Ross was the first to propose that people experience five stages of grief when faced with their own imminent death, which she wrote about in her book *On Death and Dying*. The stages were later applied to the emotions that survivors may experience after losing a loved one. They have also since been applied to people experiencing a major life change, such as a divorce or unemployment.

You are likely familiar with the five stages of grief, and I've given brief examples here based on my own and others' experiences with anticipatory grief and grief after loss:

1. Denial. "This can't be happening." Or "My dog won't die because of this. Something else must be going on." Or "I can't believe my dog is gone. My dog can't be gone."
2. Anger. "I can't believe someone let this happen! Why?!"

3. Bargaining. "If I try this, maybe I can save my dog." Or "If I do this to become a better person, I won't lose my dog." Or "If only this one thing had been done differently, I wouldn't have lost my dog."

4. Depression. "What will I do without my dog? I'll be alone." Or "I feel hopeless." Or "I am overwhelmed and numb."

5. Acceptance. "I'm helping my dog in every way I can as she nears the end of her life. I am grateful for my wonderful companion." Or "I did everything I could to help my dog toward the end of life and to pass as peacefully as possible. She was the most amazing being." And "I'm thankful for our time together."

The five stages of grief are popularized in media and culture, but evidence that people experience grief in stages is lacking. Studies show that most people don't grieve in stages and don't experience a clear end point that indicates recovery from grief. (Shermer 2008, Stroebe 2017) Healthcare professionals and counselors are now discouraged from using these stages as clinical guidelines for their bereaved clients because if they're expected to go through these stages but don't, they may be harmed by feeling that they're grieving incorrectly. (Stroebe 2017)

Instead, research indicates that grieving is not an orderly and predictable stage-like process, and that grief can involve complex, fluctuating "roller coaster" emotions. Toward the end of her career, Kübler-Ross regretted that her stages of grief had been misunderstood and wrote that grief doesn't work in a predictable, linear way. (Feldman 2017) Different patterns and ways of "normal" grieving exist, along with individual and cultural differences in reactions to loss. (Stroebe 2017) Most people experience loss in their own way over time. The bottom line is that people who are grieving should not expect or be expected to go through a specific set of stages.

The space of duality

Every time I've lost one of my pets, I find myself spending time in a "space of duality" between being brokenhearted and being happy in knowing my pet is whole again. I cringe when people say to me, "She's better now, she's no longer suffering, she's in a better place," as if I had been selfishly holding her prisoner on Earth with me. I know the good intentions behind statements like these, but they don't help me much. It takes time for me to move away from the wrenching heartbreak. What has always helped me is to focus on the pictures and videos of my pets from years prior. They make me smile and help me imagine and hope for my pet's new state of perfect being, in whatever form that may be.

426

Serissa's picture-perfect opportunity

One of the things I planned for Serissa was a professional photoshoot. I desperately wanted one picture in particular—Serissa "rooing" (it's a special Samoyed howl-speak). And the photographer nailed it! She also captured some really sweet moments that I'll treasure forever. I cried a bit during that photography session, but if I hadn't taken the opportunity then, I would've cried more for not having Serissa's photos at this stage in our life together.

Serissa being a model.

Serissa's gorgeous smile.

Dare I say, Serissa is rooing to me that she loves me in this picture!

427

Questions to ask your veterinarian

- What can I do to help my dog stay comfortable until it's time to say goodbye?
- If veterinary hospice care isn't available in this area, can we work together to create a hospice care plan for my dog?
- What plans or preparations should I make before it's time to say goodbye?
- What options are available during and after regular business hours for in-home or in-hospital euthanasia for my dog?
- Do you have suggestions for aftercare of my dog's body? Do you have a pet cemetery or cremation service you recommend?
- Do you have pet loss information available or resources to recommend?
- Can you suggest a local pet loss support group or grief counselor?

 READING RECOMMENDATIONS

- Anderson Allen M. *Coping with sorrow on the loss of your pet.* Dog Ear Publishing, LLC; 2007.
- Behrikis Shanahan N. *There is eternal life for animals.* Pete Publishing; 2002.
- Carmack B. *Grieving the death of a pet.* Augsburg Books; 2003.
- Davis C. *For every dog an angel.* Lighthearted Press; 2004.
- Dolan-Del Vecchio K, Saxton-Lopez N. *The pet loss companion: Healing advice from family therapists who lead pet loss groups.* CreateSpace Independent Publishing Platform; 2013.
- Ellis C. *Pet Parents: A Journey Through Unconditional Love And Grief.* iUniverse; 2011.
- Friedman R, James C, James JW. *The grief recovery handbook for pet loss.* Taylor Trade Publishing; 2014.
- Hanson W. *Pawprints in the stars: A farewell and journal for a beloved pet.* Tristan Pub; 2008.
- Katz J. *Going home: Finding peace when pets die.* Random House Trade Paperbacks; 2012.
- Klein A. *I never wanted to say goodbye: A collection of poems.* Designing Poet; 2004.
- Kowalski G. *Goodbye, friend: Healing wisdom for anyone who has ever lost a pet.* New World Library; 2012.

- Kurz G. *Cold noses at the pearly gates: A book of hope for those who have lost a pet.* Citadel; 2008.
- Luz Quintana M, Veleba SL, King H. *It's okay to cry: Warm compassionate stories that will help you find hope and healing after the death of a beloved pet.* Mariposa Press; 2000.
- Montgomery M, Montgomery H. *A final act of caring: Ending the life of an animal friend.* American Animal Hospital Association; 1993.
- Sife W. *The loss of a pet: A guide to coping with the grieving process when a pet dies.* 4th ed. Howell Book House; 2014.
- Wolfelt A. *When your pet dies: A guide to mourning, remembering and healing.* Companion Press; 2004.

 SUPPORT RECOMMENDATIONS

- *Lap of Love Pet Loss Support.* Offers free virtual group support and paid one-on-one support. *https://www.lapoflove.com/our-services/pet-loss-support*
- *Two Hearts Pet Loss Center.* A wonderful resource including courses to help with grief. *https://twoheartspetlosscenter.com/*
- *Center for Loss & Life Transition.* Founded and led by death educator and grief counselor Dr. Alan Wolfelt. **https://www.centerforloss.com/**
- *The Association for Pet Loss and Bereavement.* Includes an every-other-week (Thursday evening) online support chat room. **https://www.aplb.org/**
- *Everlife Memorials.* Includes a nationwide pet loss support group list. **http://www.everlifememorials.com/v/pet-loss/pet-loss-counselors.htm**

CHAPTER 35

Young grief:
When children bid farewell

"The tree I had in the garden as a child, my beech tree, I used to climb up there and spend hours. I took my homework up there, my books, I went up there if I was sad, and it just felt very good to be up there among the green leaves and the birds and the sky."

— JANE GOODALL

My fur kids—cats and dogs—have always been my only children. And I would love to have a couple of goat kids someday! When I first became a veterinarian, I struggled with finding the right things to say to children when their pets were being euthanized. But I quickly learned that a child's presence during a pet's euthanasia can be beneficial for everyone. Children share the most amazing, insightful thoughts, and they often help the adults during the experience.

Lola's Zowie

Zowie, an ornery 15-year-old mixed-breed dog, was the beloved fur kid of her mom, Jennifer. Zowie had multiple ailments, and Jennifer called me to help their family say goodbye to their sweet girl. When Jennifer was planning Zowie's euthanasia, she told me she had initially decided she did not want her 6-year-old daughter, Lola, to be

Zowie

Lauren (my summer intern), Lola, Dr. Mary, and Zowie

present. But after she read up on the subject and talked with Lola, she realized that Lola should have the opportunity to be there.

I remember their lovely family clearly; they were so welcoming and warm. I sat on the floor, and Lola proudly held out a handmade envelope for me, covered with an array of shiny, sparkly stickers. I thanked her and admired the envelope. I asked her if I could read her card right then. Lola eagerly nodded, then plopped down in my lap so that she could read along. I gingerly opened the envelope to avoid tearing the stickers.

Lola's handmade card was covered in even more stickers—the highly kid-treasured kinds—the cat stickers were holographic! I had a brief, tender flashback to my own sticker books of the '80s. I began to read Lola's card out loud: "I love you, Dr. Mary." Instantly I got teary-eyed. How sweet and tender this little girl was.

Lola stayed sitting comfortably in my lap while I explained everything to the family about the process of saying goodbye to Zowie. Lola was inquisitive, but she also respected the silence when the time came, and gently hugged her cherished friend.

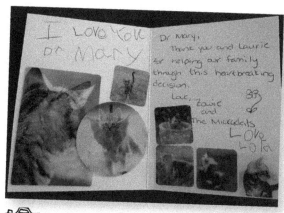

Lola's lovely card.

Zach's Rocky

Zach's response was quite different from Lola's. He was 13 years old when I helped his family say goodbye to their yellow Labrador retriever, Rocky. We had gathered around Rocky in the family's backyard. During most of my visit, Zach gave me the stink eye and aggressively tossed a basketball against the side of the house. But he also briefly walked into and out of our little group, and questioned everything I did.

A few of Zach's comments:

"You're a doctor—don't you think you could give him medicine to help?"

"Are you really a doctor?"

"I don't think Rocky is that bad."

Zach also asked whether I should be doing anything in the first place. And then he added, "Maybe you're just wanting to make money?!"

I have to admit, those words stung. But I took no offense to Zach's comments because I knew he was grieving.

After Rocky peacefully passed, Zach walked back over and looked down at Rocky, began sobbing, and then ran into the house. My heart broke for him.

Explaining euthanasia

Every child differs in how they respond to a pet's passing, and every parent differs in how they want to explain death to their child. I, of course, defer to the parents' thoughts on how best to teach and help their children, but parents often ask me for suggestions.

My first suggestion is for parents themselves to understand the euthanasia process beforehand and the changes they and their children may see as their pet passes. At the time of the appointment—whether the appointment is in your home or in the veterinary clinic—veterinarians typically describe the process and the changes that will occur in the pet. Veterinarians are also available to talk with you ahead of the appointment if you'd like, so don't hesitate to speak with your veterinarian.

In general, I like having children present during the euthanasia appointment. I speak to everyone in the room and explain the euthanasia process so that each family member feels included in these important moments. I discourage families from scheduling the appointment at a time when their children are at school, or from telling their children that their pet "went to the farm" or "ran away." I also suggest that parents consider whether their children may wish to have time alone with the pet—both immediately before and after the euthanasia, if their children wish.

For young children who do not understand the concept of death, I usually say that the body is no longer working, and that when a pet dies, the pet doesn't breathe or move, get cold or hungry, or hurt anymore. I remind them that plants die, too, and that it is a natural process. I find it beneficial to talk with them about why their pet's euthanasia is needed and what euthanasia is. I explain that the pet is already dying, and that euthansia simply ends the dying process sooner and more peacefully, rather than say we're ending the pet's life. If the pet's euthanasia is needed because of an accident, I explain that the pet was badly hurt and its body cannot heal. If the euthanasia is related to terminal illness or to old age, I explain that the pet's body stopped working because of a disease that cannot be cured, or because the body wore out naturally after a long, happy life.

Parents can help children understand that for pets who will not get better and who are suffering, the pet's family can ask a veterinarian to assist their pet to die comfortably and peacefully. Explain to children that euthanasia means "good death." Tell them that for pets who can't be healed, veterinarians help pets experience a good death by giving a medicine that will help the pet relax quietly for several minutes, and then they give a special drug that painlessly slows the body down so the pet passes peacefully.

Let children know that by gently helping a pet die, veterinarians help prevent their pet's suffering and it allows the family time to tell their pet how much they mean to them. Explain that euthanasia can give the child an opportunity to say goodbye with extra kindness and love. I think it's helpful for children and adults to understand that their pet is already experiencing the dying process and that I'm ending that process rather than ending the pet's life.

I'm by no means an expert with children. As I mentioned, I don't have children myself. I offer guidance based on my experiences in helping families with children say their final goodbyes to their best furry friends. Based on these goodbyes, I typically see that childrens' involvement in and reactions to their pet's euthanasia differ among three broad age groups:

2 to 5 years old. Children in this age group usually don't fully grasp the concept of death and its permanence. I suggest involving these youngest children before the pet's euthanasia, such as asking them to draw a picture of the pet or gather flowers for the pet's gravesite. During the euthanasia appointment, children of these ages can be a distraction to other family members. It's often easier for the entire family if a friend or other family member stays with the child in another room while the family concentrates on saying goodbye to the pet. However, it's always up to the parents to decide whether they wish to include their children in saying goodbye, and I support their decision either way.

6 to 12 years old. Children of these ages typically do well in handling an ailing pet's final goodbye. They understand that death is permanent and that their pet won't return to them. They often tenderly want to participate in making the preparations, such as writing letters to their pet, choosing their pet's last treats, making a cake, and selecting music.

They also ask the best questions during my visit. I have been asked: "Where does she go after?" (*I'm not totally sure, but one thing I know without a doubt is that she will live forever in your heart.*) "Will he visit me tonight in my dreams?" (*He may visit your dreams. Sometimes we remember our dreams when we wake up, but sometimes we forget them. So even if you don't remember your dream, it still may mean he visited your dream.*) "How will you know for sure he is dead—can he come back to life?" (*I will listen for the silence of his heart and the silence of his breathing. This means his dying is done, and he cannot come back to life.*) "Can I keep his tail?" (*If you keep his tail, it will change and not be as nice as it was before, so it's better to let him keep it. Plus, he needs it—how will he wag in heaven* [or I'll say—*how will he wag in your dreams?*]) "Are you allowed to do this?" (*Veterinarians are allowed to help end the dying process in animals who are very sick or suffering and who cannot be healed.*) "Can he keep his eyes open during it so we can look at each other?" (*The first medicine I give makes him relaxed and sleepy, so his eyes may not stay open. But he will be able to hear you, so he would like to hear your voice, even if his eyes are closed.*)

Children don't sugarcoat things, so I usually answer them just as directly, and they seem to appreciate it. If they are eager to help me, I may also encourage them to hold my stethoscope, help collect fur keepsakes, and make a clay paw print.

I remember a family I helped in Los Angeles. They had six adopted children between the ages of 5 and 13 years, and they all wanted to be as close as they possibly could be to their dog to say goodbye. We were crammed into a tiny bathroom, and four kids kneeled in the bathtub, each putting a hand on their dog who was lying on the cool tile floor next to the tub. The two other kids kneeled next to me while the parents stood behind us all in the doorway. Each child was curious about every step of the process and was not afraid. The process went smoothly, and although everyone cried a bit, no one was inconsolable. Each child also got a ball of clay to make a paw impression. Afterward, they held a mini awards ceremony to honor their dog and the paw impressions they had made. Then they scattered off to their rooms with their prized possessions.

Teenagers. I personally struggle with this age group the most during euthanasia visits. They usually have strong reservations about the reasons for euthanasia and often believe we're giving up when more could be done to help their pet. I highly encourage parents to allow their teens to take part in their pet's caregiving and hospice care long before the euthanasia appointment. This helps them better understand and witness their pet's struggles and decline. Ask teenagers to do their pet's quality of life assessments with you. Talk about the disease and its progression and how it affects the pet. Giving teens more information about their pet's illness and getting them involved in their pet's care sooner helps them better accept why and when it's time to say goodbye.

Saying goodbye on the spectrum

Based on my many visits when children who have autism spectrum disorder (ASD) are present, I want to give brief examples of how they may change the dynamic of the euthanasia experience. My first few experiences with children who have ASD were challenging for me because I kept saying the wrong things or focusing on the wrong person in the room. I hope I have gotten better over the years! The insights I've gained may have relevance for all families wanting to include their children in the euthanasia experience.

If you have a child with ASD, you know better than I do, but children with ASD may have difficulty expressing emotions or they may have an intensely dramatic emotional response. They may react in the opposite way than is expected, such as laughing when others are crying. Children with ASD may ask more questions or may seem more disengaged. They may also ask questions that seem harsh or make direct statements that upset or shock other family members. I have learned that it is, of course, important to validate every child's feelings.

With both of the children I describe below, I felt totally inadequate, and the experiences were humbling for me. In both cases, I checked in with the family more often than I usually do over the few days after my visit.

Tori's Jack

My first experience with a child with ASD was when I went to help Jack, a Jack Russell terrier. Jack's mom told me that she, along with her mother and her two daughters, ages 6 and 11 years, would be there that day.

Jack's mom and I said goodbye to Jack on the back patio while the girls played inside with their grandmother. Afterward, mom wanted each daughter to come out to the patio separately to say goodbye to Jack. The older daughter came outside and was softly crying. She kissed Jack's head and said goodbye.

Her mom then said to her older daughter, "Tell Tori to come out now." Then her mom told me that Tori had ASD.

Tori came out to the patio and plainly asked her mom, "What do you want?"

Her mom said, "Say goodbye to Jack."

Tori looked at Jack and responded, "Why? He is dead. He can't hear me." And her mom started to cry. (I thought to myself, "Well, she is correct, but that sounded harsh.") Then Tori said, "Why are you crying? It's just a dog, and he is dead."

Her mom snapped back, "Go back inside with Grandma!"

Tori immediately turned away and walked back inside, and her mom cried harder.

Mom was clearly upset about Jack and also upset that Tori didn't express the same tenderness that her older daughter had shown. I stayed longer at that visit to empathize with the mom about losing Jack.

Austin's Bandit

Another family I helped had an Australian shepherd named Bandit with severe mobility issues. Their 8-year-old son, Austin, had ASD. He wanted to be a part of the whole experience. He was sweet and gentle with Bandit and cried the whole time. He even painted a lovely picture for me to take to the crematory. But Austin was angry with me. He greeted me by yelling, "You're going to kill my dog!"

I told Austin that I was there to help Bandit because he was struggling and could not be fixed. I did my best to explain that this was the kindest way to help Bandit, and I promised Austin that Bandit would feel no pain as I helped him.

I thought that I was making good progress with Austin until I started to take things out of my doctor bag. Then he looked at me and said, "I have a pet cougar, and he is on your back right now. He is going to bite you if you hurt Bandit."

I was momentarily stunned. How to respond? Then I looked straight at him and said, "Well, it's a good thing that I won't hurt him." Austin scowled at me and narrowed his eyes, then turned back to Bandit.

Explaining what happens to the dog's body

If you plan to cremate your dog, you may wish to explain to children that the dog's body will go to a special pet memorial place where the body will be cared for and become a powdery sand called ashes. You may describe that the dog's body turns to ashes after being placed in an intensely heated room (cremation) or by using special heated water (aquamation). Let children know that the dog's body cannot feel this. Tell them your family will then get the dog's ashes back (if the family chooses to) and you can decide together whether to keep the ashes in a special container called an urn in the home, bury them in a pet cemetery or in the backyard, or scatter them (if allowed) in a location that the pet loved to visit.

If you plan to bury the dog's body in a pet cemetery or other location, explain that the dog's body will carefully and lovingly rest in the ground. Let children know that you will place an extra special marker there to honor their dog. And tell them how lovely it will be that grass and other plants will grow there naturally to protect their dog's gravesite. You can even have your children help you choose a native grass or native wildflowers to plant at the gravesite.

Tips that may help children cope with pet loss

I cry a lot when my pets die, and I'm not shy about it. I'm a hot mess! My eyes are swollen and red for days from nearly continuous streams of tears. My other fur kids seem to know I'm not my usual self and they stick closer to me than they usually do. I make an effort to give them extra affection and attention in return.

A parent's reaction to losing a dog often heavily influences a child's reaction. Keep in mind that some young children may get more upset by seeing their parent's reaction than by the dog's death. It's perfectly acceptable for parents to show grief in their children's presence. Let your children know that you're sad because of the dog's death, in case they may think you're sad because of something they did.

In the years that I've been helping families provide pet hospice care, I've seen many ways parents have involved their children in the process of a pet's passing. Here are a few ideas from those experiences, along with other wonderful suggestions I've read about:

- Note time with a visual gratitude marker. Children can place a penny or marble in a vase for every day they share with their dog after a terminal illness is identified. Or place a small stone in a special spot near a favorite path every time the dog feels well enough to walk there. (Hawn 2015)
- Invite children to help create their dog's bucket list beforehand, participate in the experiences, and mark them as completed.
- Involve children in their dog's end-of-life care.
- Ask the child to write a story about their dog.
- Select a pretty bowl or jar to hold colorful scraps of paper on which family members jot down happy memories or funny moments with their dog. Read these together or separately at any time, especially when a family member feels particularly sad. (Hawn 2015)
- Ask the child to write a letter to God about their dog.
- Suggest that the child create a card for their dog, which can go with the dog for cremation or burial if they wish.
- Keep a battery-powered LED candle flickering next to a favorite photo or drawing of the dog. (Hawn 2015)
- Purchase a customized plush animal made to look like their dog. (www.mypetsies.com)
- Involve children in creating memorial scrapbook pages that include their dog's name, a drawing or photo of their dog, and their reflections on why their dog was special. Children can write what they will miss most about their dog, what silly things their dog used to do, why the dog was their friend, the names of others who loved their dog, and what makes them smile most when they think of their dog. (Young)
- Frame original artwork created by the child or a large photograph of the dog to be displayed in the home. (Hawn 2015)
- Customize a blanket or pillowcase with the dog's photograph.
- Craft a keepsake of the dog's collar or bowl.

438

- Involve children in creating a tribute video or digital slideshow of special moments throughout the dog's life—and also in choosing the background music. (Hawn 2015)
- Paint memorial stones (with acrylic paints) to place on the ground at the dog's gravesite. (Our Small Hours website)
- Hold a memorial service.
- Take children along when you pick up the dog's ashes.

 Lap of Love veterinarian Dr. Rachel Kilckman helping a family saying goodbye to their dog at home.

- Involve children in selecting and planting a native tree or shrub, or native wildflowers or grasses in honor of the dog.

Zowie's send off, and listening for silence

I could not have been more impressed by Lola's interaction with Zowie, with her parents, and with me during Zowie's euthanasia. Dare I say that Lola held it together better than I ever have for my own pets' departures.

After I gave Zowie the final medication, I put my syringe in my doctor bag and pulled out my stethoscope. I put the earpieces in my ears, placed the bell of the stethoscope on

 Lola saying goodbye to Zowie.

Zowie's chest, and I bowed my head and closed my eyes to focus on listening. I soon felt a soft tap on my arm, and I looked up at Lola. She had her own toy stethoscope. She said, "I want to hear, too." So I shifted over a bit and she put her stethoscope bell on Zowie's chest. I could see that she was intensely listening. Lola finally looked at me and said, "I don't hear anything."

I said, "I know. We are listening for silence. But after the silence, I can sometimes hear angel wings flapping."

Lola's eyes widened a bit and she went back to listening. Her concentration was intense for about 30 seconds. Then a slight smile spread across her face, and she whispered to me, "I can hear it!"

 Lola and I listen for Zowie's silence and her angel wings.

 READING RECOMMENDATIONS

- Anderson Allen M. Helping children cope. The Pet Loss Support Page website. 2007. Accessed Dec. 18, 2020. **https://www.pet-loss.net/children.shtml**
- Tousley M. Explaining pet loss to children. Grief Healing website. Accessed December 18, 2020. **http://www.griefhealing.com/article-explaining-pet-loss-to-children.htm**
- Chance's Spot: Pet Loss and Grief Support website. Accessed December 18, 2020. **https://www.chancesspot.org/index.php**
- Helping children cope with the death of a beloved pet. Rainbows Bridge website. Accessed Dec. 18, 2020. **https://www.rainbowsbridge.com/Grief_Support_Center/Grief_Support/Chrildren_and_petloss.htm**
- The Ohio State University Veterinary Medical Teaching Hospital. Helping children cope with the serious illness or death of a companion animal. Accessed Dec. 18, 2020. **https://vet.osu.edu/vmc/sites/default/files/import/assets/pdf/hospital/companionAnimals/HonoringtheBond/HelpingChildrenCopeFactSheet.pdf**

Books about pet loss for children to read, or to read with children

- Asher M. *Humphrey was here: A dog owner's story of love, loss and letting go.* CreateSpace Independent Publishing Platform; 2009.
- Bareis Rigabar B. *A rainbow bridge for Gus: A story about the loss of a pet.* Barb Rigabar; 2014.

- Brill PA. *Don't say goodbye, just say see you! (Dog tales collection)*. Functional Fitness LLC; 2015.
- Buscaglia L. *The fall of Freddie the leaf (A story of life for all ages)*. Slack Incorporated; 1982.
- Ellis C. *Pet parents: A journey through unconditional love and grief*. iUniverse Publishing; 2011.
- Gollub P. *Remembering Baymore*. Peter E. Gollub; *2015*.
- Gut C. *Being brave for Bailey*. 2nd ed. Corey Gut, DVM; 2014.
- Hanson W. *The next place*. Waldman House Press; 2002.
- Klise K. *Stay: A girl, a dog, a bucket list*. Feiwel & Friends; 2017.
- Meng C. *Always remember*. Philomel Books; 2016.
- Ringtved G. *Cry, heart, but never break*. Enchanted Lion Books; 2016.
- Rogers F. *When a pet dies*. Puffin Books; 1998.
- Rylant C. *Dog Heaven*. Blue Sky Press; 1995.
- Tillman N. *The heaven of animals*. Feiwel & Friends; 2014.
- Tousley M. *Children and pet loss: A guide for helping*. Our Pals Pub; 2014.
- Van de Poll W. *Healing a child's pet loss grief: A guide for parents*. Center for Pet Loss Grief LLC; 2016.Viorst J. *The tenth good thing about Barney*. Atheneum Books for Young Readers; 1987.
- Wilhelm H. *I'll always love you*. Dragonfly Books; 1988.Wolfelt AD. *My pet died: A coloring book for grieving children*. Center for Loss & Life Transition.
- Young W. *Saying goodbye to a beloved pet: A workbook for kids and guidelines for adult caregivers*. Kidlutions: Solutions for Kids website.

An activity book that I co-created with Coleen Ellis. This book can help children going through the loss of a dog:

Activity Book

CHAPTER 36:

Housemates: Furry family members who lose their furry friends

Help your brother's boat across, and your own will reach the shore.

— HINDU PROVERB

Families who schedule euthanasia for a dog often ask me, "Should my other pet be present during the euthanasia?" And I usually tell them, "Let's let that pet decide." If the other pet is unlikely to disturb or disrupt the family or the process for the pet who is earning their wings, then I think it's acceptable to have them present, for as much as they wish to be.

I have been amazed by the variety of reactions from other pets in the home during a euthanasia of their "sibling." Reactions range from whining to being oblivious! I have come to realize that some of our furry family members may be similar to us in the variety of ways we react to death and manage grief.

Boston siblings

One year, near Christmastime, I helped a family who had two grey muzzle Boston terriers. Both Bostons had been well cared for, but the sick one's illness had stolen his vitality. He was skin and bones and ready to say goodbye. The family's home was merrily decorated, and I remember how the twinkling lights reflected off of his fur as he slept peacefully under the Christmas tree.

As soon as I sat down on the floor with the family, the ailing dog's "sister" Boston immediately popped up from her

443

spot. She climbed into my lap, flipped belly up, and begged for my attention. I gave her a few minutes of love and bel-lyrubs, then moved her off my lap to focus on my patient. She quietly stayed nearby while her "brother" earned his angel wings, and she seemed con-tent to be close to everyone. After my visit, I was surprised to learn from the family that she had shown no changes in activity or behavior in response to losing her companion.

 This Boston terrier sister craved a moment of love before her brother's crossing.

Bonded brothers

Another one of my senior patients was a light-tan, mixed-breed dog. He had terminal cancer and was a sweet love bug. He had a "twin" sibling who was just as sweet but still healthy.

After I gave the initial sedative injection to the sick dog, his brother came over and laid next to him. He gently rested his head on his feeble brother, who seemed comforted as he relaxed into slumberland. The family and I were happy the brothers cuddled for a few minutes before I gave the euthanasia injection to the ailing brother.

They were a bonded pair, and I suspected that the brother who was left behind would struggle a bit, and he did. The family told me that for a week afterward he was more melan-choly, only ate about half of his meals, and was not as excited to go on walks. He also slept in his brother's bed.

 These love bugs had a last cuddle before the sick brother earned his wings.

Weighing grief in pets: What the studies say

In 1996, the American Society for the Prevention of Cruelty to Animals (ASPCA) conducted a Companion Animal Mourning Project and surveyed pet owners about behavior changes they'd seen in their pets after a companion pet died. Of the dogs who were left behind, 36% showed less interest in their food, and about 11% stopped eating completely. And 63% of the dogs either vocalized more or were quieter than they normally were. Many of the dogs became more attached to their caregivers. Many dogs also changed their habits, such as where they slept. (Schultz 1996)

The cats who were left behind showed similar changes. After a companion cat passed, 46% of the remaining cats ate less, 70% vocalized more, and more than half became more clingy with their humans. (Schultz 1996)

Another large survey of pet owners in New Zealand and Australia published in 2016 collected information about 159 dogs and 152 cats who had lost a companion pet. The pets' behaviors that were assessed related to affection, territory, vocalization, eating, and sleeping, among others. (Walker 2016)

In categorizing the pets' responses to loss, the researchers considered grief as a biological response to separation, which has active and passive phases of behavior responses. Active responses occurred during the first phase after loss and involved pets searching and vocalizing. During the second phase after loss, passive responses involved pets reducing activity and withdrawing from the environment, which help animals conserve energy. Animals respond in this way because they're expecting to see the missing companion again soon and want to help make sure that happens. For example, farm animal mothers and their offspring who undergo artificial weaning (which is the common practice of separating the offspring from their mothers before weaning would normally occur) first attempt to reunite by vocalizing more, then they show altered feeding patterns and stop playing. (Walker 2016)

Similar to the ASPCA survey, this survey showed that 61% of dogs and 62% of cats solicited more attention from their owners or became more clingy. However, some pets (13% of dogs and 16% of cats) sought less attention or avoided contact with their owners. And no changes in affection were seen in 26% of dogs and 22% of cats. The researchers indicated that changes in pets' affection may be a reflection of:

- the pet's grief, anxiety, or distress;
- less competition for access to the pet owner; or
- having fewer opportunities to interact with the owners (if social interactions were previously sparked by the other pet's presence). (Walker 2016)

When it came to territory-related behaviors, 30% of dogs and 36% of cats kept checking their deceased companion's favorite spots. A few pets (10% of dogs and 5% of cats) avoided those spots. But 41% of dogs and 37% of cats showed no territory-related behavior changes. In addition, 27% of dogs and 43% of cats vocalized more after their loss. (Walker 2016)

The researchers suggested that pets who seek out a deceased companion's favorite spots and those who vocalize more may be experiencing the active phase of grief. Alternatively, they stated that pets who check these spots could also be claiming the newly vacated spot as their own because they don't have to compete for it. (Walker 2016)

Eating less occurred in 35% of dogs and 21% of cats, and eating slower occurred in 31% of dogs and 12% of cats. The amount of food eaten did not change in 58% of dogs and 67% of cats. Changes in the amount the pets ate or how fast they ate were attributed to either a negative effect of a pet losing their friend, or to less competition for food. (Walker 2016)

Sleeping more was reported for 34% of dogs and 20% of cats. Pets' sleep changes were attributed to either the passive phase of grief, or to the pet no longer receiving stimulation from their companion (Walker 2016). No more, "Hey bro, whatcha doin'?" moments.

Some pets had the opportunity to see their deceased companion's body. Of these pets, 78% of dogs and 74% of cats sniffed and investigated their friend's body. But 13% of dogs and 18% of cats showed no interest, and 7% of cats hissed or growled (none of the dogs growled). (Walker 2016)

Interestingly, the behavioral changes reported for pets who saw their deceased companion did not differ from the behavioral changes reported for pets who didn't see their deceased friend. (Walker 2016) To me, this finding suggests that regardless of whether a pet views their deceased friend, if the pet left behind is going to be sad, they will be sad, and if they're going to be neutral, they'll be neutral. It also suggests to me that while it may not necessarily help for a pet to be present during their friend's euthanasia, it probably doesn't hurt, either. Although we can't be sure how our pets process the "meaning" of such an event, being present during euthanasia or seeing their deceased friend when possible and if appropriate may at least give them an opportunity to learn.

The researchers also mentioned that pets who lose a companion from other types of separation (such as sale, rehoming, relinquishment to a shelter) may exhibit many of the same behavior changes. However, they suggested that this type of separation and the behavioral responses to it should be studied separately. (Walker 2016)

Jetty and Ranger

According to his family, Jetty was a very aloof cat. He always ran from anyone new who visited their house, and he never wanted to be near the family's dog,

Ranger. When I visited their home to help Ranger at the end of his life, Jetty casually strolled into the room as if he was fashionably late to the gathering.

Jetty quietly crept onto the back of the couch where I was sitting with Ranger. He perched there, with his beautiful fluffy tail draped over the cushion, gently swaying. He watched me intently. At the time I didn't know that Jetty wasn't a fan of strangers, and I reached up and gave him a few strokes, which he didn't resist.

The family was shocked! They whispered to me, "Jetty NEVER does that!"

"Does what?" I asked.

"He never lets anyone other than us pet him. And he normally doesn't come out of the bedroom when a stranger is here."

Ranger was resting comfortably on the couch under Jetty's perch. Jetty continued to watch my every move as I helped Ranger earn his wings. Everything went smoothly, and Ranger peacefully passed.

Afterward, I gave Jetty a few more strokes. I heard him purr! The family sat there, now teary-eyed because of Ranger's passing, but still amazed by Jetty's calm, friendly interaction with me.

I said, "I'm no cat whisperer, but maybe Jetty knew his friend was not well and wanted to be near."

The family didn't quite buy my explanation because they felt like Jetty had never really liked Ranger.

Two days later, the family called me and said that Jetty was whining and seemed irritable. I suggested they consider that because of Ranger's absence, their normal routines were probably disrupted. And because cats are not the greatest at adapting to change, maybe the altered household dynamics had upset him. They later told me that Jetty acted upset for a few more days, and then settled back into his normal, aloof demeanor.

Handling grief in pets

Even with the limited data from published surveys and my wealth of experiences with my patients families' and my own pets, I'm still unsure whether it helps for other pets to be present when their companion passes. Pets have jumped into my car before I drive away with their friend, pets have lain on top of their friend during the euthanasia, and pets have stepped over their friend as if they didn't notice a difference after their friend passed. But after helping thousands of multi-pet families, I don't think it hurts for other pets to be present. This is why I let the furry friends decide.

In my experience with my patients' families, the pet who is left behind exhibits behavior changes within the first day or two after the loss of their friend, and the changes usually last about two weeks. And I often wonder whether some of the pet's behavior changes occur in response to the owner's grief. In my household

I have not noticed a big difference in any of my pets after the loss of a companion pet. However, almost all of them gave me more attention, as if they sensed my grief and knew I needed extra love. I especially remember that when I lost Serissa, I was very sad and depressed and cried a lot for a few days. During that time, all three of my cats laid on me, head-butted me, and just stayed close to me at least twice as much as normal.

For pets who exhibit behavior changes and seem to be grieving, conflicting advice on how to help abounds. Recommendations range from sticking to regular routines and refraining from giving the pet extra attention to switching up their routines and providing extra attention. In my experience, giving the pet extra love and attention is never a bad thing. You can try new games, food treats, catnip (for crestfallen cats), and adding walks (for the doleful dogs). Changing their daily routine a bit may help, such as taking them for a walk in the late morning instead of in the early morning and feeding them in a different location. The number and types of changes you can comfortably make in familiar routines depends on your pet's health status and age, because as I've mentioned in many other chapters, sticking to routines is beneficial for many senior pets and may be especially important for pets who have cognitive dysfunction.

Calming measures such as pheromone sprays or collars (like Adaptil or Feliway) may help. Keep the deceased pet's items—such as bedding, bowls, toys, and leashes—in their usual locations for a while. Some pet parents have told me they have placed the deceased pet's collar on the remaining pet and it seemed to help the pet relax.

The bottom line is that the mechanisms that may help a pet adjust to their loss and the length of time it takes to adjust will likely be highly individual for each pet. I have no doubt that animals are sentient beings and possess emotions that we may never be able to explain. Anticipating their reactions when another pet passes is definitely worth consideration.

Welcoming a new furry friend

What about bringing a new friend into the family? I believe it is good to first give the whole family time to grieve and adjust to the loss of their friend. When the remaining pet's anxiety has passed, appetite has improved, and the sleeping pattern is normal—and when all human family members agree that everyone is ready—then I think filling the void may be helpful to everyone. Alternatively, consider making play dates with other pets in the neighborhood or with your friends. Even just a little activity with another animal or different people may bring sparks of joy back into your pet's life.

READING RECOMMENDATIONS

- Colorado State University College of Veterinary Medicine website: How Animals Grieve. **https://www.vetmed.wsu.edu/outreach/ pet-loss-hotline/support-for-bereaved/other-pets http://csu-cvmbs.colostate.edu/vth/diagnostic-and-support/argus/ Pages/how-animals-grieve.aspx**
- Grief Support Center Rainbows Bridge website: Do Pets Grieve? **https://rainbowsbridge.com/Grief_Support_Center/Grief_Support/ Do_Pets_Grieve.htm**

CHAPTER 37:

Natural passing: What to expect

"Death was a friend, and sleep was death's brother."

— JOHN STEINBECK, THE GRAPES OF WRATH

Toward the end of Neo's life, I had planned for his passing. It was going to be in the early evening when the temperature was a bit cooler so we could be outside. He'd have a bowl of ice cream with whipped cream on top. (He loved to share my sundaes.) I'd give him a ton of kisses and snuggles to make sure he knew how much I loved him as he sailed forth into his next adventure. That was my perfect scenario for Neo to pass.

I know exactly how I want the passing of each of my pets to go when they pass with my help, and each experience will be unique to them. I always want to be there, making sure they have all the comforts I can provide. Most importantly, I want them to know I am there with them—loving them and thanking them for their love and companionship.

Another part of me wishes that my pets would pass on their own so I don't have to make that decision. And I know many pet parents wish the same thing. They often tell me, "I just want my pet to die peacefully in her sleep."

That is also how I'd like to die—sleeping and dreaming of something great after having had a wonderful dinner with a stack of Oreos to top off the night; to not know I'm dying and to not feel anything. Perhaps you have a similar wish for yourself.

Pondering that final wish

Most of us will die as a result of a disease or an accident or other trauma. We may be able to choose to die at home or in a hospital or a hospice facility. Some people choose assisted death, which is allowed in a few states and countries that have right-to-die laws. Depending on the circumstances, death may be painless and peaceful, or it may be painful and distressing. Euthanasia, which is deliberately and painlessly ending someone's life to relieve suffering, isn't available and is illegal for people in the United States. But for our pets, euthanasia is acceptable, available, and legal. Yet many pet parents wish for their pet's natural passing instead—as long as it occurs without suffering. Many people don't realize that natural passing doesn't always occur quickly or without pain or suffering.

Pet parents occasionally call me for hospice services and tell me they're against euthanasia for a variety of reasons; they believe only in natural passing for their dog. I understand and respect these families' requests for their dogs, and I want to make sure each dog's needs are met. Pain and suffering must be mitigated to the best of our ability. I think, and I hope, that most pet parents wouldn't want their dog to suffer, whether they agree with euthanasia or not.

For dogs to not suffer, pet parents must be able to accurately recognize and acknowledge the signs of pain, anxiety, or suffering in their dogs. Sometimes these signs are subtle. Pet parents may also not understand that their dog has a disease that will take years before death to occur naturally and, in that time, their dog suffers if the effects of the disease are not adequately managed. One example is dogs who have arthritis. They may be barely able to walk, but that doesn't mean their organs will fail and death will occur.

Properly understanding the disease or condition your dog has, what can be done to treat the disease or relieve the signs, as well as what occurs during the death process will help you determine the best options for your dog and you.

Preparing for a dog's death

Regardless of whether euthanasia or natural passing is chosen, I encourage all owners of geriatric dogs or dogs who have a terminal illness to make these preparations:

- Learn the signs of the disease or condition your dog has.
- Know the signs of pain and anxiety in your dog so you can promptly determine how to alleviate them. Your veterinarian or hospice veterinarian can prescribe pain and anti-anxiety medications appropriate for you to give your dog or have on hand, and give guidance on how to administer them. Talk with your veterinarian about the medical concerns you have.
- Know that pet hospice and palliative care in your home is an option during the final weeks or days of your dog's life.
- Consider all methods to mitigate suffering. Although further studies are needed, acupuncture has been reported to help ease pain, tiredness,

insomnia, nausea, dyspnea, and anxiety in human hospice patients, which could bring comfort to your dog in their final days. (McPhail 2018, Romeo 2015, Zeng 2018)

- Decide whether you'd like to be present when your dog passes. It's an important decision that some pet parents don't stop to consider. Learn about what occurs during natural death, and keep in mind that it may be difficult to witness. If you don't wish to be present but want someone to be present for your dog, consider asking a family member or friend to be available, or reconsider whether euthanasia may be the more appropriate choice.
- Consider the wishes of family members or friends involved in the dog's care. Decide whether and how children will be involved and whether they'll be present when your dog passes.
- Consider how you may want to memorialize your dog, and have the proper supplies on hand (such as clay or ink and paper to make a paw print).
- Research options for handling your dog's body. Will your dog be buried or cremated? Where will your dog's remains rest—at home, in a pet cemetery, or at another location? By taking the time to reflect on this information beforehand, it's easier to act on the desired plan rather than having to choose in the moment.
- Make arrangements for handling your dog's body. Identify a cool (below 70 F [21 C]) holding area, decide on transportation, and determine what payment will be needed.
- Consider which arrangements may need to change and how to handle those if your dog passes during the night.
- Try to avoid leaving your dog alone during the final days.
- Learn about the natural stages of dying. It's important to know what changes your dog may exhibit.
- Learn about the changes in a dog's body that occur after death so you're prepared.
- Continue to give love and attention to other furry family members.
- Take care of yourself. Try to get adequate sleep and good nourishment. Ask for help and take time out as needed.
- And remember, if you decide you no longer want a natural death for your dog, you can change your mind. Natural does not mean it will be painless or nontraumatic to witness. Veterinary in-home or in-clinic euthanasia should remain options. (Keep information on hand for in-home veterinary hospice and euthanasia services, veterinary emergency clinics, and your primary care veterinary practice in case you decide that you no longer want your dog to experience a natural death.)

Keep the unexpected in mind

With natural passing, you won't know exactly when it will happen. So you need to be prepared for the fact that you may not be there when your dog passes, or that it may happen at an inopportune time. Your dog may pass in her sleep or while you're at work. She may pass when you are sitting down to have dinner, or when you're getting your kids ready for school.

Also consider whether being present when your dog passes is your priority, which in-home euthanasia can provide. If you want to be present when your dog dies and are not, this may leave an emotional scar. I have learned that most pet owners want to be with their dogs during euthanasia, but many do not want to be present when their dog passes naturally.

An example of the truly unexpected: During the COVID-19 pandemic, many veterinary clinics didn't allow pet owners to come into the clinic to be with their dogs during euthanasia. These were agonizing situations for the pet parents and the veterinary teams. So given unprecedented circumstances like this, even if you want to be present and schedule an in-clinic euthanasia or take your dog to an emergency service for euthanasia, it's possible you may not be able to be present. I mention this in the hopes of helping you be prepared for and accept that such circumstances could arise.

The natural death process

Understanding the dying process for your dog and being aware of what you and your family may experience is essential. What happens to the dog naturally in those final days and hours are especially important to consider. The natural dying process has many stages that manifest in different ways as the end of a dog's life approaches.

If your dog still has an appetite or is thirsty, then, of course, continue to provide this support. Don't be alarmed if your dog seems to waste away despite eating a fair amount. Her body may no longer fully absorb or process the nutrients normally. Similarly, though she may drink, she may not drink enough to stay hydrated or may become dehydrated because her kidneys are malfunctioning. Keep in mind that it's important to differentiate weight loss and dehydration associated with dying from those signs associated with a treatable illness.

Disinterest in food and water are normal at the end of life. If your dog truly doesn't want to eat or drink, don't continually place food or water in front of him and don't try to force him to eat or drink. This can cause nausea and other distress. His body is going through the natural steps of shutting down, and we may cause harm or pain by interfering in this way.

Other changes you may see in your dog as death approaches, and what you can do to help keep your dog as comfortable as possible:

- **Spending time in out-of-the-way locations in your home or seeking to be alone.** Allow your dog to rest where she feels most comfortable. Provide comfy bedding, although keep in mind she may choose not to use it. Keep the environment quiet and calm, and avoid loud noises and lots of activity. Supervise other pets in the household and monitor their interactions with the ailing dog, limiting any interactions if needed. Your pets may prefer to remain close to one another, or they may prefer to stay apart.
- **Diminished or—on the opposite end—intensified signs of pain associated with the dog's underlying disease.** It's important during this time and until the end to administer pain medications as prescribed by your veterinarian and to consider whether anti-anxiety medications may be needed as well. Talk with your veterinarian about how best and when to administer medications, because in the later stages of dying, swallowing may not be possible. Injectable options are available, or patches can be placed on your dog's skin that deliver medication to give him more comfort.
- **Abnormal postures that may look uncomfortable.** Turn your dog every two to four hours or adjust her position as needed if she is too weak to move.
- **Twitching, trembling, and shaking.** Be a reassuring presence.
- **Low body temperature or pale gums.** Keep a warmer room temperature and put a light blanket over your dog—one that doesn't feel too heavy or constrictive of your dog's breathing. Leave your dog's face uncovered.
- **Severe weakness that progresses to little to no movement when awake, then an almost comatose state.** Provide a reassuring presence and quiet environment.
- **Lack of fecal and urine control and no attempt to move away from the soiled area or groom themselves.** Place puppy pads under your dog and help keep him clean and dry by removing soiled pads and gently washing soiled fur and skin.

As time passes, dogs will begin to display more drastic changes that lead to the moments right before they pass. These changes are often more difficult to witness than you might anticipate, and they can last for several hours. But it can be helpful to expect that they may occur:

- Complete unresponsiveness
- Lack of blinking; their eyes may seem blank and dull
- Restlessness or agitation
- Seizures
- Stretching of their limbs

- Backward arching of their neck or head
- Evacuation of their bowels or bladder
- Vocalization
- Twitching, tremors, or paddling
- Complete lack of movement
- Long gaps between breaths, progressing to gasping breaths, and then no breathing.

Considerations for the family during the dying process

When the time comes and a dog is passing, it can be difficult to remember what you should be doing. It can be helpful to take a little time to remind yourself and those around you of what you wanted to do during the dying process:

- Continue to talk to your dog and comfort him. Hearing is one of the last senses to fade.
- Don't move your dog if possible. She may react, or it may be distressing or painful.
- Be as present and calm as possible. Focus on the love of your furry family member.
- Remember to say or read or do what you and your family members prepared for these moments.
- Leave your dog's collar on if he is used to wearing one. He may feel more comfortable wearing it.
- Excuse yourself and take a breath if you feel overwhelmed in the moment and it's safe for you to do so.
- Breathe, and remember that the dying process is natural. As difficult as it may be to watch your dog in the final stages of dying, don't try to administer CPR to stop your dog from passing, and don't try to hasten your dog's death as she is passing naturally. If your dog seems to be struggling for a prolonged period, consider using a veterinary service for emergency in-home or in-clinic euthanasia.

What happens after a dog passes

After your dog has breathed his or her final breath and is completely at rest, look for the continued absence of breathing. You may also have been able to feel, hear, or see your dog's heart stop beating.

It's helpful to familiarize yourself with other bodily changes that may occur after a dog has passed. This way you can manage your and others' expectations and be respectful of your dog's remains. You may notice one or more of these changes:

- Voiding of feces (or diarrhea), flatulence, voiding of urine
- Muscles twitching in the face and lips
- Open eyelids
- Open mouth
- Cooling of the body. A dog's normal temperature is about 100 F (38 C), so it may take a few hours to cool to room temperature.
- Change in the pet's odor
- Fluid discharge from the mouth or nose. Whether this occurs often depends on what the dog's ailments were, and the fluid sometimes appears frothy and bloody.
- Progressive stiffening of the limbs and body (rigor mortis). This typically occurs two to four hours after death in dogs. This time may vary with the ambient temperature and the dog's size. In general, rigor mortis occurs faster in small dogs.

What should I do after my dog's death?

After your dog passes, you and others present first need to take time—within reason, and with respect to your dog's body—to take care of yourselves. You may want to sit with your dog for a few minutes and continue to talk to him. Then take a moment for yourself, reflect, talk to your friends or family, and do what brings you comfort.

Although you feel grief, you may also feel relief that your dog is no longer suffering. A part of your own suffering has been relieved. Allow yourself to experience relief. It's a good and normal emotion.

When you're ready, consider the next steps:

- You may want to allow other family pets or pet friends to see and sniff their deceased friend. Because grief in pets hasn't yet been extensively studied, we don't know precisely how pets process being exposed to a deceased companion. According to one study, seeing a deceased companion does not change the behavior of the pet left behind. (Walker 2016) However, we also don't know whether being present gives pets an opportunity to learn, so we may not want to deny them that opportunity.
- If you planned to make a clay or ink paw print, it is easier to obtain before your dog's body has stiffened. You may want to trim your dog's

toenails and fur between the paw pads if needed to provide a better imprint.

- Remove your dog's collar if you would like to keep it.
- Get help lifting and moving your dog if you need assistance.
- To contain body fluids and help preserve your dog's body, place her inside a thick plastic bag or wrap her in a blanket, and then place her in a plastic container.
- Move your dog's remains to the appropriate place in preparation for cremation or burial, such as a box, bag, or basket, before rigor mortis has occurred. If stiffness sets in, you will likely be unable to place him in the carrier you've chosen.
- Place your dog in a cool location and chill her body if possible to delay natural decay, which can happen quickly, especially in warmer climates.
- Inform the chosen crematorium or other service who will pick up your dog's body.
- As soon as you feel comfortable, call or write and inform your primary care veterinary practice (and referral hospital, if applicable) that your dog has passed away. The veterinary team will appreciate your sharing the news of your dog's passing with them. It also allows the team to update your dog's medical records and will prevent you from receiving healthcare reminders for your dog who has passed.

As difficult as this process may be for you and your loved ones, remember to be kind to yourself and those around you. Prepare as much as possible, but give yourself a break during the extremely difficult moments. It's normal to feel and display a wide range of emotions.

Neo's passing

The day after Thanksgiving in 2010, I went to help a family in Fort Lauderdale, Florida, who requested in-home euthanasia for their cat. They were so grateful that I was working during the holiday weekend. I always say to myself on holidays, and in the middle of the night, and during hurricanes, that death doesn't avoid holidays, wait for a more convenient time, or care about the weather. The appointment went smoothly for the family, and their cat passed peacefully with my help. On the drive back afterward, I reflected on the comfort I had provided for the cat and the family. And as I got closer to home, my thoughts turned to Neo and what to make for his dinner. At that stage in his illness, I was feeding him home-cooked meals to entice him to eat better.

Whenever I needed to leave Neo for a few hours, I had to put him in a hallway blocked off with a baby gate and cover the floor with towels in case he urinated—a frequent problem associated with his illness. I hated confining him. But he didn't seem to mind as long as I gave him his squeaky toys, which he happily played with, including that afternoon when I left. And he always eagerly pranced at the gate, happily welcoming me when I got home.

When I returned home and opened the front door that afternoon, silence greeted me. No clicking of Neo's toenails. He wasn't prancing. I thought, "Maybe he's sleeping and didn't hear the door." I felt a slight pang of anxiety as I rounded the corner to look down the hallway.

 Neo was a pro in his confined area when I had to leave the house.

There was Neo, lying on the floor. He was not asleep. His handsome body was lifeless. His long legs were outstretched and stiff. Feces and urine were spread over his hind end and on the floor behind him. His eyes were open, completely dull and blank. My heart clenched and seemed to drop into my gut. The shock of his death washed over me, and I sank to my knees and screamed his name. I had not been prepared for him to leave me this way. It was not what I wanted for my boy. To be alone, to be in the hallway, to be covered in feces. No treats. No love. No feeling of calm.

I will always regret not helping Neo to pass peacefully sooner. Now, whenever I think for a second that I wish Mother Nature would take one of my pets, I remember that moment when I found Neo. And I start to plan for a euthanasia instead.

 Questions to ask your veterinarian

- What measures (such as pain and anti-anxiety medications, acupuncture, massage) will be most beneficial, given my dog's underlying condition, in the days leading up to my dog's passing?
- What options are available to administer the medications my dog needs?
- Do you offer telemedicine or video conferencing services so I may check in with you if I have questions or concerns while I'm supporting and monitoring my dog?

459

- What are my options during or after regular business hours for in-home or in-clinic euthanasia services?
- Do you have suggestions for aftercare of my dog's body? Do you have a pet cemetery or cremation service you recommend?

RECOMMENDED READING ON HUMAN MORTALITY

- *Being Mortal: Medicine and What Matters in the End* by Atul Gawande (2014, Picador).
- *A Beginner's Guide to the End: Practical Advice for Living Life and Facing Death* by BJ Miller and Shoshana Berger (2019, Simon & Schuster).

CHAPTER 38:

Euthanasia: The ending is what matters most

"It's not that I'm afraid to die, I just don't want to be there when it happens."

— Kleinman in Death, A Comedy In One Act by Woody Allen

I never considered I would be good at euthanizing animals, and students certainly don't win awards for it in veterinary school. However, providing euthanasia requires skills that rival successfully performing many complex surgical techniques. But as odd as it may sound, I'm good at it. I've learned that I love helping families during these heartrending moments. I'm honored to bring care, comfort, pain relief, and love to animals at the end of their lives. But euthanasia comes with challenges—emotional and technical.

It's helpful for pet parents to better understand the euthanasia process. This knowledge may bring some peace and reassurance to those struggling with or afraid to make this decision. It may provide answers to lingering questions for those who have gone through a pet's euthanasia. In this chapter I'll share important considerations for you in relation to the euthanasia process—whether you experience it with your pet in the veterinary clinic or at home.

When possible, I've always been the one to euthanize my pets. Not all veterinarians can do this for their own pets, and I can understand that. Believe me, I never want to have to say that final goodbye to my pets, just like you. But when I must, I want to be the one to relieve their struggles and usher them into their next adventure. As I write this book, I know my dog Sam will be next, and that thought aches to my core. I also know I'll make Sam's last day a really good day and her last moments will be those of looking at the face of her friend—me. My goal is for every pet to have a really good last day with their family, and to be surrounded by their family's faces and love at the end.

The Day

Of course for pet parents, there is no true good day, ever, to lose a pet. But we can do our best to make our pet's last day a good one. Our pets certainly deserve that whenever possible.

Families usually don't think about planning euthanasia for their pets. Most of us tend to delay it for as long as we can. About a quarter of the families who contact Lap of Love Veterinary Hospice schedule their pet's euthanasia on the same day, and about half schedule it for within 48 hours. While this time frame is often understandable and not unreasonable, I encourage families who do have time to plan ahead, to think about and plan for several things in order to make their pet's last day as good as possible.

Start by asking yourself some important questions, then talk with your veterinarian in advance to learn what options are available to you. Where would you like to say goodbye to your pet? In the veterinary hospital? At home? Which room at home? At a park? In your backyard? What time of day? Can your veterinarian accommodate your wishes?

If you prefer to say goodbye to your pet at the veterinary clinic, what are the clinic's business hours? If a veterinarian comes to your home or meets you at a park, at what times are they available and what is the additional fee? If your veterinarian does not make house calls, do they recommend an in-home euthanasia service such as Lap of Love? What happens if you book an appointment and want to cancel? Will there be a fee?

When

All of us at Lap of Love fully understand how difficult the decision to euthanize a pet is. I've pulled into families' driveways and saw them peeking out through their blinds, when they called to tell me "we just can't," and they canceled the visit. I usually ask them if I may still come in to say hi to their pet. I offer to assess their pet and discuss hospice care and help with assessing the pet's life quality. I want to make sure their pet isn't suffering. But we never charge a cancellation fee. We understand. We know that doubt can be overwhelming, and we want to support the family as best as we can. Some say our policy is a bad business practice, but the gratitude we receive in such situations is payment enough.

Some pet parents want to schedule their pet's euthanasia on a weekend so they can have more time to spoil their pet and have other family members present. Some have to say goodbye during the week because their pet's decline hastens. Many families tell me they want an appointment first thing in the morning so they can "get it over with." That may sound harsh, but usually their pet is struggling and the family doesn't want to wait another hour to relieve their pet's discomfort, or they may want to avoid prolonging their own dread and anxiety about the appointment. Conversely, some pet parents want to schedule for the last appointment of the day so they know they shared every possible second with their pet. I remember one woman who wanted an appointment toward the end of the day, but before dark. She told me she did not want to immediately be left alone in the dark, and that she needed to have at least an hour afterward, before sunset.

I always do my best to schedule according to the family's wishes. This is why it's a good idea for families to start thinking about The Day, especially before it becomes last minute. Then you can plan to make your pet's last day a good last day.

If you can plan ahead (even if it is within a day), and if your pet has had a veterinary exam within the past 12 months, your veterinarian should be able to pre-prescribe medications you can give your pet at home before the euthanasia appointment. Medications can help alleviate your pet's pain or anxiety, especially if you're planning to travel to the veterinary hospital for your pet's euthanasia. Depending on their medical conditions, pets often experience pain or nausea toward the end of life. Giving a veterinary-prescribed analgesic or antinausea drug can ease the experience of getting pets into the car or into their carriers and riding in the car. If your pet tends to be aggressive when around other people or in unfamiliar situations, your veterinarian can prescribe a mild sedative to take the edge off. Contact your veterinarian to ask whether your pet can receive one or more of these medications.

Also think ahead about the memorial items you wish to obtain before your pet's passing, whether it's photos, videos, a lock of fur, or a paw print or nose impression. Pre-planning ensures that you capture all the mementos you want..

After your pet is gone, the last thing you may want to have to decide is what you wish to do with your pet's body. This is a personal decision, and it's helpful to decide ahead of time.

Preplanning for prescriptions

Your pet will need to have been seen by your veterinarian within the last 12 months in order for your veterinarian to legally prescribe medication for your pet. This is a requirement of the Veterinary Practice Act in most states. I mention this because in a study I conducted that reviewed data from over 400,000 pets who were euthanized, more than half of these pets had not been seen by their veterinarian during the final 12 months of their lives. (M. Gardner, unpublished data, August 2019) So in addition to not receiving veterinary evaluation to determine whether other potential therapies would've been beneficial during their final months, these pets didn't have the option to have medications prescribed before their euthanasia appointment if needed. It's beneficial—for many reasons—for your pet to receive a veterinary examination at least once a year, including when they're nearing the end of their life.

Who

All who wish to be present for the pet's euthanasia are more than welcome. But some pet parents or family members don't want to be there. Again, I respect the family's wishes. I've been left alone with pets for euthanasia, and I've been a guest at a pet's final block party! There is no "right" number of people. What is best is the pet's comfort. And the pet loves their family most!

Some pet parents who can't imagine not being with their pet during euthanasia harshly judge those who don't want to be present. Even some veterinary professionals harbor negative feelings toward pet parents who don't want to be present. But a clear distinction exists between those who don't care to be present because they don't care much for the pet and those who can't bear to be present for their pet's death. In either case, it doesn't matter to me because I'll be there to give the pet lots of love and kisses. For the pet whose owner seems indifferent—and those cases are rare—I get a chance to give that pet extra love. However, many pet parents cannot bear to witness the death of their pet. I understand and accept their position without judgment. They love their pet.

I remember one pet parent, Elizabeth, who couldn't bear to be present during her dog's euthanasia. She also asked that her dog be laid to rest in a special place in her backyard on that day. And she didn't want to return home until after the burial.

I had known Elizabeth for many years and I knew this dog was her whole world. I knew the dog had had a wonderful life. But when it came time, Elizabeth wanted to kiss her dog goodbye and leave.

And so she did.

I was alone with her beloved dog, gently stroking, hugging, kissing, and talking to her as she took her final breaths. I continued stroking and softly speaking to her for several minutes afterward, ensuring her transition was as beautiful as she was.

After the burial, I called Elizabeth to tell her she could come home.

She barely squeaked out her tiny reply, "OK."

Typically, all the family members in the household are present. I love this because I hear stories, I see tears, and I feel the love they have for their pet. I'm thankful for that emotional boost that helps me do this bittersweet work. I'm gratified to witness how much the pet was loved.

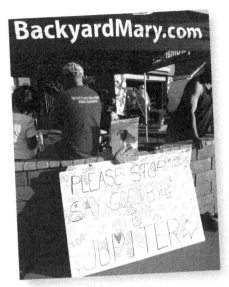

 An outpouring of love from family and friends at Jupiter's farewell celebration.

And sometimes, the pet gets to party like it's 1999! I fondly remember a dog named Jupiter. On a sunny June day in Westminster, California, I was having trouble locating the house I was called to for a euthanasia. I slowly drove down the street reading the house numbers, and I could see a large gathering at the far end. As the house numbers increased, it finally hit me that the one I was looking for was on the corner at the end of the block. The house that was having a party! For Jupiter!

Jupiter was an English mastiff who had chronic mobility problems, and during the previous three months his condition had progressively worsened to the point he could barely walk. His mind and stomach worked fine, but those darn hips weren't cooperating. Jupiter was clearly a popular boy. A huge sign that said "Please Stop, Say Goodbye to Jupiter" was propped against the low brick retaining wall in front of his family's house. The sign was covered in handwritten messages for Jupiter. On top was a lovely beach photo that featured the dog of the hour.

I was enthusiastically welcomed like I have never been welcomed before. Jupiter and his family members wore decorative leis! There were tears, smiles, swollen eyes, and runny noses, and the love for Jupiter was palpable. A long table held photo albums and poster boards filled with pictures of Jupiter's life adventures, as well as other memorabilia. Some guests were enjoying fruity cocktails and toasting Jupiter.

I was a little nervous with about 50 people intently watching my every move, but Jupiter's euthanasia went perfectly. After Jupiter passed, his dad lifted the front half of Jupiter's body to hug his boy and cry. I was sad for the family, but so happy that Jupiter had such an adoring family and amazing life!

Deciding who will be present for a pet's euthanasia is deeply personal. No one should judge you if you can't be present. No one should judge you if you want to be the only one there. No one should judge you if you want to give a goodbye party like Jupiter's. No final farewell playbook exists. Find a veterinarian who will help you achieve the best experience possible.

If you're unable to be present for your pet's euthanasia because of work, school, vacation, or another conflict, ask to attend via a video conference. Once when I was traveling to speak at a conference, my cat Lilu who had diabetes got sick. We learned that she had a severe urinary tract infection that had spread to her kidneys. And although she had the best care at a specialty veterinary hospital, Lilu took a sudden turn for the worse and she stopped producing urine. Lilu's condition was life-threatening and irreversible. I was taking a cross-country flight and would not make it home in time. So my wonderful colleague and friend who also provides in-home veterinary euthanasia services picked Lilu up from the speciality clinic and took Lilu back home for her goodbye. My friend video-called me, and there was Lilu on my bed, surrounded by her furry siblings. I talked to Lilu, and I got to see her get her wings.

Where

Determining the location for a pet's euthanasia is also a personal choice, but your options may be limited by your pet's ailment or the weather. I believe that pets love their home, and whenever possible, we should try to honor that and say goodbye where they are most comfortable. I have been called to help pets earn their angel wings in thousands of living rooms, hundreds of master beds, many backyards, and a few parks. I have also delivered pets' sendoffs on beaches, under a grand piano, beneath a pool table, and on a sailboat!

Once you decide on a location, make sure it's comfortable for your pet and for you. Does it allow easy access for you to love on your pet? Will the veterinarian be able to perform the procedure? In some cases it may be difficult to say goodbye exactly where you hoped or planned to, especially if your pet is too sick to move. It's best to leave your pet where he or she is most comfortable, even if it's not perfect for you. Your pet's comfort is paramount—your plans and desires come second.

If you'd like to choose a public location, select a time of day when it will be the least occupied to provide the fewest distractions for your pet and the most privacy for you. Consider the weather, too, because extreme heat or cold makes everyone uncomfortable, and you want to ensure everyone's comfort—especially your pet. Choose a spot that is sufficiently far from the usual traffic for that time of day and one that allows easy access to your car to transport your pet back to your vehicle afterward. Bring your pet's bed, a stretcher, or a basket that will help you carry your pet.

One Sunday morning I went to help a veterinary practice manager whose clinic did not provide in-home euthanasia. Her shepherd-mix dog had been fighting nasal cancer. Dogs breathe primarily through their noses, and the cancer had finally blocked so much of her dog's nasal passages that breathing was uncomfortable for her dog in nearly every position.

I parked in the driveway and walked between my car and hers. I noticed her car's hatchback was open and she was sitting in the back, quietly loving on her dog.

She explained, "She loves the car and going for rides, so we just went for one!"

I thought for a split second, then offered, "If she loves the car so much, we can say goodbye in the car, if you want." She turned to me, incredulous. "Are you serious?" she asked.

I thought I had accidentally insulted her. Sheepishly, I nodded my head. She answered emphatically, "Yes. That would be amazing."

Relieved, I realized she was happy with this suggestion. I opened the rear passenger door and leaned in, which gave me perfect access to her dog's hind leg to administer the injections.

Not only did her dog remain comfortable and content, she got to say goodbye to her dog in a place where her dog had exhibited pure joy throughout her entire life.

That's something I'll always treasure.

I experienced another unusual situation with Daisy, a shih tzu with extreme cognitive dysfunction. Daisy lived with her pet parents in a lovely single-story condominium with a small porch that overlooked a gorgeous lake. Daisy's mom was retired and spent nearly

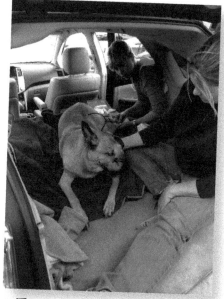

This sweet dog got to take a final joy ride and earn her wings in a favorite spot.

every waking moment caring for Daisy. They had a toddler playpen in the living room with all of Daisy's necessities inside so Daisy would be safe if they were not home—which was quite possibly never more than 30 minutes at a time.

Daisy's mom was terribly distraught at the thought of losing Daisy, and the moment I walked into the home, I sensed that her anxiety hit the ceiling. I did all I could do to reassure and calm her, but I soon realized that this would be how her body and mind would handle this moment.

She was standing, holding Daisy in her arms and rocking back and forth, which appeared to comfort her a bit. It seemed to soothe Daisy, too.

I gently asked where she wanted to say goodbye. Her anxiety spiked again. Frantic, she looked around the house—at the playpen, the couch, the patio, and the couch again. Then she looked at me and implored, "I just don't want to have one spot in this house where I look and think, 'That's where she died.'"

She hesitated for a moment and then asked, "Can you just do it with her in my arms, while I stand and maybe walk around a little? This is what we do every night before she goes to bed, and it calms her down."

That request was a first for me. But Daisy was comfortable and her mom seemed certain. I couldn't think of one good reason against it.

So I agreed. "Yes, I can do that."

Daisy's mom's shoulders instantly relaxed, and calmness settled across her wide eyes and tense jaw as her anxiety diminished. I gently asked Daisy's dad to sign the necessary paperwork.

I gave Daisy a dab of peanut butter to distract her while I injected a small amount of sedative under her skin. She looked back at me for a second, and then turned forward to continue licking the peanut butter.

Her mom held her and started walking around the living room and into the kitchen. Daisy slowly began to relax and snooze in her favorite place—mom's arms. When I knew Daisy was completely asleep, I told her mom I needed to perform the next step and give the euthanasia solution. Typically I inject it into a leg vein, but other injection sites are acceptable, and I decided to use a different one for Daisy that would allow her mom more time for their final walk.

I asked her mom to stand still for a few seconds, and I injected the final medication into Daisy's liver. Daisy still snoozed comfortably in her mom's arms.

I said, "OK, I gave her the medication. It will now travel slowly to her brain and let her drift off to her final rest. You can walk around as much as you want."

Daisy's mom started to cry, then turned away from me and started back on her path—around the living room, into the kitchen, and back around the living room. She spoke softly to Daisy the whole time.

Finally, she stopped at the sliding glass door and looked out at the lake, gently rocking back and forth, quietly saying sweet things to her little Daisy as she left her world for the next one with a full heart and mind.

In the veterinary hospital

It's still most common for pet parents to say their final goodbyes to their pets in the veterinary clinic. Some clinics have a comfort room that's used only for pet euthanasia. It makes the experience a little more comfortable and less clinical.

 One example of a comfort room at a veterinary clinic.

If you say goodbye to your dog at the veterinary hospital, feel free to bring your dog's bed, favorite toy, treats, and other familiar comfort items—perhaps a shirt recently worn by a family member who can't be present. I often suggest that other pets ("siblings") accompany the family to the clinic if feasible. They, too, are losing a friend. They may also help calm and reassure their friend in their final moments. They will also most certainly provide comfort for the family. The hospital team will support you and will understand that you want to make your pet as comfortable as possible.

What about feeding my pet?

If your dog still has an appetite, then they can eat any table food they want on the day you say goodbye. Steak, chocolate cake, cheese, hamburgers, ice cream, pizza, or whatever special treat delights them! My boy Duncan got a huge plate of French fries from In-N-Out Burger, a popular fast food restaurant that started in California and Californias love, including Duncan!

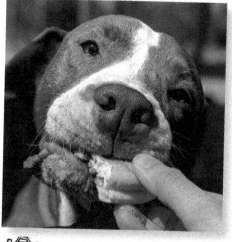

Also give your pet their regularly scheduled medications for that day— whether they're medications to treat pain, anti-anxiety pills, anti-seizure medications, insulin, or others. Your pet's medications won't interfere with the euthanasia process.

Gravy Boat, a Lap of Love patient, enjoys a burger on his last day.

One client, Greg, called me to schedule a euthanasia visit for his boy Yogi, a yellow Labrador retriever who had severe joint disease. Yogi could no longer get up and get around on his own. Like most of my patients with mobility problems (and most Labs!), Yogi still had a good appetite. So I suggested that Greg give Yogi whatever he wanted to eat that day.

When I arrived at Greg's home, a row of Harley-Davidson motorcycles were parked out front. A small cluster of men clad in leather vests, sunglasses, and American flag bandanas—some of whom also had impressive ZZ Top beards— were gathered near the porch. They greeted me kindly and ushered me into Greg's home.

As I entered the house, the smell of delicious food was overpowering! The food was all neatly lined up and covering the coffee table: an extra-large pizza, cheeseburgers, and hot dogs. And Yogi was resting right in front of it, his eyes laser-focused on his spread, with the biggest grin on his face.

Yogi got a fill of all his favorites during his goodbye gathering.

The euthanasia process

The process by which veterinarians euthanize pets varies, and there are big differences in some countries compared with the United States. One crucial component is required in all techniques: that veterinarians do not induce suffering.

Sedation

Most veterinary hospitals in the United States will give your pet a sedative before they give the euthanasia solution. The level of sedation can vary from mildly drowsy but still alert, to deep anesthesia. If the euthanasia solution is delivered by injecting it into a vein, sedation is not required, but I highly suggest the pet be sedated anyway. It's comforting for all involved to thoroughly relieve a pet's pain and anxiety before we say goodbye. Innumerable times, once their pet is sedated, pet parents have told me, "This is the best sleep she has had in days," or "He seems so comfortable now."

Comfort is the primary benefit of sedation. It also provides a transitional state between being awake and being gone. I believe it's difficult for anyone to see an awake, alert pet one moment and a lifeless pet the next moment. Even as a veterinarian performing euthanasia, I struggle with that. Sedating the pet first provides an intermediate stage that is emotionally gentler for everyone involved.

The sedation injection is usually a combination of an analgesic to relieve pain and a mild sedative to bring relaxation and drowsiness. The injection can be given in a muscle (usually in the rear leg or back), in the subcutaneous tissue (under the skin, like most vaccines), or in a vein. I give the sedation injection in a back muscle or under the skin. The body location, or route of administration, that I choose is based on the patient's body condition and position. By giving the medication under the skin or in a muscle rather than in a vein, the medication more slowly takes effect—usually over a few minutes. This prevents a sudden change from the pet being awake to instantly falling asleep, which can be startling to some pet parents.

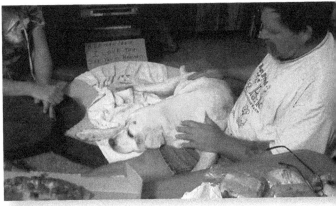

Many veterinary teams follow a process in which they take your pet to the Yogi peacefully relaxing into sedation.

hospital's treatment area to place an indwelling intravenous catheter in their leg, and then bring your pet back to the room to be with you. Some teams place this catheter in the room with you so your dog doesn't have to move. The catheter allows your veterinarian to easily administer the sedative and the euthanasia solution into the vein. When and how the veterinarian gives the sedative may vary depending on a pet's demeanor and degree of discomfort. Some veterinarians inject the sedative under the skin after they've placed the catheter instead of injecting it into the catheter. That way the sedative's effects are more gradual, and your pet will not be drowsy yet when they return your pet to you in the room.

Instead of giving a sedative, some veterinarians give an anesthetic induction agent called propofol, which is given only in a vein. From a medical standpoint, there is nothing wrong with giving propofol, and we use it in pets before many surgeries. But unless propofol is needed for specific medical or behavioral reasons during the euthanasia process, I'm not a proponent of giving pets this medication in place of a sedative that is given under the skin. Administering propofol immediately induces unconsciousness. This happens quickly and can startle some pet parents. Pet parents often think their pets have already passed, and may get upset if the drug's effects aren't carefully explained beforehand. Again, every veterinary hospital has determined which euthanasia protocol works best for them, and using propofol is not wrong. It's simply not my preference to induce unconsciousness so quickly.

If you prefer that your pet stay with you in the room for the catheter placement, you should feel comfortable asking your veterinarian whether this is possible. Your veterinarian will assess the stability of your pet's condition and your pet's demeanor, as well as the circumstances in the room and discuss the options with you. For example, a toddler who pets and pulls on the pet's legs during catheter placement and a parent unwilling to discourage this makes the veterinarian's job hard to do and is unsafe.

Does the sedation hurt? As most of us know from receiving flu shots or giving blood, a needle penetrating the skin can hurt. Pets who are already in pain may have a heightened sensitivity to pain, so a needle stick may hurt when normally it would not bother the pet. Some may not feel a thing, while others may flinch, yelp, or growl when the needle goes through the skin or when they feel the medication being injected. This is not a veterinarian's or nurse's lack of skill; it's a normal reaction in many pets. We do our best to avoid it because we never want to inflict pain. But, fortunately, most pets don't even notice, especially if they are distracted with a delectable treat. Placing an indwelling catheter also requires piercing the skin with a needle, so it can cause the same reaction, but you won't see that if the pet isn't in the room with you. I do everything in front of the owner, unless they don't wish to be there. I always hope that the pet doesn't react, because I would never want an owner to think I caused their pet a moment of pain. But pets do react to the sedative injection or catheter placement sometimes.

The sedative normally induces a good snooze. Sometimes a pet may still have a blunted awareness. Pets who have respiratory disease or who have a painful condition do not snooze as easily and can be roused. Again, this is normal. And some pets feel really good when the sedation starts to take effect because it's combined with a pain reliever. I've seen dogs with incredibly painful hips suddenly be able to get up. And I've seen cats who have had nausea and little interest in food for days mosey to their food bowl. Pet parents sometimes interpret this to mean their pet is telling them, "It's not time." But it's simply a normal bodily reaction to feeling temporarily good. I encourage family members to find comfort in their pets having that moment of comfort.

Although pets are usually calm and comfortable in just a few minutes after one sedation injection, there are times when giving more sedative is needed to achieve a comfortable level of relaxation. So it's not unusual for veterinarians to give two sedation injections.

During my speaking and teaching engagements at veterinary conferences abroad, I learned from veterinarians in European and African countries that they do not routinely give pets sedation before euthanasia. Again, sedation is not a required component of euthanasia if the euthanasia solution is delivered through a vein, so whether sedation is used may simply be a cultural difference.

The euthanasia injection

After the pet is serene and comfortably sedated, it's time to give the euthanasia solution. This injection for euthanasia is an overdose of a barbiturate, an extremely powerful central nervous system depressant. An overdose of this medication travels through the bloodstream to the brain and stops brain function. When the brain activity has stopped, all other bodily functions then stop. I want to assure you that the pet does not have a heart attack, as some people think. The pet simply falls into a deep, irreversible, anesthetic sleep. It's totally painless.

The route by which the euthanasia solution is given varies. It's most commonly injected into a vein. It can be injected through an indwelling intravenous catheter, a butterfly catheter (also known as a butterfly needle), or a syringe attached directly to a needle:

- An indwelling intravenous catheter is a small plastic tube with an injection port and a connector on its external end. The internal end of the catheter is guided into a vein by inserting a needle through the skin and vein. Once the needle and catheter are introduced into the vein, the needle is removed and the catheter remains in place. The catheter is then secured by taping it to the patient's skin. The catheter is not as rigid and sharp as a needle is, so it allows flexibility and patient movement during medication administration, it reduces the likelihood of puncturing the vein during medication administration, and it can remain in the vein for a longer time than a needle can (such as when hospitalized people or pets receive intravenous fluids).
- The butterfly catheter consists of a needle with two attached flexible "wings" and a long, small, flexible tube with a connector on its external end. Although the needle remains in the vein, the wings and long tube allow for more patient movement during medication administration. Because the needle remains in the vein, these catheters are used only temporarily (such as when people donate blood).
- A syringe attached to a needle is simply that, and it can be used to inject a medication directly into a vein, muscle, organ, or body cavity or under the skin. It provides the least flexibility and allows the least amount of patient movement during medication administration.

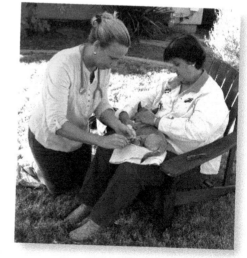

Pepe is sedated and snoozing comfortably in Gloria's lap. I'm giving the euthanasia solution through a butterfly catheter placed in a rear leg vein.

For my patients, I wait until the pet is sedated and snoozing. Then I locate a good vein for butterfly catheter placement. I place my thumb on the flexible wings to hold the catheter in place and do not need to tape it to the patient's skin.

Regardless of the type of catheter placed or whether it's placed in the pet in the treatment room or in front of you, the pet's veins do not always cooperate. And geriatric pets' veins are very fragile. Often, the vein will "blow." This means that the vein has a tiny rupture whereby blood (and the medication) leak out. Both old age and some medical conditions (such as liver failure or a decrease in the platelet cells that help blood clot) can cause these leaky veins. In some cases, a vein "blows" because it rolls away from the needle as soon as it is pricked, also leaving a tiny, leaky hole and no access to that vein.

If a vein blows, we'll most often try another vein. A butterfly catheter can be placed in a vein in a different leg, in a vein in their paw, or in a vein on the outside of their ear. Veterinarians may need more than one try to access a pet's vein. It can be difficult to do even in healthy animals, but with disease and age, the difficulty triples. If this happens, continue to love up on your pet while your veterinarian proceeds.

If a vein can't be reliably accessed, the veterinarian may choose a different administration route. Or we may prefer a different route based on your pet's condition or demeanor or, as in Daisy's case, based on the situation in the room. Using a route other than a vein is common, and as long as the pet has been adequately sedated beforehand (must be unconscious), using a route other than a vein is approved by the American Veterinary Medical Association. The animal's unconscious state helps ensure that the alternative route injection is painless. I have selected an alternative administration route in all of my own pets. For example, in cats, the most common alternative route is intrarenal administration, which means injecting the euthanasia solution into a kidney. I used this method with my cat Herbie. After injection, the pet usually passes within a minute or two. Kidneys are harder to feel in dogs than in cats, so I rarely use this method when helping a dog.

Another alternative administration route is through the liver, which is called intrahepatic injection. Like the kidneys, the liver contains many vessels that shuttle blood to the brain. A syringe with a needle attached is used to penetrate the skin in the pet's midsection below the rib cage, and the euthanasia solution is injected into the liver. With this route, the pet usually takes about 15 minutes to pass. This is the method I used for Daisy, and for my dog Duncan.

Another route, called intraperitoneal, involves injecting the euthanasia solution into the abdomen—the pet's belly (not the stomach). Because the blood supply differs in the abdomen compared with the blood supply in the organs, intraperitoneal injection takes longer for the pet to pass—usually about 45 minutes. I used this method for Serissa.

Me resting next to Serissa as she peacefully passes.

An intracardiac route may also be used, which means the injection is given directly into the heart. Unfortunately, pet parents are often afraid of this method. But remember, the pet is completely asleep before the injection is given. And keep in mind that veterinarians perform surgery in unconscious pets all the time—surgery that is much more invasive than a small needle penetrating the chest. Also know that the needle itself does not stop the heart. The needle delivers the medication to the heart, where it's rapidly carried in the blood to the brain, where it then stops brain function.

One Wednesday, I received a call from a woman about her Boston terrier, Benny. She told me he had liver failure and wasn't eating much. She said his belly was swollen like a basketball and his legs were also swollen. She wanted to schedule his euthanasia appointment for Monday, but after hearing about Benny's condition, I asked if I could visit to evaluate Benny that evening. Boy, am I glad I did.

I could tell Benny had once been a spry little guy, and he still had an adorable, signature Boston terrier smile: an outstretched tongue curled between two big eyeballs! As Benny waddled toward me, I was amazed he could walk at all. His belly nearly scraped the ground—it truly was almost basketball-sized. I could detect a slight swish of the fluid in his legs. They were the puffiest I'd ever seen. He greeted me and then waddled back to his bed and lay next to his best friend, who was a boxer.

I told Benny's family that his fluid buildup was severe, especially in his belly where it impaired his breathing because it put so much pressure on his diaphragm. I explained it was similar to how I feel after Thanksgiving dinner, but much worse and much more distressing. After more discussion, Benny's family decided that it was time to say goodbye to Benny that night. There was no doubt in my mind that they were making the best decision for Benny.

Then my mind turned to the euthanasia process. It would be easy to sedate Benny, but how would I give the euthanasia solution? I knew I wouldn't be able to find a vein in his swollen legs. The kidneys are hard to feel in dogs, so that route would not be an option. And his liver was in the middle of his basketball-sized abdomen and not functioning anyway, so that was out. I also couldn't inject it into his abdominal cavity because fluid was leaking *out* of his veins there, so the euthanasia solution would not be absorbed!

The intracardiac route was my only option. And as any veterinarian who has to explain this process to a pet parent knows, this is when our hearts sink because we know this seems odd and can be upsetting to hear. I explained the whole process to the family, starting with the sedation. I told them that after Benny was soundly asleep, I would give the second medication in his chest cavity, where it would go into his heart and travel to his brain, which would stop all body functions. I assured the family that this was the best route for Benny, and I promised he would not feel anything.

True to my word, Benny passed peacefully, with his boxer bestie next to him and his 12-year-old human bestie snuggled in front of him, kissing his little black nose as he passed. If Benny were my dog, I would have not done anything differently.

The body's responses during euthanasia

Whichever route we use, the euthanasia medication travels to the pet's brain and stops brain function. Then the pet's breathing stops, and then heart function stops. This usually happens within seconds to a few minutes after brain function has fully stopped. Veterinarians then listen with a stethoscope for a heartbeat, check for a pulse, and also check for a blink reflex by lightly touching the eyelids. When all indicators of life are absent, I say, "Your pet is an angel now."

Euthanasia means "good death"—and it usually is. But some of the body's automatic reflexes or responses may make a pet's passing appear 'not so good' to a pet parent. It's important to know that pets are not suffering when these things occur—they are normal biologic processes. Seeing the body shut down can be difficult, and that's why some people elect not to be present. I think if everyone better understood these natural processes, they wouldn't be as afraid. These same responses occur when a pet passes naturally.

After brain function stops, the body gradually shuts down. I prepare pet owners for two of the body's responses that happen in all pets at the time of passing. First, the bladder relaxes. The bladder wall is muscular and the sphincter that holds urine inside is also a muscle. After one passes, all the muscles relax, including the bladder and sphincter. So if your pet has urine in their bladder, it will leak. This is why we place an absorbable pad under pets before euthanasia. Feces may also pass from the bowel, but this occurs more commonly in pets with diarrhea in the preceding days or who have not defecated in a while.

The second response is that the eyelids remain in a relaxed state. The eyelids require the activity of small muscles to open them wide or to keep them closed.

When a pet dies, the eyelids relax, so the eyelids remain half open. You won't be able to keep them closed. This occurs in people, too. It frustrates me to watch scenes in movies when someone runs their hands over a deceased person's open eyes and they stay shut. This is a fallacy. In fact, morticians use glue or other methods to keep a deceased person's eyelids closed for a viewing at a funeral home. As the body shuts down, other reactions can occur, but they occur so infrequently that I don't wish to frighten pet parents by describing them beforehand. So I don't typically explain them unless their pets exhibit these reactions. Muscles contract, and twitching or tremors may occur as the nerves stop firing and the last electrical impulses leave the muscles. The diaphragm is a large muscle that sits between the abdomen and chest, and when it contracts it forces air from the lungs. And as the brainstem shuts down from lack of oxygen, this may trigger a reflex known as agonal respiration, and it looks like gasping for air. This can startle everyone watching—even myself. Please know that this is not the pet breathing. The jaw muscles also relax at death, and when the air is forced from the lungs, the jaw drops and it looks like a gasp. If this happens, it usually occurs within the first two minutes after the heart has stopped. And it invariably happens after I have declared that the pet is an angel! This raises pet parents' doubts and they sometimes don't believe me.

Very rarely, during the sedation process or right before the pet passes, the pet has a seizure. This has happened to animals I have euthanized only three times in 10 years, but when it does, it's upsetting to everyone. No definitive reason is known, but in people these seizures may be related to lack of oxygen or glucose as the brain shuts down, and it may occur in response to certain medications or in patients with a history of seizures, brain trauma, or brain cancer. (Tradounsky 2013) Take comfort in knowing that the pet is unconscious and has no knowledge of the experience. Yet the family remembers the seizure. Every veterinarian dreads the rare occurrence when a pet has a seizure during the farewell.

During sedation or euthanasia, some pets may also vocalize. Vocalization is common during any anesthesia process, and even people will chat, moan, or yell as we go under anesthesia. And sometimes the muscle twitching that occurs in pets as the nerves stop firing can result in vigorous leg paddling. Again, this is normal as anesthesia sets in. All of these things can upset a family if they interpret them as the pet suffering. I can assure you that the pets are not suffering. In fact, these responses let me know the medication is starting to work and they are not feeling discomfort. I prefer to wonder what pleasant moments the pets are dreaming about while they're kicking their legs or flicking their tails.

After the medication travels to the brain, it usually takes only a few minutes for the body to shut down. However, there are times when it can take longer. I have had a few patients whose heartbeat gradually slows and stops after up to 20 minutes, even when I give the euthanasia solution intravenously, which is the quickest route.

Talk to your pet

I encourage pet owners to talk to their dogs as they are being sedated and as they are passing. I think it's not only nice for dogs to hear their humans' voices, it also helps comfort the pet parents to say loving things to them. A study found that hearing still occurs in people who are unresponsive and dying (Blundon 2020), so one might cautiously presume this is also the case for our pets. Hearing may be the last sense to stop functioning as we (and our pets) die, so use your voice to comfort your pet throughout the end.

Duncan's good goodbye

When it came time to let my boy Duncan go, I knew I would be the one to perform the euthanasia. The day before, he had visits from all his human girlfriends. And the next day was even more perfect—he got a plate full of French fries!

I gave him the sedation cocktail, and he stretched out on his giant orthopedic bed that had his name embroidered on front and started to drift off. I talked to him the whole time, telling him how much I loved him and how much he blessed my life. I told him to give Serissa some love from me because I missed her dearly, and to do the same for my other fur kids Goldie, Bodhi, Herbie, Neo, Lilu, my first dog of my own, Snow White, and my childhood family dog,

Duncan got treated to an entire meal of fries and a burger from a fast food restaurant he loved.

Listening to the sound of silence after Duncan passed.

Lump. Then Duncan started to snore, a sweet sound to my ears. His lips relaxed and a bit of drool dribbled out. His third eyelid shifted upward and I knew he was in a good, deep sleep.

I had thought hard about how I would give Duncan the euthanasia solution. If I injected it in his leg vein, he would die fairly quickly. And I didn't want him to die while I was still performing my doctor duties. I wanted what all my patients' families got to do—to snuggle next to their pet and talk to them. I wanted to continue telling Duncan how thankful I was for his companionship. Death is a phase, it doesn't have to be a fleeting moment.

I decided I would use the intrahepatic method. I drew up the pink medication into the syringe. I attached a two-inch-long needle (he was a big boy) and found the spot to put the needle in. I pushed the needle through his skin and into his liver, took a deep breath, and slowly, steadily pushed the plunger to deliver the thick medication. My tears swelled as I knew there was no turning back. The solution took about 10 seconds to inject, and I pulled the needle out.

I placed the syringes and needles in their appropriate containers to discard later and returned the medications to my bag and shoved it aside. As I lay close to Duncan, his back to my chest, I hugged him tightly, whispering sweet nothings. I felt his breathing slow. Through his chest, I could feel his big heart beating and could imagine its familiar sound with each pulse: lub-dub....lub-dub.......... lub..... dub..... lub......... dub...... lub. Then silence. He was an angel.

 Such a handsome, sweet boy. We seemed to make each other smile.

CHAPTER 39:

Burial and cremation: A final place to rest and remember

"Near this spot are deposited the remains of one who possessed beauty without vanity, strength without insolence, courage without ferocity, and all the virtues of man, without his vices. This praise, which would be unmeaning flattery if inscribed over human ashes, is but a just tribute to the memory of Boatswain, a dog."

— From "Epitaph to a Dog," Lord Byron, poet

In the 1970s in rural New York where I grew up, it was customary to bury your deceased pet. I don't recall having gravestones—we buried Lump, our family dog, near a tree and planted flowers at her gravesite. But over the years, it grew over and her final resting place was unrecognizable. I didn't think about pet burial or cremation again until the late 1990s, when I had to decide what to do for my own first dog.

I was not prepared for Snow White, who you first met in this book's introduction, to die, so I certainly had never thought about what would happen with her body afterward. When that evening came and I sat crying, holding my lifeless friend, I only knew I would need to bury her. At that time, I hadn't heard of pet cremation. I took Snow White home and called friends to help me dig the gravesite and help settle her snugly in her final resting place.

I didn't realize how hard it would be to create her gravesite. When developers built homes near the Everglades in South Florida, they filled the marshland with coral rock. My friends and I took turns using a pickaxe to break through the rock in my yard. It took us three hours to dig a 5-ft-deep hole. We tried to gently lay Snow White at the bottom, which was no easy task. I placed flowers on her body and said a prayer. We filled in the hole, and I placed a special rock on top. A few days later I planted white flowers at the gravesite to honor her resting place. I always thought fondly of Snow White when I passed that spot.

When I sold my house to move to Gainesville, Florida, to attend veterinary school, I lost that space to visit and honor Snow White. The new homeowners never knew the importance of that spot. But I have pictures of Snow White, and her life inspired me to become a veterinarian. Each letter of my DVM degree carries some part of her spirit.

Since then, I also buried my cat Herbie, but all my other pets have been cremated. I don't have a personal preference; my own choice is influenced by each pet and situation. The choice of aftercare is a personal decision, and I support every family's choice. So let's take a closer look at the options available so you can feel more confident, prepared, and at peace with your decision.

Burial

When a body is buried, microbes break down the tissues, and the soil pH can help accelerate the process. Depending on what a pet is buried in, the body may break down within a few months, leaving bones behind. Humans have been burying their deceased pets for centuries. Archaeologists have identified what appears to be a pet dog burial site from 14,000 years ago. (Alex 2018) Pet burial may be done on the family's property if local regulations permit it, or in a pet cemetery. The oldest and largest pet cemetery in the United States is in Hartsdale, New York. It was founded by a veterinarian in 1896 and now is the final resting place of more than 80,000 animals. (Schulz 2020) A sign of the closeness between pets and their human family members, Hartsdale worked hard on New York law to allow people to place their cremated ashes with their pets in pet cemeteries. (Place 2013) Together forever, truly.

Pet cemeteries are not necessarily widely available, so if you prefer this option for your dog, preplanning is wise. A burial and gravesite can cost thousands of dollars and require an annual maintenance fee. Burying your dog in your yard may be acceptable, so here are things to consider first:

- Check your city or county ordinances for restrictions, because not all areas allow pet burial.
- Call your local public utilities office to mark your yard before you dig so you can avoid damaging gas and water lines or other utilities.

 In 1881, a dog named Cherry was the first pet to be laid to rest in what became Hyde Park Pet Cemetery in London, England.

- If your household accesses well water, choose a site away from the well.
- Will you need room for future additions (other pets) in the location you choose?
- Are you OK with leaving your dog's gravesite behind if you move?
- Are you physically able to dig the hole, or do you have someone to assist—a family member, friend, or hired help?
- Is the weather cooperative? Burying your pet on your property in Buffalo, New York in January, or in your yard in South Florida during the rainy season probably isn't feasible. (Tip: Your veterinary clinic or local crematory may hold your dog's body in a chilled facility until the land thaws or dries out.)

If you choose burial, here are some tips:

- If you need to delay the burial by a few days, you may want to place your dog's body in an air-tight plastic container and place it in a refrigerator or freezer.
- When you're ready to bury your dog, wrap your loved one in a small blanket, t-shirt, or pillow case. Avoid plastic bags or boxes because they slow the natural process of absorption into the soil.
- An urn or box isn't necessary, but if you prefer one, a pet crematory can provide options. PawPods.com is one option for biodegradable containers. One family I know bought a single kitchen cabinet unit from a home improvement store to use as their dog's casket, and the cabinet door served as the lid.
- An adequate depth for the hole allows four to five feet of soil to be placed above the dog to prevent other animals from investigating the area.
- Sprinkle 1 cup of lime powder (calcium hydroxide) on the bottom of the grave and 1 cup on top of the coffin, blanket, or pet. Lime can be purchased at most hardware or livestock feed stores.
- Place at least four feet of soil on top of the body or casket. If the pet was euthanized, the euthanasia medications remain in the tissues, and the pet's body can be deadly to or cause severe illness in curious pets or other scavenging animals. Again, avoid burying your pet in a location near your water supply if your source is well water.
- Use a headstone or decorative piece to discourage future digging in that spot.
- If you elect to have your dog cremated and then bury their ashes yourself, use an organic soil mixture along with the cremains (cremated remains) to create a nutrient-rich

R I P REX

2008 - 2021

mixture that will benefit the earth and help plants around the burial site flourish. Burying cremains alone can adversely affect the soil and inhibit plant growth.

Traditional (furnace-based) cremation

Cremation reduces the body to its basic elements of bone fragments through the use of intense heat. Cremation of deceased people on an open funeral pyre is an ancient tradition and began thousands of years ago. Cremation using high heat in an enclosed space began in Europe and North America in the late nine-teenth century.

In the late twentieth century, dedicated companion animal pet cremation centers began opening. Hundreds of pet-only crematories exist around the U.S. today, and some human crematories also offer pet cremation services. Based on nation-wide data from Lap of Love's veterinarians and a crematory in South Florida that I co-own, families elect cremation for their pet 80% of the time. Modern-day cre-mation uses a special furnace that generates extreme heat (at least 1700 F (927 C)) from burners fueled most often by natural gas and sometimes by propane, fuel oil, or electricity. The body is not directly exposed to flames.

Because bodies are about 70% water, the water evaporates in the extreme heat and the remaining tissue breaks down. The process takes between one and six hours, depending on a dog's size. Any items (toy, leash, blanket) placed in the crematory with the dog will be cremated as well. Large metal implants, such as a bone plate that was placed during an orthopedic surgery, do not break down in the heat and are left behind. Small metal pieces such as microchips or thin surgical wires dissolve in the heat.

After a human or dog body is cremated, bone fragments are left behind (many still retain their original shape, but they're very fragile when touched). These bone fragments are then placed in a pulverizer machine and ground into smaller pieces which resemble sand. This pulverized material is what is typically referred to as *ashes, cremated remains*, or *cremains*.

Depending on the wishes of a pet's family, the ashes are then either spread by the crematory or returned to the family. If you plan to spread your dog's ashes after cremation, check your local laws and federal regulations. For example, spreading ashes in national parks or on public beaches is often prohibited.

For people, each deceased person is cremated individually and the ashes are returned to the family in an urn that the family chooses (or multiple urns, if the family wishes to divide a loved one's ashes among family members). For dogs, a family can choose a communal, private, or individual cremation. Based on the Lap of Love and my crematory data, of the families who choose pet cremation, 50% elect communal cremation and 50% elect private cremation.

Communal cremation

This style of cremation involves cremating a deceased pet with other deceased pets without separation between them. The pet's ashes are not returned to the pet parents. Without sugarcoating this process, this means that pets are placed on top of each other (sometimes a dozen or more) and cremated. Each crematory may have different protocols regarding the number of pets that they allow to constitute a communal cremation, so it's a good idea to learn about the process for the crematory you select. Communal cremation costs less than private cremation.

The crematory disposes of the ashes of pets who are communally cremated, and this is done in accord with local and federal regulations, which may be stricter in densely populated cities. Such disposal (I hate using that word, but that is exactly what they do) may mean that the ashes are put in the trash. That may sound shocking, but in some places, no alternative way exists to spread ashes. Some crematories spread the ashes (or a portion of the ashes) in a memorial garden, some obtain special permits and may spread them in rivers or oceans, and some bury the ashes on their property.

I want to emphasize that communal cremation does not suggest that the dog was unloved or less loved. Some people are simply not attached to their pet's body and do not want the ashes returned to them. I have known many families who went to the ends of the earth to save their pets, shared their beds with them, cooked for them, and much more, but in the end they did not wish to receive their pet's ashes—a perfectly acceptable preference.

Private cremation vs. true private cremation or individual cremation

This method of cremation means a deceased pet is separated from other deceased pets during cremation, and the family receives their pet's ashes. However, the manner in which pets are separated differs among crematories.

Historically, crematory machines had only one large chamber, called the retort. Multiple pets would be placed in the chamber at one time, and they were separated by distance or by bricks, or pets were placed on individual metal trays. This method could be prone to mistakes if the pets were not properly organized and identified. The crematory's protocol to retain organization and keep pets identified is vital. Mixing of ashes could also theoretically occur. I am not aware of any scientific studies on whether bone fragments become airborne during cremation, and, in my opinion, not much of this type of mixing occurs. I have seen questionable "private cremation" methods where too many pets were placed in one chamber, too close together. Not everyone agrees with me, but I believe three feet between pets, with bricks separating them is acceptable and can be considered a private cremation. It may seem odd to you, but when Serissa was cremated, I felt some comfort knowing that other pets were close by.

The machines used for pet cremation have dramatically changed over the years. Some have multiple small chambers so that one pet can be placed in an individual chamber, which leaves no doubt that all the ashes belong to that pet alone. Some crematories refer to this as *true private* or *individual* cremation.

Because no regulation exists regarding body spacing and the terminology used to describe it, some crematories use these three terms interchangeably. So you may need to ask for more details about the crematory's process if you prefer a true private or individual cremation.

After a private cremation, the bone fragments are scooped up, pulverized, and placed in a container or urn to be returned to the pet's family.

Aquamation (water-based cremation)

Aquamation is a relatively new type of cremation gaining traction in the United States for both people and pets. Aquamation is a gentle, quiet, and eco-friendly process that uses a combination of heated flowing water and alkaline compounds (sodium and potassium hydroxide) to accelerate the same natural course of tissue breakdown that occurs during burial in the earth. Aquamation is also known as bio-cremation, alkaline hydrolysis, or green cremation.

The crematory I co-own with my brother Allan, Monarch Pet Memorial Services in Boynton Beach, Florida (**www.monarchpetservices.com**), provides only aquamation. It's a safe, natural, and environmentally friendly alternative to burial or furnace-based cremation. It produces no toxic air emissions and uses a fraction of the energy of traditional cremation.

Aquamation machines provide communal or private cremation. Most have a long metal basket that holds one very large dog, but it also allows placement of metal sheets to separate small pets. The pets and their bone fragments remain in their private chambers and the water passes through all the containers through small holes. Because of the water circulation, whether this can be called true private or individual cremation is debated. With a private aquamation option, each pet is carefully tracked through the process and pet parents receive their pet's ashes back.

The aquamation process can take up to 24 hours, and then the bone fragments need to be dried, which can take another 24 hours. The "bone ash" from aquamation is mostly made up of calcium (bones, teeth) and other minerals. It is softer, whiter, and lighter bone ash and the process produces more ash than that produced by extreme heat cremation. Any non-organic material placed with the pet remains intact afterward. So if a toy is placed with the pet, it will be there after the process. Sometimes we find items that pet parents may not have known their pets had eaten—hair ties, socks, small toys, and more!

Composting

A new, limited option in the United States for pet aftercare is body composting. Like burial, furnace-based cremation, and aquamation, composting breaks down body tissues and bone fragments remain. Pet composting may be done indoors or in a greenhouse, and composting of farm animals has been done outdoors for many years. The pet's body is placed in a special aerated, temperature- and moisture-regulated container with wood chips and soil to promote growth of helpful bacteria and fungi that catalyze the process. Done correctly, the process also neutralizes disease-causing microorganisms and chemicals. This process takes about eight weeks, and the compost that remains can be used in gardens or to plant trees and houseplants.

The body's elemental nature—a recap of aftercare options

Whether a family chooses pet burial, furnace-based cremation, aquamation, or composting, the end result is the same—each body is eventually reduced to its basic elements of bone ash. Apart from cost and availability, the primary differences among these methods are the amount of time the process takes, the catalyst that supports the decomposition, and the environmental impact of the process:

- Burial results in slow decomposition that can take several months to years, is catalyzed by microbes and certain soil conditions, requires land use, and may release toxins into the soil or water.
- Furnace-based cremation takes up to six hours, is catalyzed by extreme heat that requires a large amount of energy to produce, creates smoke, and has a high carbon footprint.
- Aquamation (with drying) takes up to 48 hours, is catalyzed by alkaline hydrolysis, and has a small carbon footprint. The byproduct is sterile water that contains nutrients, salts, amino acids, and sugars. The water is processed the same as other wastewater is.
- Composting takes about two months, is catalyzed by microbes, and has a small carbon footprint. The byproduct is heat.

Viewings

I have attended a few pet memorial services, but memorial services are not as common for pets as they are for people. Because I am a veterinarian focused on end-of-life care, I consider the euthanasia visit to be one element of a pet's funeral. I try to make it as peaceful as possible while providing the family the opportunity to celebrate their dog's life.

Sometimes pet parents want to view their dog again before cremation. They may wish to say one last goodbye, or oftentimes a family member who wasn't present to see the dog before they passed can obtain closure during a viewing. Most crematories can provide a viewing opportunity, and the dog is placed lovingly on a table to allow a family to pay their last respects.

Care of the body and ashes

Veterinary clinics and in-home veterinary euthanasia services typically partner with one nearby crematory (there may be only one option). Pets' bodies are delivered to the crematory directly or kept in cold storage at the veterinary clinic until the crematory picks them up—usually once or twice a week. The crematory returns the ashes to the clinic within a few days to two weeks. The family may pick them up, or the end-of-life-care veterinarian may deliver them to the family. A few veterinary hospitals have their own crematory on site.

 ## Questions you may wish to ask your veterinarian

- If I wish to, may I choose a different crematory than the one you typically use? (This may require that the crematory makes a special trip to the clinic to pick up your dog or you may have to take your dog to the crematory.)
- Has a team member from the veterinary hospital toured the crematory and watched their process?
- If I choose a communal cremation, where will my dog's ashes be spread?
- What memorial items will be returned?
- What options for urns are available?

 ## Questions you may wish to ask a crematory representative

- What are the hours for drop off? (This may affect the time you elect for your dog's euthanasia appointment if you take your dog's body to the crematory.)

- What are my options if my dog passes after regular business hours?
- Do you provide a viewing opportunity before cremation?
- What type of cremation do you offer (water-based aquamation, furnace-based cremation, or both)?
- Are memorial items available?
- What options for urns are available? (If you would like your dog's ashes divided into multiple urns for family members, a crematory may provide this option for a small additional fee.)
- What is your protocol to ensure dogs are separated and properly identified throughout the cremation process?

CHAPTER 40:

Keepsakes: Memorializing your dog to honor their life story

"It's surprising how much memory is built around things unnoticed at the time."

— SOURCE UNVERIFIED
(THE INTERNET ATTRIBUTES THIS QUOTE TO
BARBARA KINGSOLVER, NOVELIST)

I've been asked to help families memorialize their dogs in many ways. Some are common and traditional, and others are quite uncommon. When someone requests a memorial I haven't done before, I enjoy the challenge of trying to make it happen. The first time a family asked me to take a sample for their dog's cloning, I had no idea what to do, which I confessed to the pet parent. But with help from the company that provides dog cloning, I obtained the sample they needed.

I've also been asked to pull a dog's tooth, shave an entire Alaskan malamute so the family could make a sweater with their dog's fur, store a dog's body for days so family members could gather for a viewing and memorial service, transport a dog's body to a freeze-dry preservation center, transport a dog's body to a taxidermist, allow a photographer to be present for a dog's euthanasia, and remove a deceased dog's ear because the family would miss its softness (I did not remove the dog's ear, and I offered other memorial options). I have attended dog memorial services, dog walks organized in honor of a deceased dog, and pet memorial tree planting ceremonies!

I'm in awe of the creative ways people have honored and remembered their dogs. For some families, their thoughts are all they need to remember, while others want physical remembrances. Many companies and artists that produce awesome pet memorials have asked me to recommend them, but discussing such products during euthanasia appointments would be awkward and sound uncomfortably promotional. Instead, this chapter is dedicated to sharing memorial ideas and products I have learned about during my career, and it isn't intended to be promotional.

Scan to go
to memorials

I hope you find these suggestions helpful or that they may inspire you to create something different. It's also helpful to think about memorial items you may want before your dog passes so that you can prepare and fulfill your wishes when the time comes. Related to the list I've included here, I've created a webpage **drmarygardner.com/resources/memorials** that provides additional examples and direct links to the sources of many of these ideas.

1. Create a paw print impression in clay. I love a good paw print. Air-dry and oven-bake clays are available in craft stores. You may want to trim your dog's toenails and fur between the paw pads to provide a better imprint. Many veterinary clinics and almost all crematories have the supplies to create a paw impression, so just ask.

ColorBox is one example of many inkpad options.

Moisten the footpads with a damp paper towel, then add lots of ink to each pad.

Press the dog's paw onto paper or clay.

2. Create a paw print impression with ink or paint. Using ink or paint is a bit messier than clay alone, and it may take a few tries to get a good print. Again, you may want to trim your dog's toenails and fur between the paw pads. You can also have your colorful print scanned and use it to help create jewelry or a tattoo.

3. Keep your dog's ashes. More than half of families who elect cremation want their dog's ashes returned to them. This gives many people a sense of closure or that their dog is "back." You'll see many keepsakes in this list that can be created to hold or incorporate a dog's ashes.

4. Create a custom memorial blanket. Many internet retailers will create a blanket from one or more photos of your dog.

5. Create custom memorial clothing: t-shirts, socks, scarves.

6. Have a plush animal made that looks like your dog.

7. Keep fur clippings. These can be a treasure to sniff and touch to help you remember. Many keepsakes can also be created to hold your dog's fur or can be made from their fur.

8. Hold a memorial ceremony—alone or with a few family members or friends, or invite everyone who knew your dog.

9. Create a scrapbook to memorialize the wonderful moments in your dog's life. We often keep pictures on our phones and computers but don't take time to print them. You can make or order a custom cover for your dog's photo album or scrapbook.

10. Create a nose print. Similar to a clay paw impression, you can make a nose impression in clay. These impressions are easier to make after the dog passes. The nose is even more unique to your dog than their paw—like a person's fingerprint.

11. Make or purchase custom lockets, charms, or other jewelry created based on your dog's paw or nose print impressions.

Press the dog's paw
Charlie's nose print in clay.
onto paper or clay.

12. Consider a trip to your dog's favorite spot or spots to sprinkle their ashes or a smidge of their ashes. Check your local regulations before doing this, and think about others who visit the area and how you would want the area treated as well.

13. Obtain a sample that will give you the option to have your dog cloned. Talk with your veterinarian and the company you choose before the

euthanasia appointment, because specific procedures that require fast action may be needed to preserve the sample.

14. Preserve your dog with taxidermy. Research this option before the euthanasia appointment so that the best preservation can be achieved.

15. Preserve your dog with freeze-drying. This process differs from traditional taxidermy. It is applied to the whole animal and stops the decaying process by using ultra-low temperature and a vacuum procedure to remove all moisture.

16. Preserve and remember your dog with cryonics. This process is available for deceased people as well. Research this option thoroughly beforehand because special preparations and fees are required. A dog's body is specially prepared and suspended in a liquid nitrogen tank and must stay at the cryonics facility. With this method, the hope is that one day reanimation of frozen bodies will be possible.

17. Get a tattoo of your dog, their paw print, or their nose print. You may also investigate options to incorporate some of your dog's ashes into the ink.

18. Light up the night sky with your dog's ashes! Ashes can be incorporated into fireworks.

19. Plant new life and boost local biodiversity by planting one or more native trees, grasses, wildflowers, or an entire memorial garden dedicated to your dog on your property.

20. Plant new life by donating in memory of your dog to an organization that plants trees in national forests, such as the Arbor Day Foundation.

21. Plant a memorial tree urn. A tree will grow from this urn that contains some of your dog's ashes. (Keep in mind that if dog's ashes are placed alone in a planting location or gravesite, the ashes can inhibit plant growth, so use special soil mixes or biodegradable urns.)

22. Place a memorial bench in honor of your dog in your yard or garden.

23. Write lyrics and music for a song in your dog's honor, or commission an artist to do this. Websites such as UpWork may be helpful in finding independent artists.

24. Write your dog's eulogy or obituary and post it online. Many websites invite dog lovers to share stories about a dog who has passed.

25. Donate in memory of your dog to a local or national dog rescue or shelter facility.

26. Donate in memory of your dog to a local veterinary primary care or specialty practice that has a charitable fund to help clients who qualify and cannot afford their dog's emergency or chronic illness care. Not all hospitals offer this, but national organizations such as Frankie's Friends also provide this service.

27. Donate in memory of your dog to an organization that researches dog diseases or provides funding for research, such as a veterinary school, Morris Animal Foundation, or Winn Feline Foundation.
28. Purchase a personalized dog memorial stone to keep at home or in your garden, or to place on your dog's gravesite.
29. Create a silhouette portrait of your dog made of buttons and fabric.
30. Repurpose your dog's identification tags and have them made into jewelry.
31. Create your own or order a customized dog memorial holiday ornament.
32. Create a shrine in your home dedicated to your dog with photos, battery-operated LED tea lights or flickering LED candles, flowers, their collar, favorite toy, locks of fur, ashes, or other items.
33. Make a planter out of your dog's food and water bowls.
34. Create felted beads from your dog's hair instead of using wool.
35. Have a bracelet made from your dog's collar or leash.
36. Make a dog photo collage—a great project to do with children.
37. Write a letter to your dog and send it with them to be cremated.
38. Have a portrait painted or other illustration created from a photograph of your dog. Wonderful watercolor, acrylic, and even cartoon options are available.
39. Paint your dog's portrait using a decoupage medium such as Mod Podge, or attend a paint-your-pet class.

40. Commission a portrait painted with your dog's ashes.
41. Incorporate your dog's ashes into a memorial sculpture or stone.
42. Create your own or purchase a customized dog sculpture.
43. Incorporate your dog's ashes into glass art or jewelry.

 Mya Wiggle and her family. Love all the tennis balls! (Photo by Fearless Legacy—Carli Calapa)

44. Incorporate your dog's ashes into a memorial glass paperweight in a form meaningful to you.
45. Place your dog's ashes in a specially made urn hourglass.
46. Have a professional photo shoot done before your dog passes. This directory will help you find a pet photographer: **https://greyboypetportraits.com/pet-photographers/**

47. Make your own dog plush toy with felt.
48. Create your own or order a personalized flower or floating candle vase.
49. Make a hanging jar candle or other memorial candle with a personal message.
50. Make a framed memorial photograph that includes your dog's collar.
51. Get a personalized window decal.
52. Create a custom coffee cup.
53. Engrave your dog's name on a personalized wind chime.
54. Send a portion of your dog's ashes to orbit the Earth, or to the moon, or into deep space!
55. Name a star after your dog.
56. Create a dog hair keepsake, such as a glass jar, wooden box, or locket.
57. Write a short story, poem, novel, biography, or children's book about your dog.
58. Place your dog's ashes or hair in various resin memorials.
59. Turn your dog's ashes into diamonds
60. Turn your dog's ashes into pottery.
61. Include your dog's ashes in an eternal reef. The ashes are incorporated in an environmentally safe cement and dropped in the ocean to erode safely over time.
62. Create a memorial keychain with a photo of your dog or engraved remembrance.
63. Create a ring, pendant, or charm with a lock of hair with or without flowers and captured in resin.
64. Incorporate dog hair with beads the color of your dog's birthstone to be crafted into a necklace or pendant.
65. Create a pet memorial wall or shelf that features photographs of all your beloved pets who've passed on.
66. Purchase an urn that matches your dog's breed.
67. Have your dog's photograph engraved on drinking glasses.
68. Incorporate your dog's ashes into snow globe art.
69. Complete a special home or personal project, participate in a community charitable event, or volunteer at a shelter or elsewhere in your community to fulfill a personal goal while honoring your dog's memory. Decide how you will commemorate or dedicate your special project to your dog.
70. Organize your own community fundraising or charitable event in honor of your dog, such as a walk or fun run and donate all proceeds to a local pet shelter.
71. Create your own video memorial montage, short film, or movie about your dog.
72. Make or order a personalized memorial bird feeder.

73. Celebrate your pet's life with a toast, cheers, and customized bottle opener.
74. Paint a birdhouse that resembles your house from a kit and incorporate a small portrait of your pet. (You can also order a custom birdhouse designed to look exactly like your house!)
75. Honor your beloved pet by adopting a new pet to share your love anew if this is right for you.

CHAPTER 41:

After they are gone:
The silence is deafening

They can inhabit all aspects of our daily lives for over a decade. We care for them as our "furry children." And when the end nears, our lives become even more entwined. To make their remaining time better, we alter our own routines. We sleep in the living room to stay nearby, we cancel trips, we work from home, we don't go out to dinner with friends, we don't have friends over because our homes are messy and we're embarrassed …

…. we have constant worry, we scour the internet for answers, we try every product available hoping it'll help them a little bit more …

… we offer dozens of foods to spark their appetites so they'll show us they still have an appetite for life, we have countless sleepless nights, we deal with unholy smells, we have frustrations that no one else seems to understand, we argue with our family members ….

Yet most of us would do it for as long as our pets need us to.

Caring for an ailing pet brings stress, but it can also bring joy. The room where I'm writing this smells odd because my dog Sam smells odd. I can no longer get her to the groomer, and no mobile groomer is equipped to handle her, so tufts of her hair are scattered all over the house. She has lost 20% of her body weight over the last few months, and the harness she wears that helps me help her get around is now too big for her. My to-do list for today includes going back to the store to get baby wipes to help keep her clean and stocking up on deli meat so she'll take her medications. Yet hearing Sam snoring softly and seeing her lying there comfortably dreaming, I smile. I'm happy to attend to her needs for as long as she needs me to.

As sad as I'll be to say goodbye to Sam when the time comes, I'll know I have done all that I possibly could for her. And based on similar experiences with my other grey muzzle fur kids, I know that after a period of rest and "time off," I'll welcome another pet into my life. So many animals out there need a loving home. I'm sure that Sam and all of her predecessor "fur siblings" would agree.

Every one of my pets has taught me more about life, disease, caregiving, and loss. Each experience I've had with them has made me a better veterinarian (and human), and I've used that knowledge to help families. I thank my pets for the love they provided and for their gifts that I can share.

I've had the amazing privilege of providing end-of-life veterinary care for thousands of pets, and I've met thousands of phenomenal families along the way. People often ask me whether I'm numb to euthanasia because I've performed so many. And my answer will always be, "No!" Never have I visited a home and felt that a pet represented a routine appointment. Every family and every pet brings a new experience, a new love story, and a new set of angel wings I can deliver. Have I gotten technically better? Yes. I have muscle memory for the process. And this advantage allows me to be more present for the family and their pet. I also send a silent wish with every pet to please say "hi" to one of my grey muzzle angels above. I feel like I'm sending a friend to all my loves that I miss so much. In many ways, I'm now more affected by a pet's passing and their family's experience than I was when I began practicing so many years ago. And that's OK. The day that I become numb will be the day I need to stop providing this care.

I'm grateful for the treasured lessons I've learned from my patients and their families. My wish for this book is to give families answers, tips, and hope in caring for their senior pets, especially in times when they may feel helpless.

Praise your time together

I often hear pet parents say one of two things as their pet is being sedated or as their pet is passing. Some say, "I'm sorry!" I worry when I hear this because it sounds like they have regrets. And I wonder—do they feel they should've done more? Or perhaps they're quietly expressing sorrow for their pet's illness. Grief and sadness are expected, but regret seems unjustified. I hope at the end of your pet's life, you don't feel regret. Instead, I hope you can say what I hear many pet parents say to their pets, "Thank you!" I hope you can allow yourself to express that you're grateful that your pet was a part of your life. You're all good pet parents. Do what you can for your pets, and be gentle on yourself. Because if your pets could talk, I'm sure they would say, "thank you," right back.

One of my patients, Scooby, was a 12-year-old vizsla who had an incurable nasal tumor. I visited his family's home in Southern California for his euthanasia. The moment I entered their tranquil home, I felt an overwhelming sense of serenity. The family softly spoke German to each other, and they switched to English with ease for me. The parents and both of their children had dressed alike in white clothing in honor of Scooby's goodbye.

They led me to the backyard where Scooby was resting. He got up to greet me and then went back to his bed. It was laden with red roses and sheltered by white curtains hanging from a trellis. The curtains floated in the breeze and filtered the sun. It was lovely and ethereal. The children picked up the flowers that had rolled off Scooby's bed and carefully replaced them around him. They all spoke lovingly to him. I admired the angelic scene in awe.

I talked with the family about Scooby, and then explained the steps involved during my visit. They all agreed that it was time to set Scooby free from his disease. I injected the sedative and sat back to give them their space and final moments together. They all gathered closer, and I heard them each say, "Danka, Scooby, Danka!" Followed by lots of kisses. Scooby was one lucky boy!

Their spirit survives

I still have my dog Neo's collar. It has lost his "gorilla" smell that I miss. I saved a lovely wad of fur from my dog Serissa. How I miss her tufts of "snow" that would tumble through my house. I have only pictures of my first dog, Snow White, and I treasure them. I have many pictures and videos of my cats Goldie and Bodhi. I also still have my dog Duncan's heart medications in his multi-dose pill box! It has been three years since he has passed, and I cannot bear to throw them out. I miss that handsome boy so much.

Our pets share our space and occupy our hearts. When they are gone, the expanse of their absence engulfs us. We miss their greetings, expectant looks, smell, fur, drool, nose prints on the windows, and warmth on our lap. We simply glance at their spot on the couch or favorite perch, and the pang of its vacancy breaks like a wave crashing through our being. The empty dog bed, the deserted path of non-slip rugs, the lone toy in the corner, the treats left at the bottom of the jar—all sting, yet soothe us, and we can't bear to put these reminders away just yet. The familiar background symphony of our pets' barks or meows, panting or purrs, snores, and toenails tapping across the floor or claws digging into the scratching post is forever muted. I even pray to hear their special sounds one more time, even if it's only in my dreams. The silence in my house after I've lost a pet is deafening.

How blessed we are to love a pet and to receive a pet's love. Loving a pet expands our capacity to love, and losing a pet doesn't limit it. Still, we know that no matter how much time we have our pets in our life, it will simply never be long enough.

In Memory of Sam

Like all of my geriatric fur kids, Sam, too, inspired my work as a veterinarian and in writing this book. I learned abundantly from caring for each of them, but perhaps I learned the most from Sam. The COVID-19 shelter-in-place requirements cancelled my work travel obligations and allowed me to stay home with Sam consistently during the last nine months of her life. I took her to chemotherapy

 Sam with a mouthful of pancake on her last day.

 Sam's valentine treats.

Watching "The Crown" soothed Sam (and me).

 One of Sam's empty spots. I waited two weeks to pick up all the rugs.

Healthy, smiley Sam.

appointments, radiation treatments, rehabilitation and massage therapy, and the groomer (while she could still manage it). I was grateful and fortunate that I could be home nearly 24 hours a day to care for her. And she needed a lot of care and caring.

I slept on the floor with her, played a soothing sound machine to help her fall asleep, picked her up from awkward positions, stimulated her to poop, coaxed her to eat, petted her for hours to calm her anxiety, cleaned up her accidents, and simply loved on her. As hard as it was, I'd do it all again. And as hard as I tried to do all I could for her, she was already spoken for. On Sam's final day, Valentine's day, she got anything and everything she wanted to eat, including pancakes for breakfast and cupcakes after dinner. I spent hours loving on her, and we even watched a little of "The Crown" together—her favorite show.

I euthanized Sam myself. I gave my angel back. Delivering the medication is not the hard part. Saying goodbye is. I gave Sam the beautiful, peaceful send-off that she deserved. Rest well, my dear friend and silent guardian.

Thoughts of Sam will always bring a smile to my face.

Acknowledgments

Writing this book has been swirling in my mind for several years. My everlasting gratitude goes to many people, pets, and patients who have inspired and motivated me, and helped me shape and bring this book to life.

Dr. Theresa Entriken gave me exceptional help in researching this book, edited my words while riding the same wavelengths of my thoughts, and was an amazing sounding board for my crazy ideas. I say humbly and without hesitation that this book is better because of your involvement.

Mindy Valcarcel, thank you for your editing goddessness—for catching my grammatical mistakes, excising my overabundant exclamation points, teaching me about Oxford commas (they're optional!) and making me look polished!!!

Portia Stewart, thank you for sharing your awesome doodle skills! Your creations always surprised me, and they bring lightness to these sometimes heavy topics.

Deepest thanks to my friends—Holly Russo, Dr. Dave Nicol, Eric Garcia, Dr. Caitlin DeWilde, Nikita Pavlov, and Dr. Faith Banks. You gave me phenomenal encouragement throughout my years of writing this book, and beyond—throughout life's charms and trials overall!

Thank you, Dr. Sheilah Robertson, my fellow grey muzzle lover and perpetual helper and guardian of geriatric pets everywhere. Your constant support and encouragement and inexhaustible knowledge have made me a better veterinarian.

My sister, Sharon Sherman, has been my biggest cheerleader in life and has been pushing me along during my writing and publishing endeavors. And my brother, Allan Gardner, who is there whenever I need him…even when it's to open an aquamation service.

Stacy Bennett, my banana split maker! For years you've helped me research all the questions that pop into my head about grey muzzle pets, geriatric people, and age-related conditions. I asked for a scoop of vanilla ice cream, and you brought me a banana split.

Thank you, Suze Orman, for kicking me in the rear and getting me to move ahead when I was dragging my feet. Your no-nonsense, no excuses, get-it-done attitude is invaluable, my friend.

To all the families who allowed me to share their stories and pictures, THANK YOU! Each and every one of you and your pets has touched me personally and made me a better human and veterinarian. Your beautiful dogs live on and will continue to enhance many more lives.

To my canine fur kid angels above—Snow White, Neo, Serissa, Duncan and Sam—you've taught me countless lessons about love, caring, and all the wonder that exemplifies the human-animal bond. You've brought unbounded joy to my life. Not a single day goes by that I don't think of you all!

Finally, thank you to Dennis. You were my champion through veterinary school and all my crazy ideas. Most importantly, you loved our dogs just as much as I did, and trusted me to care for them in the best way I could. (Sorry about all the poop and pee accidents!)

References

I have referenced a lot of sources throughout this book and have decided to keep a webpage for the resources with up to date information. Please use the QR code below to navigate to them.

Index

CPSIA information can be obtained
at www.ICGtesting.com
Printed in the USA
LVHW052151011221
704784LV00005B/23/J

9 781956 343007